The Mountain Pine Beetle
A Synthesis of Biology, Management, and Impacts on Lodgepole Pine

edited by Les Safranyik and Bill Wilson

Sponsored by the Government of Canada through the Mountain Pine Beetle Initiative, a program administered by Natural Resources Canada, Canadian Forest Service.

Natural Resources Canada,

Canadian Forest Service,

Pacific Forestry Centre

Victoria, BC

Canada

2006

Pacific Forestry Centre
506 West Burnside Road
Victoria, British Columbia
V8Z 1M5
Phone: (250) 363-0600
www.pfc.cfs.nrcan.gc.ca

Printed in Canada

Library and Archives Canada Cataloguing in Publication

Safranyik, L., 1938-

The mountain pine beetle : a synthesis of biology, management,
and impacts on lodgepole pine / by Les Safranyik and Bill Wilson.

Includes bibliographical references.
Available also on the Internet and on CD-ROM.
ISBN 0-662-42623-1
Cat. no.: Fo144-4/2006E

1. Mountain pine beetle. 2. Lodgepole pine--Diseases and
pests--Control--Canada, Western. 3. Lodgepole pine--Diseases and
pests--Economic aspects--Canada, Western. 4. Lodgepole pine—Diseases
and pests--Control. 5. Forest management--Canada, Western. I. Wilson,
Bill, 1950- II. Pacific Forestry Centre III. Title.

SB945.M78S33 2006   634.9'7516768   C2006-980019-7

This book presents a synthesis of published information on mountain pine beetle (*Dendroctonus ponderosae* Hopkins [Coleoptera: Scolytidae]) biology and management with an emphasis on lodgepole pine (*Pinus contorta* Dougl. ex Loud. var. *latifolia* Engelm.) forests of western Canada. Intended as a reference for researchers as well as forest managers, the book covers three main subject areas: mountain pine beetle biology, management, and socioeconomic concerns. The chapters on biology cover taxonomy, life history and habits, distribution, insect-host tree interactions, development and survival, epidemiology, and outbreak history. The management section covers management strategy, survey and detection, proactive and preventive management, and decision support tools. The chapters on socioeconomic aspects include an economic examination of management programs and the utilization of post-beetle salvage timber in solid wood, panelboard, pulp and paper products.

Le présent ouvrage offre une synthèse de l'information publiée concernant le dendroctone du pin ponderosa (*Dendroctonus ponderosae* Hopkins [Coleoptera: Scolytidae]), sa biologie ainsi que la lutte qu'on lui fait. L'accent porte sur les forêts de pins tordus latifoliés (*Pinus contorta* Dougl. ex Loud. var. *latifolia* Engelm.) de l'Ouest du Canada. Préparé à l'intention des chercheurs et des aménagistes des forêts comme ouvrage de référence, ce dernier traite de trois sujets principaux : la biologie du dendroctone du pin ponderosa, la lutte qu'on lui fait et les questions socioéconomiques qui y sont liées. Les chapitres sur la biologie comprennent la taxonomie, le cycle de vie et les mœurs, la répartition, l'interaction entre l'insecte et l'arbre hôte, son développement et sa survie ainsi que l'épidémiologie et l'historique des infestations. La section sur la lutte et la gestion traite de stratégies de lutte, de détection et de relevés, de lutte préventive et proactive ainsi que d'outils d'aide à la décision. Les chapitres sur les aspects socioéconomiques examinent, d'un point de vue économique, les programmes d'aménagement et l'utilisation du bois récupéré après le passage du dendroctone dans la fabrication de produits en bois massif, de panneaux ainsi que des pâtes et papiers.

Front cover:
Mountain pine beetle outbreak in lodgepole pine.

Back cover:
Lodgepole pine salvage with splits and blue stain.
Photo courtesy of Pulp and Paper Research Institute of Canada.

Disclaimer:

Contents

Part 1 – Biology

Part 2 – Management

Part 3 – Socioeconomic impacts

Editors

Safranyik, Les
Natural Resources Canada, Canadian Forest Service, Pacific Forestry Centre
506 West Burnside Road, Victoria, BC, Canada V8Z 1M5
e-mail: lsafranyik@pfc.cfs.nrcan.gc.ca

Wilson, Bill
Natural Resources Canada, Canadian Forest Service, Pacific Forestry Centre
506 West Burnside Road, Victoria, BC, Canada V8Z 1M5
e-mail: bwilson@pfc.cfs.nrcan.gc.ca

Contributors

Alfaro, Rene I.
Natural Resources Canada, Canadian Forest Service, Pacific Forestry Centre
506 West Burnside Road, Victoria, BC, Canada V8Z 1M5
e-mail: ralfaro@pfc.cfs.nrcan.gc.ca

Byrne, Tony
Forintek Canada Corporation
2665 East Mall, Vancouver, BC, Canada V6T 1W5
e-mail: byrne@van.forintek.ca

Carroll, Allan L.
Natural Resources Canada, Canadian Forest Service, Pacific Forestry Centre
506 West Burnside Road, Victoria, BC, Canada V8Z 1M5
e-mail: acarroll@pfc.cfs.nrcan.gc.ca

Dymond, Caren C.
Natural Resources Canada, Canadian Forest Service, Pacific Forestry Centre
506 West Burnside Road, Victoria, BC, Canada V8Z 1M5
e-mail: cdymond@pfc.cfs.nrcan.gc.ca

Erickson, Bob
Natural Resources Canada, Canadian Forest Service, Pacific Forestry Centre
506 West Burnside Road, Victoria, BC, Canada V8Z 1M5
e-mail: berickso@pfc.cfs.nrcan.gc.ca

Fall, Andrew
Gowland
220 Old Mossy Road, Victoria, BC, Canada V9E 2A3
e-mail: fall@cs.sfu.ca

Hawkes, Brad C.
Natural Resources Canada, Canadian Forest Service, Pacific Forestry Centre
506 West Burnside Road, Victoria, BC, Canada V8Z 1M5
e-mail: bhawkes@pfc.cfs.nrcan.gc.ca

Peter, Brian
Natural Resources Canada, Canadian Forest Service, Pacific Forestry Centre
506 West Burnside Road, Victoria, BC, Canada V8Z 1M5
e-mail: bpeter@pfc.cfs.nrcan.gc.ca

Riel, Bill G.
Natural Resources Canada, Canadian Forest Service, Pacific Forestry Centre
506 West Burnside Road, Victoria, BC, Canada V8Z 1M5
e-mail: briel@pfc.cfs.nrcan.gc.ca

Safranyik, Les
Natural Resources Canada, Canadian Forest Service, Pacific Forestry Centre
506 West Burnside Road, Victoria, BC, Canada V8Z 1M5
e-mail: lsafranyik@pfc.cfs.nrcan.gc.ca

Shore, Terry L.
Natural Resources Canada, Canadian Forest Service, Pacific Forestry Centre
506 West Burnside Road, Victoria, BC, Canada V8Z 1M5
e-mail: tshore@pfc.cfs.nrcan.gc.ca

Stennes, Brad
Natural Resources Canada, Canadian Forest Service, Pacific Forestry Centre
506 West Burnside Road, Victoria, BC, Canada V8Z 1M5
e-mail: bstennes@pfc.cfs.nrcan.gc.ca

Stonestreet, Cameron
Natural Resources Canada, Canadian Forest Service, Pacific Forestry Centre
506 West Burnside Road, Victoria, BC, Canada V8Z 1M5
e-mail: cameron.stonestreet@gov.bc.ca

Taylor, Steve W.
Natural Resources Canada, Canadian Forest Service, Pacific Forestry Centre
506 West Burnside Road, Victoria, BC, Canada V8Z 1M5
e-mail: staylor@pfc.cfs.nrcan.gc.ca

Wagner, William L.
Natural Resources Canada, Canadian Forest Service, Pacific Forestry Centre
506 West Burnside Road, Victoria, BC, Canada V8Z 1M5
e-mail: wiwagner@pfc.cfs.nrcan.gc.ca

Wang, Sen
Natural Resources Canada, Canadian Forest Service, Pacific Forestry Centre
506 West Burnside Road, Victoria, BC, Canada V8Z 1M5
e-mail: senwang@pfc.cfs.nrcan.gc.ca

Watson, Paul
Pulp and Paper Research Institute of Canada
3800 Westbrook Mall, Vancouver, BC, Canada V6S 2L9
e-mail: pwatson@paprican.ca

White, Joanne C.
Natural Resources Canada, Canadian Forest Service, Pacific Forestry Centre
506 West Burnside Road, Victoria, BC, Canada V8Z 1M5
e-mail: joanne.white@pfc.cfs.nrcan.gc.ca

Whitehead, Roger J.
Natural Resources Canada, Canadian Forest Service, Pacific Forestry Centre
506 West Burnside Road, Victoria, BC, Canada V8Z 1M5
e-mail: rwhitehead@pfc.cfs.nrcan.gc.ca

Wilson, Bill
Natural Resources Canada, Canadian Forest Service, Pacific Forestry Centre
506 West Burnside Road, Victoria, BC, Canada V8Z 1M5
e-mail: bwilson@pfc.cfs.nrcan.gc.ca

Wulder, Michael A.
Natural Resources Canada, Canadian Forest Service, Pacific Forestry Centre
506 West Burnside Road, Victoria, BC, Canada V8Z 1M5
e-mail: mwulder@pfc.cfs.nrcan.gc.ca

Preface

Les Safranyik, Bill Wilson, and Allan L. Carroll

Our main objective in producing this book is to provide a comprehensive review and synthesis of the biology and management of the mountain pine beetle (*Dendroctonus ponderosae* Hopkins [Coleoptera: Scolytidae]) in lodgepole pine (*Pinus contorta* Dougl. ex. Loud. var. *latifolia* Engelm.) with a special emphasis on western Canada. In addition, the synthesis is intended to assist in identifying the incremental research necessary to effectively respond to the major beetle epidemic in British Columbia and to provide a benchmark to measure the research contribution of Natural Resources Canada's Mountain Pine Beetle Initiative.

The extensive lodgepole pine forests in western North America provide a wide range of values, including scenic and recreational areas, watersheds, habitat for wildlife, grazing for livestock, and raw materials for wood and wood fibre products. However, lodgepole pines are relatively transient successional pioneers subject to frequent natural disturbances, particularly from wildfires and from insects such as the mountain pine beetle. This creates significant challenges for forest managers. These challenges are further complicated by the apparent dependence of lodgepole pine upon disturbances related to fire and the mountain pine beetle. In the absence of disturbance, lodgepole pine is normally replaced by late-successional species such as spruce and fir. The mountain pine beetle's preference for mature pine and the consequent increased fuel loading and wildfire potential, in combination with the serotinous cone character of lodgepole pine, assist in the perpetuation of lodgepole pine forests (Raffa and Berryman 1987). The combination of these factors tends to produce mixed-age, pine-dominated landscapes.

The mountain pine beetle is an indigenous insect in pine ecosystems throughout western North America. Beetle populations are prone to periodic landscape-level outbreaks where larger diameter trees of mature stands may be heavily depleted in a few years over large areas. During large outbreaks some younger stands may also suffer considerable mortality. The extensive tree mortality that occurs during these outbreaks has important economic and ecological impacts. Consequently, the biology and habits of the beetle, as well as the nature and effects of its interaction with its pine hosts, have been studied and foresters have attempted to manage the problem over the past century or so, both in Canada and the United States.

Despite the large inventory of pine, the increased vulnerability of these pine forests and the scale of outbreak impacts, little of the beetle research is recent. The last comprehensive publications on mountain pine beetle biology and management in lodgepole pine were published over two decades ago (Safranyik et al. 1974, 1975; Amman et al. 1977; Berryman et al. 1978; McGregor and Cole 1985; Amman and Cole 1983). Some of these publications are out of print and others are not readily available to forest managers. Furthermore, even though these past publications were generally comprehensive for their time, there have been important advances since then. Accordingly, this book presents a synthesis of published information on mountain pine beetle biology and management with an emphasis on lodgepole pine forests. The goal is to interpret the diverse and often complex literature within the context of operational mountain pine beetle management. Where possible, sections have been augmented with new, unpublished information, especially on aspects of beetle population biology and epidemiology. As deemed appropriate, information sources relating to host species other than lodgepole pine (e.g., ponderosa pine, *Pinus ponderosa* and jack pine, *P. banksiana*) and other geographic regions (i.e., the western United States) were also included.

The book covers three main subject areas: mountain pine beetle biology, management, and socioeconomic concerns. As such, it is intended to be the most comprehensive treatment of mountain pine beetle to date. The chapters on biology cover taxonomy, life history and habits, area distribution, insect-host tree interactions, development and survival, epidemiology, and outbreak history. The management section covers management strategy, survey and detection, proactive and preventive management, and decision support tools. The chapters on socioeconomic aspects include an economic examination of management programs and the utilization of post-beetle salvage timber in solid wood, panelboard, pulp and paper products.

Our synthesis of mountain pine beetle biology highlights the importance of climate and the evolved interaction between the beetle with its associated blue stain fungi and lodgepole pine in determining the onset and course of beetle epidemics. Significant new information is presented on factors affecting change from endemic to incipient population phase, possible effects of climate change on range expansion, and the structure, growth and development of residual stands following epidemics.

In the management section, new information includes an assessment of remote sensing tools in beetle survey and detection, the role of decision aids in management programs, and the potential of preventive forestry practices to reduce losses from the mountain pine beetle.

The synthesis of the economic aspects of management points out the relatively minor role economic theory has played in beetle management and suggests ways to increase this vital component of decision making. The chapter on the characteristics of post-beetle salvage timber for manufacturing wood products reveals that in spite of considerable published information and local experience with the utilization of salvage timber, there are important gaps in knowledge, especially in relation to changes in the manufacturing qualities of trees as a function of time since death.

The material presented necessarily includes complex technical information, but the book should be a valuable reference for forest managers as well as researchers. As much as it was practicable, each chapter is self-contained and the need for the reader to refer to other chapters for additional information is kept to a minimum. Indeed, for readers with specific topics of interest, electronic copies of individual chapters are available for downloading from the Canadian Forest Service's electronic bookstore at bookstore.cfs.nrcan.gc.ca.

Acknowledgements

Preparation of this publication was only possible through the hard work and commitment of the contributing authors. We greatly appreciated their willing cooperation. We acknowledge the prompt and thorough reviews provided on the various chapters of the book by the following persons: Brian Aukema, Hugh Barclay, Nicholas Coops, Tim Ebata, Ken Gibson, Vince Nealis, Ken Raffa and Ken White. Any errors or omissions are the responsibility of the book editors. The Canadian Forest Service, Pacific Forestry Centre publications group expeditiously brought the book into a publishable format - Joanne Stone and Steve Glover completed the editorial work.

This project was funded by the Government of Canada through the Mountain Pine Beetle Initiative, a program administered by Natural Resources Canada, Canadian Forest Service.

LS, BW & AC

25.11.05

References

Amman, G.D.; McGregor, M.D.; Cahill, D.; Klein, W.H. 1977. Guidelines for reducing losses of lodgepole pine to the mountain pine beetle in unmanaged stands in the Rocky Mountains. USDA Forest Service Intermountain Forest and Range Experiment Station, General Technical Report INT-36. 19 p.

Amman, G.D.; Cole, W.E. 1983. Mountain pine beetle dynamics in lodgepole pine forests. Part II: Population dynamics. USDA Forest Service Intermountain Forest and Range Experiment Station, General Technical Report INT-145. 59 p.

Berryman, A.A.; Amman, G.D.; Stark, R.W., eds. 1978. Theory and practice of mountain pine beetle management in lodgepole pine forests. Symposium Proceedings, Washington State University, Pullman, WA. 223 p.

McGregor, M.D.; Cole, D.M.1985. Integrating management strategies for the mountain pine beetle with multi-resource management of lodgepole pine forests. USDA Forest Service General Technical Report INT-174. 68 p.

Raffa, K.F.; Berryman, A.A. 1987. Interacting selective pressures in conifer-bark beetle systems: a basis for reciprocal adaptations? The American Naturalist 129: 234-262.

Safranyik, L.; Shrimpton, D.M.; Whitney, H.S. 1975. An interpretation of the interaction between lodgepole pine, the mountain pine beetle and its associated blue stain fungi in western Canada. Pages 406-428 *in* D. Baumgartner ed. Management of lodgepole pine ecosystems. Washington State University Extension Service, Pullman, WA.

Safranyik, L.; Shrimpton, D. M.; Whitney, H. S. 1974. Management of lodgepole pine to reduce losses from the mountain pine beetle. Environment Canada, Canadian Forestry Service, Pacific Forest Research Centre, Victoria, BC, Forestry Technical Report 1.

Part 1

Biology

Chapter 1

The biology and epidemiology of the mountain pine beetle in lodgepole pine forests

Les Safranyik and Allan L. Carroll

Abstract

The biology, habits and epidemiology of the mountain pine beetle, *Dendroctonus ponderosae* Hopk. (Coleoptera: Scolytidae), are reviewed with particular reference to lodgepole pine, *Pinus contorta* Dougl. ex Loud. var. *latifolia* Engelm., the main host in Canada. Critical aspects of mountain pine beetle life history (i.e., those that have large impacts on establishment and survival) include (i) efficient host selection and dispersal, (ii) a highly evolved mutualistic relationship with blue stain fungi that aids the beetle in overcoming host resistance, (iii) a semiochemical communication system that mediates mass attack and regulates attack density, (iv) stage-specific development thresholds that ensure synchrony of development within and among growing seasons, and (v) development rates specific to sub-populations that ensure univoltinism over a large part of the geographical range.

Mountain pine beetle populations exist in one of four phases: endemic, incipient epidemic, epidemic (i.e., outbreak) and post-epidemic (i.e., declining). Each of these phases is defined in terms of population size relative to the abundance of available host. Endemic populations principally exist in weakened, often small-diameter trees, and interactions with other bole-infesting bark beetle species are an important determinant of mountain pine beetle establishment and survival. Incipient-epidemic populations develop when the larger-diameter host trees can be successfully colonized either because of a local decline in host resistance or increases in population size due to immigration or favourable breeding conditions, or a combination of these factors. Epidemics exist at the landscape level, and develop mainly as a consequence of large, highly contiguous areas of susceptible host and favourable weather conditions. Epidemics decline either due to adverse weather conditions, or depletion at the landscape level of the host component in which increasing populations can be maintained (i.e., large-diameter trees).

Due to the nature of the interaction between the mountain pine beetle and its host trees, effective management requires detailed yearly surveys and prompt, thorough action against emerging incipient-epidemic infestations. However, given that the mountain pine beetle has evolved as a natural disturbance agent of pine forests, long-term mitigation of large-scale epidemics can only be achieved through management strategies that reduce the susceptibility of lodgepole pine over the landscape.

Résumé

La biologie, les mœurs et l'épidémiologie du dendroctone du pin ponderosa (*Dendroctonus ponderosae* Hopk. [*Coleoptera: Scolytidae*]) sont examinées en rapport avec le pin tordu latifolié (*Pinus contorta* Dougl. ex Loud. var. *latifolia* Engelm.), hôte de prédilection du ravageur au Canada. Les principaux aspects du cycle vital du dendroctone du pin ponderosa (c.-à-d. ceux qui ont une incidence importante sur l'établissement et la survie de l'insecte) comprennent : i) une sélection d'hôte et une dispersion efficaces; ii) un mutualisme très évolué avec des champignons agents du bleuissement qui aident le ravageur à vaincre la résistance de l'hôte; iii) un système de communication sémiochimique qui sert d'intermédiaire aux attaques massives et règle la densité des attaques; iv) des seuils de développement propres au stade, qui assurent une bonne synchronisation du développement au cours d'une même saison de croissance et d'une saison à l'autre; v) une vitesse de développement propre à chaque sous-population, qui assure le maintien de l'univoltinisme à l'échelle d'une grande partie de l'aire de répartition du ravageur.

Les populations de dendroctones du pin ponderosa passent par quatre stades : le stade endémique, le stade de préinfestation, le stade de l'épidémie (c.-à-d. l'infestation) et le stade postépidémie (c.-à-d. le déclin de l'infestation). Chacun de ces stades se définit en fonction des effectifs du ravageur par rapport à l'abondance de l'hôte. Les populations endémiques sont associées principalement aux arbres affaiblis, souvent de petit diamètre, et les interactions avec les autres espèces de scolytes qui infestent le tronc jouent un rôle déterminant dans leur établissement et leur survie. Les populations atteignent le stade de préinfestation lorsqu'elles parviennent à coloniser des hôtes de fort diamètre en raison soit de la baisse localisée de la résistance des hôtes, soit de l'augmentation de leurs effectifs due à l'immigration ou à des conditions propices à la reproduction, ou d'une combinaison de ces deux facteurs. Les populations d'épidémie se retrouvent à l'échelle du paysage, et elles se propagent principalement en raison des vastes régions contiguës d'hôtes vulnérables et de conditions météorologiques favorables. Le déclin de l'épidémie se produit soit en raison de conditions météorologiques défavorables, soit de la diminution à l'échelle du paysage du nombre d'hôtes permettant la croissance des populations du ravageur (c.-à-d. des arbres de grand diamètre).

En raison de la nature de l'interaction entre le dendroctone du pin ponderosa et son hôte, une gestion efficace de la situation exige des relevés annuels détaillés et l'application rapide et rigoureuse de mesures contre le ravageur au stade de préinfestation. Toutefois, comme le dendroctone du pin ponderosa a évolué en agent de perturbation naturelle des forêts de pins, l'atténuation à long terme des épidémies à grande échelle ne peut se réaliser que par des stratégies d'aménagement qui réduisent la vulnérabilité du pin tordu latifolié à l'échelle du paysage.

Introduction

The mountain pine beetle, *Dendroctonus ponderosae* Hopk. (Coleoptera: Scolytidae), is the most destructive biotic agent of mature pine forests in western North America. Normally, mountain pine beetle populations are innocuous, infesting only a few damaged, decadent or suppressed trees scattered throughout a forest. However, populations periodically erupt into large-scale outbreaks capable of causing the mortality of mature trees over many thousands of hectares (Fig. 1). In Canada, the most extensive outbreaks have been situated within the southern interior regions of British Columbia (Unger 1993), while in the United States the largest epidemics have occurred in the Rocky Mountain states (Amman and Cole 1983). In addition to extensive timber losses, mountain pine beetle epidemics may increase fuel loading, alter successional trajectories, affect watershed quality, wildlife composition, and recreational values (Safranyik et al. 1974; McGregor 1985).

Due mainly to the severity of these impacts on forest resource values, the biology and management of the mountain pine beetle has been researched extensively over the past 50 years both in Canada and the United States, and a large body of published information exists. The earlier publications are referenced in Safranyik et al. (1975) and Berryman (1976), while examples of more recent work are found in Amman and Cole (1983), Borden et al. (1983b), Cole et al. (1985), Raffa and Berryman (1986), Bentz et al. (1991), and Carroll and Safranyik (2004).

The following review of the biology, habits and population dynamics of the mountain pine beetle is based on the published literature augmented by unpublished data from our files. We will concentrate on the biology of mountain pine beetle in lodgepole pine (*Pinus contorta* Dougl. ex Loud. var. *latifolia* Engelm.) due to the extent, severity and commercial impacts of epidemics in lodgepole pine forests. We have emphasized the interactions between the beetle with its associated blue stain fungi and lodgepole pine, with particular reference to western Canada.

Figure 1. Mountain pine beetle-caused mortality in a lodgepole pine forest in central British Columbia, Canada.

Distribution, life history, and habits

Taxonomy

Detailed descriptions of the taxonomy of the mountain pine beetle are given in Wood (1982) and Amman and Cole (1983). The following is a brief overview. Hopkins (1902) described *D. ponderosae* from specimens collected from ponderosa pine (*Pinus ponderosa* P. Laws. ex C. Laws) in the Black Hills, South Dakota. The early common name, Black Hills beetle, and more details on biology and habits were provided by Hopkins (1905). The mountain pine beetle (*D. monticolae* Hopk.) was described four years later (Hopkins 1909); the known hosts at the time comprising sugar pine (*P. lambertiana* Dougl.), western white pine (*P. monticola* Dougl. Ex D. Don), lodgepole pine and ponderosa pine. The Jeffrey pine beetle (*D. jeffreyi* Hopk.) was described the same year with hosts listed as Jeffrey pine (*P. jeffreyi* Grev. and Balf.) and ponderosa pine.

Experimental mating of *D. ponderosae* and *D. monticolae* (Hay 1956) indicated that these were actually one species that varied by region and host in some characteristics such as body size. In a comprehensive treatment of the genus *Dendroctonus*, Wood (1963) combined *jeffreyi, monticolae,* and *ponderosae* into a single species: the mountain pine beetle, *D. ponderosae*. Later (e.g., Lanier and Wood 1968; Pitman et al. 1968; Renwick and Pitman 1979; Zúniga et al. 2002), additional evidence supported the synonymy of *ponderosae* and *monticolae*, but indicated a distinctiveness of *jeffreyi*. Additional genetic studies showed differences in mountain pine beetle populations breeding in two varieties of lodgepole pine (*P. contorta* var. *murrayana* and *P. contorta* var *latifolia*) (Stock et al. 1978) suggesting genetic variation among widely separated beetle populations (Stock and Guenther 1979) that might be partially related to host tree species (Stock and Amman 1980).

Life stages

The mountain pine beetle has four life stages: egg, larva, pupa and adult (Fig. 2). Apart from the dispersal phase by mature adults, all of the life stages occur within the subcortical tissues of their host trees. Adult beetles construct egg galleries in newly attacked trees parallel to the direction of the stem (Fig. 2a). Once mated, the females deposit their eggs (approximately 60 per female on average) singly into niches cut in the sides of the gallery and cover them with boring dust (Fig. 2b). Eggs are pearly white to cream coloured, ovoid, and average about 1 mm in diameter. Egg size is positively related to beetle size (McGhehey 1971), and increases with distance along galleries, perhaps due to the ingestion of nutritious phloem by females during gallery construction (Elkin and Reid 2005). Unfertilized eggs remain a uniform colour whereas the colour of fertilized eggs changes with time during embryogenesis. Reid and Gates (1970) classified eggs into four development stages based on appearance. Stage 1 eggs are 1 – 2 days old and homogeneously opaque; stage 2 eggs are 2 – 3 days old and clear at one end; stage 3 eggs are 3 – 4 days old and clear at both ends; stage 4 eggs are 4 – 5 days old and have a clearly developed head capsule visible.

Larvae pass through four growth stages called instars, each of which is terminated by moulting. They have brown sclerotized heads and white to greyish bodies (Fig. 2c). The width of the head capsule increases with larval instar. On average the head capsule ranges in width from 0.50 mm (first instar) to 1.25 mm (fourth instar). The mature (i.e., fourth instar) larva is about 6 mm long (Fig. 2c). The larvae feed individually on the phloem tissue in the inner bark by excavating mines or tunnels that usually extend at right angles to the parent egg gallery. The larval mine generally becomes wider with each successive instar. When encountering another larval mine, some larvae will cross it or mine under it (Amman and Cole 1983); however, parental galleries are rarely crossed. Larvae will also occasionally back down their mines and commence feeding either in a new direction or along the sides of the original mine.

Figure 2. (a) Mountain pine beetle parental galleries in the phloem before eggs hatch, (b) eggs in niches in the parental gallery, (c) a mature (i.e., fourth instar) larva, (d) pupal chamber with pupa, (e) newly formed, teneral adults, (f) and a mature adult. Adapted from Safranyik et al. (1974).

During the latter part of the fourth larval instar, the feeding area is enlarged and cleared of debris. The prepupal and pupal periods are passed in this chamber (Fig. 2d). The pupae are white at first, changing to light brown, and are about 5 mm long. The legs and wings are folded beneath the body and the abdominal segments are exposed (Fig. 2d). This is the earliest stage in which the sexes can be determined (Fig. 3a [Schofer and Lanier 1970]).

At first, adults are pale coloured and soft. These new beetles are commonly called teneral or callow adults (Fig. 2e). They harden and become dark brown to black before emergence. Mature adults range in length from 3.7 to 7.5 mm and have stout, cylindrical bodies (Fig. 2f). Normally the females are larger than the males. For example, the mean pronotal width of female and male beetles from a population in southeastern British Columbia measured 2.08 and 1.94 mm, respectively (McGhehey 1971). The sexes can be reliably identified based on the dimorphism of the posterior margin of the seventh abdominal tergite (Fig. 3b,c [Hopkins 1909; Lyon 1958]). The pointed margin of this tergite on the male is used as part of a stridulation mechanism to produce a high-pitched rasping sound (Michael and Rudinsky 1972). Male stridulation can also be used for separation of the sexes. However, as some males do not stridulate, this method is less reliable than that based on the shape of the seventh abdominal tergite.

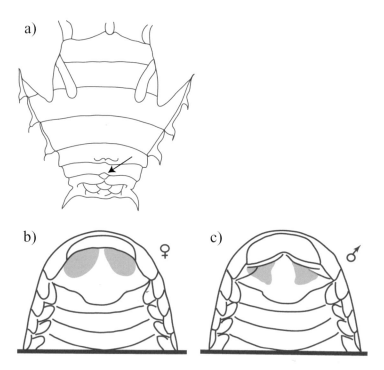

Figure 3. Ventral aspect of mountain pine beetle pupa (a) with arrow indicating characteristic lobe of females (absent in males [Schofer and Lanier 1970]), and dorsal view (elytra and wings removed) of the abdomen of female (b) and male (c) mountain pine beetle adults. Note that the posterior margin of the seventh tergite of females is gently curved, whereas in males it is angular (Lyon 1958). Adapted from Amman and Cole (1983).

Geographic distribution, host trees

The range of the mountain pine beetle extends from northern Mexico (latitude 31° N) to northwestern British Columbia (latitude 56° N), and from the Pacific Coast east to the Black Hills of South Dakota (Fig. 4). In Canada, the beetle is found as far east as the Cypress Hills on the Alberta – Saskatchewan border. The elevational range is from sea level to about 750 m near the northern limit, and up to 3650 m in the most southerly regions (Safranyik 1978).

In western Canada, the principal hosts of the mountain pine beetle are lodgepole pine, ponderosa pine, and western white pine. However, all native pines within the beetle's range, other North American pines (e.g., eastern white pine, *P. strobus* L. and jack pine, *P. banksiana* Lamb.) and some exotic species (e.g., Scots pine, *P. sylvestris* L.) can be infested and killed. Interestingly, host species can cause variation in several life-history parameters such as survival, phenology, fecundity, development rate, and body size (Knight 1959; Reid 1962 a, b, 1963; Billings and Gara 1975; Amman 1982; Safranyik and Linton 1982, 1983; Amman and Cole 1983; Langor 1989).

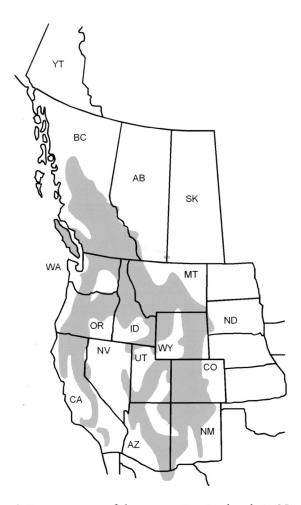

Figure 4. Present range of the mountain pine beetle in North America.

Life cycle

The length of the life cycle varies depending on ambient temperature. Normally throughout most of their range beetle populations have one generation per year (i.e., they are univoltine). During warmer than average summers, parent adults may re-emerge to establish a second brood (Reid 1962a). In cooler summers, such as those that often occur at high elevations, some or all of the brood may require two years to mature.

For univoltine populations, emergence and dispersal, host selection and colonization, and mating and oviposition normally occur during late July to mid August. Within the parental galleries of newly colonized trees, eggs normally hatch within a week or so following deposition and young larvae commence feeding immediately. Larvae often reach third or early fourth instars before temperatures become too cool for continued development. Larvae resume feeding in the spring once temperatures warm sufficiently and complete their development, transforming to pupae by June. New adults occur during late June to mid July. Depending on ambient temperatures, teneral adults require one to two weeks to mature and be capable of emergence and dispersal.

Following mild winters a high proportion of parent beetles often survive within the egg galleries they excavated during the previous season. Some of these beetles may emerge and infest new trees before their progeny complete development. More frequently, early emerging parent beetles construct galleries in the fresh phloem of trees that resisted attack or were only partially attacked (i.e., strip attacked) in the previous season (Rasmussen 1974). Alternatively, surviving parent beetles may continue to extend their galleries and oviposit in the spring if there is sufficient fresh phloem in the trees they originally attacked (Amman and Cole 1983). Progeny produced by early emerging parent beetles have little chance of contributing to population fluctuations because of their lack of coincidence with the general mountain pine beetle population (see Synchrony and Phenology).

Signs and symptoms of attack

Trees attacked by the mountain pine beetle display several distinct signs and symptoms (Fig. 5) and are grouped by the following categories: external-bole signs, crown symptoms, and under-bark symptoms (see Safranyik et al. 1974). External signs on the lower bole of mountain pine beetle-infested trees are usually a combination of (i) pitch tubes surrounding beetle entry holes (pitch tubes are cream to pinkish coloured mixtures of resin and boring dust that are extruded from egg galleries), (ii) boring dust in bark crevices, particularly around the root collar of the tree, iii) patches of bark flaked off by woodpeckers in search of bark beetle brood, and iv) small round emergence holes (about 2.5 mm in diameter) through which the new adults have exited trees once they've completed their development (see Fig. 5a,b,c). Flaked bark accumulates on the ground and is readily seen over snow in winter (Fig. 5b), but trees of low vigour may not produce pitch tubes, and boring dust, emergence holes and woodpecker activity are not unique to mountain pine beetle attacks. So, by themselves, these signs of injury are not reliable indicators of mountain pine beetle attack.

Figure 5. Symptoms of mountain pine beetle attack on the bole (a,b,c), in the foliage (d,e,f) and beneath the bark (g,h,i) of lodgepole pine. Beetles attacking a tree (a) expel light-coloured boring dust that collects around the root collar and bark crevices, while trees often exude pitch around the point of penetration, i.e., pitch tubes (a, inset). During winter, woodpeckers frequently chip away the bark in search of mature larvae (b). As new beetles emerge in the subsequent year, round holes are left in the bark of dead trees (c). The foliage of attacked trees remains green (d), usually until May and June of the year following attack, after which it begins to fade to yellow (e) and finally to red-brown (f) by July and August at approximately the time that new adults emerge. Attacking beetles excavate galleries within the phloem tissue that have a characteristic hook at the bottom and the lower ends are packed with boring dust (g). Larvae construct mines at right angles to the parental gallery (h), terminating in pupal chambers (i) once they've completed development.

Successfully attacked trees are usually killed and their crowns begin to fade from loss of moisture. The first sign of fading is a change in foliage colour from green to greenish-yellow that usually begins in the top of the crown. Later, in sequence, the crown fades to a uniform yellow, bright red and to brown by late summer the year following attack (see Fig. 5d,e,f). In situations where the mountain pine beetle develops on a one-year cycle, all or most of the beetles have emerged by the time the crowns of brood trees have turned brown.

The beginning of the visible symptoms of crown fading depends on a number of factors such as the timing of attack during the year, attack density, tree vigour and weather conditions. In western Canada, the first signs of fading normally occur in late May to early June of the year after attack. However, following hot, dry weather during late summer and early fall, faded crowns may be visible during autumn of the year of attack. Normally, lodgepole pines killed by mountain pine beetle retain some needles 3 to 5 years following attack. So, it is not possible to reliably use crown symptoms to estimate when a tree died, and it follows that aerial assessments of yearly tree mortality are unreliable.

Only the under-bark symptoms are definitive indicators of mountain pine beetle attack. However, the appearance of under-bark symptoms will vary, depending on the time of examination. During late summer, shortly after attack, beetles construct vertical galleries in the phloem with a diagnostic slight hook at the bottom (Fig. 5g). The bottom of each gallery is normally packed with boring dust. Completed galleries are usually approximately 30 cm long, but in some cases they may approach 2 m. Larvae construct their mines perpendicular to the parent gallery (Fig. 5h). During late spring of the year after attack, oval pupal chambers will be visible at the ends of some of the larval mines (Fig. 5i). From then until emergence, larvae, pupae and teneral adults will usually be present within each gallery system. In the case of new, isolated infestations it is advisable to obtain positive identification of adult beetles as confirmation.

Symptoms of mountain pine beetle attack are also visible at the stand level. During the beginning stages of epidemics, infested trees appear in groups (Fig. 6a). Locally, the groups of infested trees will grow in size and number and may coalesce to form larger patches (Fig. 6b). Within the infested patches, proportionately more of the larger-diameter trees are infested. These characteristics of infestations are frequently used for aerial assessment of damage and infestation levels over large areas.

Figure 6. Symptoms of mountain pine beetle attack at the stand level. Infested trees appear in groups (a) during the early stages of epidemics. Often, these groups will grow in size and number and may coalesce to form larger patches (b).

Population processes

Emergence

Although the phase of the mountain pine beetle life cycle beginning with emergence and ending with orientation toward, and colonization of, new host trees is arguably one of the most important aspects of mountain pine beetle ecology, it is perhaps the least understood. During this phase local infestations may grow in size (i.e., spot growth), or new infestations may develop (i.e., spot proliferation).

Prior to emergence, young beetles complete maturation by feeding on the inner bark and on spores of blue stain fungi and other microorganisms that line the walls of their pupal chambers. This enables the flight muscles to increase in size (Reid 1958b), and the mycangia (specialized invaginations of the maxilla) to become charged with fungal (Whitney and Farris 1970) and yeast (Shifrine and Phaff 1956) spores, thereby ensuring transport of necessary microorganisms to new trees (Safranyik et al. 1975). Microorganisms may also be transported from tree to tree by way of sticky spores that adhere to the bodies of emerging beetles (Whitney and Blauel 1972; Six 2003). When the density of new adults is high, their maturation feeding often causes them to coalesce together within a common feeding chamber. The result is that multiple beetles may emerge through a single emergence hole chewed through the bark (Reid 1963; Amman 1969; Safranyik and Linton 1985).

After completion of maturation feeding, it is mostly temperature that determines when emergence begins and the initiation and duration of the dispersal period. Emergence occurs only when ambient temperatures exceed 16°C (Reid 1962a; Schmid 1972; Billings and Gara 1975) and it declines above 30°C (Gray et al. 1972; Rasmussen 1974). Most beetles emerge when temperatures are above 20°C (Fig. 7). This usually occurs during the early to mid-afternoon over the main distributional range in British Columbia. The emergence and flight periods are generally preceded by warm, dry weather, but there is no apparent relationship between the duration of such dry periods and the onset of emergence (Chapman 1967).

The pattern of emergence is determined by several factors. Timing of attack by parent beetles combined with accumulation of heat above the thresholds for development of the various brood stages (Safranyik 1978; Safranyik and Whitney 1985; Bentz et al. 1991) are the primary determinants of life-stage distribution and the subsequent temporal pattern of new adult emergence. Host size (diameter), aspect, height on the bole and brood density also affect emergence. On average, beetles emerge at greater relative rates from large-diameter trees than from trees with small diameters (Safranyik and Jahren 1970). Furthermore, beetles emerge at greater relative rates from the south aspect of the bole compared with the north aspect, and the rates of emergence generally decrease with height on the stem. In addition, large female beetles tend to emerge earlier than small females.

Safranyik and Jahren (1970) found that rates of daily emergence were proportional to cumulative degree-days above 14.4°C, and captures of released mountain pine beetles were directly related to heat accumulation above 16°C (Safranyik et al. 1989). The pattern of daily emergence is controlled by an endogenous rhythm as emergence in the field and in the laboratory exhibit distinct diel periodicity even in total darkness and at constant temperatures (Reid 1962b; Watson 1970; Billings and Gara 1975).

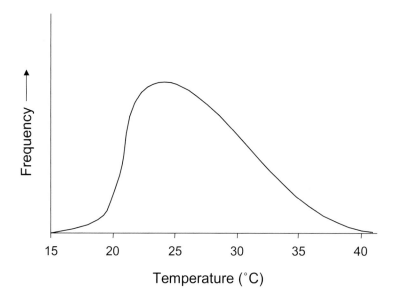

Figure 7. Frequency of emergence of mature mountain pine beetle in relation to temperature. Adapted from McCambridge (1971).

From year to year, the peak of emergence may vary by as much as 1 month, but normally it varies by less than 10 days (Reid 1962a; Safranyik 1978). Throughout most of the beetle's range in western Canada, emergence usually peaks between mid-July and mid-August. The window of peak emergence normally lasts 7 to 10 days, but can be as long as several weeks during cool or rainy periods (Safranyik et al. 1975).

Although the estimated lower and upper temperature limits for beetle flight are 19° and 41°C, respectively (McCambridge 1971), most beetles fly when temperatures are between 22° and 32°C (Safranyik 1978). Within the optimum temperature range, flight propensity increases with increasing light intensity and relative humidity almost up to the saturation point. Once temperatures exceed 35°C, flight propensity begins to decline with light intensity (Shepherd 1966), and above 38°C flight is severely restricted (McCambridge 1971). Since beetles are able to fly at low light intensities, the pattern of daily emergence is more the result of temperature than light intensity (Reid 1962a).

In general, bark beetles do not fly in winds that exceed their maximum flight speed (Seybert and Gara 1970; Meyer and Norris 1973). For large-bodied bark beetles like the mountain pine beetle, the maximum wind speed for flight, and therefore the probable maximum flight speed, is approximately 2 ms^{-1} (Rudinsky 1963).

Dispersal

The initial flight by newly emerged mountain pine beetles tends to disperse them widely throughout the forest (Raffa and Berryman 1980; Safranyik et al. 1992). Indeed, even in the presence of aggregation pheromones, the majority of beetles may disperse out of a stand (Safranyik et al. 1992). That beetles tend not to respond to aggregation pheromones immediately following emergence suggests that a flight period may enhance their host-seeking behaviour. This interpretation is supported by Shepherd (1966) who found that flight exercise increased the responsiveness of mountain pine beetle to host stimuli.

During short-range, within-stand dispersal, most beetles fly several metres above the ground – below tree crowns, but above the undergrowth (Schmitz et al. 1980; Safranyik et al. 1989). The direction of this flight is normally downwind until beetles encounter an attractive odour plume at which point they turn and fly back upwind toward the source (Gray et al. 1972; Byers 1999). Beetles that do not disperse from the stand in which they develop usually locate suitable host trees within two days of emergence, but are capable of searching for several days. In a two-year mark-release-recapture study in a lodgepole pine stand (Safranyik et al. 1992), the number of beetles recaptured following release decreased exponentially with distance from the release point, and about 90% of the recaptured beetles were trapped within 30 m. Although shorter dispersal flights may allow greater investment of energy in reproduction (Elkin and Reid 2005), longer flights may enable beetles to locate habitats with higher quality host trees.

There is a paucity of information about long-range, above-canopy dispersal by the mountain pine beetle. However, Safranyik et al. (1992) found that, based on the vertical distribution of flying beetles, up to 2.5% of a population may attempt long-range dispersal above the canopy. This estimate was determined from a relatively small population and would likely be much higher during an outbreak when locally available host trees have been depleted. Given that beetles fly during periods of warm, fair weather that are often accompanied by air inversions near the ground and by upward convection currents (Chapman 1967), it has been suggested that some beetles are caught in, and directed by, warm convective winds and could easily be carried 20 km or more (Furniss and Furniss 1972). This thesis is supported by collections of mountain pine beetles from snowfields above the timberline, many kilometres from potential host trees. In addition, there is compelling evidence for long-distance dispersal at the scale of hundreds of kilometres. During an outbreak that occurred in the extreme southwestern region of Alberta and adjacent British Columbia in the early 1980s, mountain pine beetles were discovered attacking planted pine trees in community parks and on residential properties 200 to 300 km downwind across the prairies (Cerezke 1989). More recently, mountain pine beetle infestations were discovered in the Peace River region of northeastern British Columbia, an area that was historically considered climatically unsuitable for mountain pine beetle (Safranyik et al. 1974; Carroll et al. 2004). Assessments of these infestations revealed that they originated in a single year (i.e., they did not increase from local populations), most probably as a consequence of long-distance dispersal from outbreak populations located several hundred kilometres to the southwest, across the Rocky Mountains (ALC, personal observation). These observations suggest that long-range dispersal could contribute to the spread of epidemic populations.

Host selection and colonization

Some debate exists as to the mechanism of initial host selection by pioneer beetles. Evidence suggests that vision plays a key role in locating host trees. Several authors have reported tree diameter as a landing stimulus (Hopping and Beall 1948; Cole and Amman 1969), and that large, dark silhouettes (Shepherd 1966) and vertically oriented cylinders (Billings et al. 1976) are attractive to beetles. By contrast, other studies suggest that beetles land at random during the pre-aggregation phase and that the greater number of beetles landing on larger trees is simply due to their larger surface area (Burnell 1977; Hynum and Berryman 1980).

Although the dominant theory of host selection by mountain pine beetle proposes that pioneer females utilize a combination of random landings and visual orientation followed by direct assessment of host suitability after landing (e.g., Wood 1982; Pureswaran and Borden 2003a), there is evidence that dispersing adults orient to lodgepole pine trees suffering from injury or disease (Gara et al. 1984a). Furthermore, Moeck and Simmons (1991) showed that mountain pine beetles are attracted to odours of host material in the absence of visual cues.

After pioneer beetles land on a potential host tree, the decision to initiate a gallery is made based upon gustatory assessment of compounds present in the bark (Raffa and Berryman 1982a). If a tree is considered acceptable, females begin to construct a gallery and in the process instigate a mass attack. A mass attack involves a complex synergism of host-produced (kairomones) and beetle-produced (pheromones) volatile chemicals (Borden 1982). As pioneer females penetrate the bark they oxidize the host monoterpene α-pinene to produce the aggregation pheromone *trans*-verbenol, which is preferentially attractive to males (Pitman et al. 1968; Pitman and Vité 1969; Billings et al. 1976; Libbey et al. 1985). Once males arrive they release *exo*-brevicomin, which at low concentrations attracts mainly females (Borden et al.1983a, 1987; Conn et al. 1983; Libbey et al. 1985). The kairomones α-pinene and myrcene synergize the aggregation pheromones resulting in a mass attack (Renwick and Vité 1970), a process that is normally completed in one to two days on an individual tree. In trees where attack densities are low, females may abandon their egg galleries, even after laying a complement of their eggs (Amman 1975, 1980).

To minimize the effects of intraspecific competition, the mountain pine beetle has evolved a mechanism to terminate host colonization on individual trees at or near optimum attack densities [approximately 60 attacks per m^2 of bark (Raffa and Berryman 1983b)] using chemical cues. Attack density is regulated in part by the production of high concentrations of *exo*-brevicomin and frontalin (Ryker and Libbey 1982; Ryker and Rudinsky 1982; Raffa and Berryman 1983b; Borden et al. 1987) and 2-phenylethanol (Pureswaran et al. 2000) by males, the release of 1-octen-3-ol by females (Pureswaran and Borden 2004), and by the production of the anti-aggregation pheromone verbenone (Pitman and Vité 1969) by intestinal and gallery-inhabiting microbes within both sexes of beetles (Hunt and Borden 1990). This process is not fully understood, and at least three hypotheses have been advanced to explain the process of switching attacks from a "focus tree" to a neighbouring "recipient" tree (Geiszler et al. 1980; Bentz et al. 1996). The first of these theories is that production of the anti-aggregation pheromone, verbenone, through autoxidation of the kairomone α-pinene and microbial conversion of *trans*-verbenol (Hunt and Borden 1989), in combination with the inhibitory effects of high concentrations of frontalin and *exo*-brevicomin, leads to close-range redirection of beetles to nearby trees (e.g., Ryker and Yandell 1983; Borden et al. 1987). A second theory is that cessation of resin exudation from the host tree as it becomes fully utilized (Renwick and Vité 1970), and secondarily the production of inhibitory compounds, leads to the termination of attacks. Thirdly, some authors have proposed that an increasing concentration of *trans*-verbenol emitted from the focus tree envelopes neighbouring trees leading to their subsequent acceptance and attack (Coster and Gara 1968; Geiszler and Gara 1978; Geiszler and Gallucci 1980). Several studies have shown that switching of attacks to a recipient tree often occurs before the original focus tree is fully utilized (Geiszler and Gara 1978; Bentz et al. 1996), thereby precluding the second theory. Raffa and Berryman (1983b) and Bentz et al. (1996) have suggested a combination of the first and third hypotheses where the inhibitory effects of the anti-aggregation pheromones are short range, perhaps affecting the distribution and density of attacks within a tree rather than among trees (Raffa and Berryman 1983b; Renwick and Vite 1970), while plumes of the aggregation pheromones that encompass neighbouring trees are responsible for redirection of attacks. In support of this interpretation, observations (e.g., Raffa and Berryman 1983b) and model analyses (Logan et al. 1998; Powell et al. 1998) indicate that when mountain pine beetle populations are very small (i.e., when attack densities are low) the pattern of successfully attacked trees is mainly determined by the distribution of susceptible trees. In epidemic infestations, however, the availability of susceptible trees is less important and the success of switching attacks is more dependent on factors such as distance between the focus and recipient tree (Mitchell and Preisler 1991; Preisler and Mitchell 1993).

Beetle-host interactions

The mountain pine beetle preferentially attacks large trees. This is because characteristics of the stem that are related to tree size are the primary determinants of a tree's potential to produce beetles once it has been successfully colonized (Safranyik et al. 1975; Amman and Cole 1983).

Total attacks and brood production per tree are positively related to tree age and diameter at breast height ([dbh] i.e., 1.3 m) of lodgepole pine trees (Fig. 8). This is due in part to the fact that larger trees have thicker bark (Fig. 9a). Mountain pine beetles require a minimum thickness of bark ($\approx$1.5 mm) beneath which to construct their galleries (Fig. 9b). When beetles attempt to excavate egg galleries in thin bark, they often break through to the outside. If this occurs, beetles will abandon the tree. Thick bark also affords protection from natural enemies, temperature extremes, and sapwood drying (e.g., Reid 1963; Safranyik et al. 1974). Furthermore, attacking beetles require bark scales, crevices and fissures as points to brace against to initiate boring through the bark (Shepherd 1965). The rough boles of older, larger trees tend to have a much greater density of these potential boring points than smaller, younger trees (Safranyik 1971).

Bark characteristics also affect the spatial pattern of attacks. Beetles initiate galleries with a regular spacing on the bole, apparently because of the regular arrangement of bark niches (Shepherd 1960, 1965). This conclusion is strengthened by the finding that the proximity to previously established attacks has no effect on attack initiation (Safranyik 1971). There is also a horizontal attack gradient around the circumference of the stem (Shepherd, 1960,1965; Reid 1963; Carson and Cole 1965; Safranyik 1971). In the clear bole zone, the heaviest attacks are usually found on the northern aspect and the lightest attacks on the southern aspect (Fig. 9c). Shepherd (1965) suggested that this is the result of the attacking beetles' reaction to light intensity and temperature. Since most flights occur on bright sunny days, and peak flight is in the early to mid afternoon (Reid 1960), the southern aspect of the bole usually has high light intensities and surface temperatures during this time period, conditions that stimulate beetles to continue flying (Shepherd 1966).

Beetles ultimately prefer large trees due to the positive relationship between tree diameter and phloem thickness (Amman 1969; Shrimpton and Thomson 1985). Brood production by the mountain pine beetle is directly related to phloem thickness (Amman 1969, 1972b; Berryman 1976; Amman and Cole 1983) given the greater quantity of the resource and perhaps its greater nutritional value. In trees with thick phloem, beetles lay more eggs per centimetre of gallery (Amman and Cole 1983), experience less intraspecific competition as larvae (Cole 1973), develop faster (Amman and Cole 1983), and ultimately produce larger brood beetles (Amman and Pace 1976) compared to beetles in trees with thin phloem.

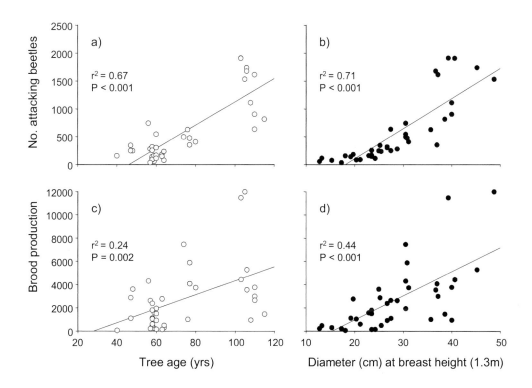

Figure 8. The number of attacking beetles and the number of brood produced per tree in relation to (a, c) tree age, and (b, d) the diameter of trees at breast height for an incipient mountain pine beetle population from southeastern British Columbia. Adapted from Safranyik (1968).

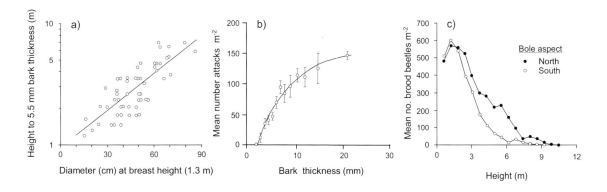

Figure 9. (a) The diameter at breast height in relation to the height on the bole at which the bark is at least 5.5 mm thick, (b) the mean (± 1 S.E.) density of mountain pine beetle attacks in relation to the combined thickness of the inner and outer bark, and (c) the mean number of brood beetles per m² of bark versus height on the bole of the North and South sides of lodgepole pine trees. Data were collected from an incipient mountain pine beetle infestation from southeastern British Columbia. Adapted from Safranyik (1968).

Although phloem thickness is generally positively correlated with tree diameter, stand conditions often affect this relationship. For example, senescing or unthrifty trees tend to have thin phloem (Berryman 1982a). In addition, competition among trees within a stand may affect phloem thickness. The number of attacking beetles and the number of brood produced are both positively related to the volume of a tree's live crown and the sum of the distances to its nearest neighbours (Fig. 10). Trees with larger crowns growing at greater distances from neighbouring trees suffer less competition for resources and in turn have thicker, potentially more nutritious phloem (Safranyik 1968). Variation in phloem thickness as a consequence of stand conditions likely explains why tree age and diameter explain much more of the variability in the number of attacking beetles (Fig. 8a,b) than the subsequent number of brood produced (Fig. 8c,d).

Because the combined thickness of the bark and phloem tends to decline with height on the bole, the density of attacks is a decreasing function of infested height (Fig. 9c). As a consequence of these relationships and the effect of tree size on beetle landing rates, young trees with thin bark, and small-diameter, older trees are rarely attacked or killed. Moreover, because brood production is much lower in small-diameter trees compared with large ones, populations breeding in small trees have a much lower potential rate of increase compared to those infesting large trees. In practical terms, this means that on average lodgepole pine trees up to 25 cm in diameter are beetle sinks (i.e., more beetles attack than emerge), whereas trees over 25 cm in diameter are beetle sources (i.e., more beetles emerge than attack [Safranyik et al. 1974]).

Although the mountain pine beetle prefers to colonize larger trees within a stand, such trees are normally the fastest growing, most vigorous trees at a given age and site quality (Shrimpton 1973a). As a consequence, they are also the best able to defend themselves from attack. Successful colonization by the mountain pine beetle depends on the death of its host tree. This intense selection pressure has resulted in the evolution of a complex array of defenses that enable lodgepole pine to resist attack. These defenses include resins released from constitutive resin ducts severed as beetles bore through the bark (Smith 1963; Shrimpton and Whitney 1968; Reid and Gates 1970; Berryman 1972), and secondary induced resinosis by tissues surrounding the wound (Reid et al. 1967; Shrimpton and Whitney 1968; Berryman 1972; Shrimpton 1973b; Raffa and Berryman 1982b; 1983a,b). The flow of constitutive resin slows attacking beetles and their accompanying microorganisms and may even expel them from a tree [i.e., pitch out (see Fig. 11)]. The induced response involves localized breakdown of parenchyma cells, the formation of traumatic resin ducts, and ultimately the production of secondary resin comprising increased concentrations of terpene and phenolic compounds (Raffa and Berryman 1982b; 1983a). The phloem becomes saturated and liquid resin exudes through the sites of attack. If the induced response is rapid and extensive, the beetles and associated microorganisms will be confined and killed in a lesion of dead tissue.

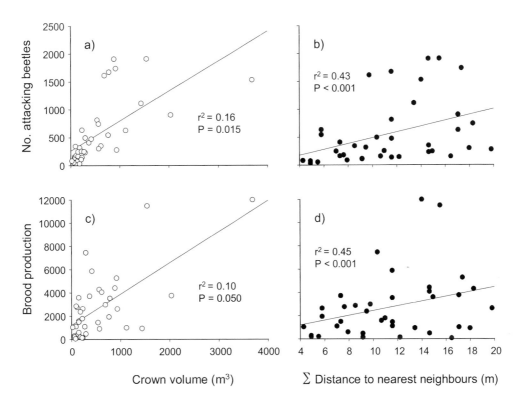

Figure 10. The number of attacking beetles and the number of brood produced per tree in relation to (a, c) volume of the live crown, and (b, d) the sum of the distances to each of the three nearest neighbours larger than 10 cm diameter at breast height (1.3 m) for an incipient mountain pine beetle population from southeastern British Columbia. Adapted from Safranyik (1968).

The mountain pine beetle employs two strategies to overcome the defenses of lodgepole pine. The first relies upon cooperative behaviour in the form of mass attack as described above. By rapidly concentrating attacks on selected trees in response to aggregation pheromones, the beetles exhaust the host's defensive response (Safranyik et al. 1975; Berryman 1976; Raffa and Berryman 1983b; Berryman et al. 1989). If sufficient beetles arrive at a rate that exceeds the resistance capacity of a particular tree, then colonization will be successful.

The second strategy derives from a mutualistic relationship between the mountain pine beetle and several species of blue stain fungi. Spores of these fungi are acquired and disseminated via the mycangia, which are paired invaginations of the exoskeleton of the maxillae present in both sexes (Whitney and Farris 1970) (Fig. 12a). The fungal spores are inoculated into trees as beetles bore through the bark. They germinate quickly and penetrate living cells in both phloem and xylem (Safranyik et al. 1975; Ballard et al. 1982, 1984; Solheim 1995) (Fig. 12b) causing desiccation and disruption of transpiration (Mathre 1964), effectively terminating resin production by the tree. As the fungus colonizes a tree, the mountain pine beetle brood develops. At the end of larval development, coincident with pupation, the fungi line the pupal chambers with a dense layer of asexual propagative spores (conidiophores and conidia; Fig. 12c). Newly eclosed beetles feed on the fungi for a period of days to weeks before emergence, during which time the mycangia are charged with spores (Whitney 1971).

The mountain pine beetle may benefit from its association with blue stain fungi in several additional ways (reviewed by Six and Klepzig 2004). Colonization of the phloem and sapwood by the mycangial fungi may: (i) protect beetle broods from antagonistic species of fungi (Whitney 1971), (ii) improve the moisture composition of phloem for larvae (Reid 1961), and (iii) provide nutrients required to complete development (Six and Paine 1998).

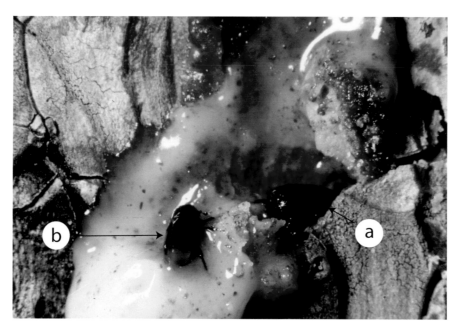

Figure 11. Defensive resin exuded by lodgepole pine in response to attack by the mountain pine beetle. Note the female beetle (a) penetrating the bark, and male (b) partially engulfed by resin.

Figure 12. Maxilla of mountain pine beetle (a) showing mycangium (indicated by arrow) with fungal material protruding. Cross section of a lodgepole pine tree killed by mountain pine beetle with characteristic blue staining of the sapwood (b) as a consequence of fungal colonization. Mountain pine beetle pupal chamber (with pupa) lined with a dense layer of blue stain fungi spores (c).

Two species of blue stain fungus, *Ophiostoma clavigerum* (Robinson-Jeffrey & Davidson) Harrington and *O. montium* (Rumbold) von Arx, are consistently associated with mountain pine beetle (Whitney and Farris 1970; Six and Paine 1998; Six 2003; Kim et al. 2005). Interestingly, recent studies have shown that *O. clavigerum* is mainly acquired and disseminated from the mycangia, whereas the sticky spores of *O. montium* are mainly carried phoretically on the exoskeletons of beetles (Six 2003). Moreover, *O. clavigerum* appears to be a mutualist with a long evolutionary history with mountain pine beetle. By contrast, *O. montium* is a more recent associate that acts antagonistically to mountain pine beetle brood, possibly parasitizing the mutualism between the beetle and *O. clavigerum* (Six and Paine 1998, 1999).

At the stand level, resistance of lodgepole pine to colonization by the mountain pine beetle and blue stain fungi is affected by the normal process of stand aging. Depending on site quality, stands tend to be most resistant between 40 and 60 years of age, and resistance then declines rapidly with age (Safranyik et al. 1974) (Fig. 13a). Resistance begins to decline at about the point when, in fully stocked stands, current annual increment peaks and basal area growth culminates (Safranyik et al. 1974, 1975; Raffa and Berryman 1982b) (Fig. 13b). Thereafter, the vigour of trees declines as they reach maturity and begin to compete for resources. Under these conditions, if trees have reached sufficient size, mountain pine beetle populations can increase rapidly. As a general rule, by the time stands reach 80 to 100 years of age, they are highly susceptible to mountain pine beetle.

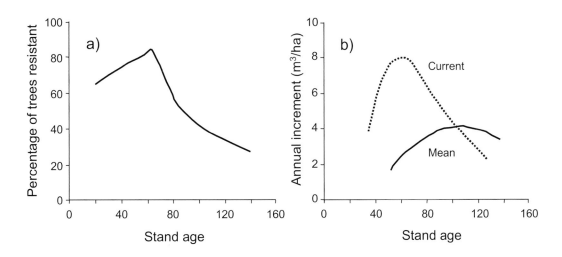

Figure 13. The frequency of trees resistant to inoculation with blue stain fungi in relation to age (a), and the current and mean annual growth increments (b) for a fully stocked lodgepole pine stand growing on a moderately productive site. Adapted from Safranyik et al. (1974).

Cold tolerance

Within the host tree, cold temperature is often the largest single source of mortality in mountain pine beetle populations (Safranyik 1978; Cole 1981). Not surprisingly, the beetle has evolved an effective mechanism by which it can tolerate temperatures commonly encountered during winter within its range. Cold tolerance is acquired through the production and accumulation of glycerol, a polyhydric alcohol, in the hemolymph (i.e., the blood) as temperatures decline during autumn (Somme 1964; Bentz and Mullins 1999). Tolerance to cold varies with life stage. Larvae are the most cold tolerant followed by adults, pupae, then eggs (Safranyik et al. 1974). Reid and Gates (1970) determined the lethal temperature for eggs to be -18°C. Logan et al. (1995) estimated that the lethal temperature range for pupae is between -18° and -34°C, and that for adults between -23° and -34°C. Larval tolerance to cold increases as they mature (Amman 1973; Safranyik et al. 1974; Langor 1989; Safranyik and Linton 1998; but see Bentz and Mullin 1999) even though the first three larval stages contain proportionately the same amount of glycerol (Somme 1964). Lethal low temperatures for larvae have been estimated as manifesting between -23° and -29°C for first instars, -23° and -34°C for second instars, and –29° and -40°C for both third-instar and fourth-instar larvae (Logan et al. 1995).

Given the gradual accumulation of glycerol, cold-hardiness is greatest during the period from December to February when winter temperatures are usually lowest. Late larval instars are the normal overwintering stage and can withstand temperatures near -40°C for extended periods during this time (Wygant 1940; Yuill 1941). However, if low temperatures occur early in the year before the mountain pine beetle is able to produce sufficient glycerol, or late in the winter after the beetle has begun to metabolize it, significant mortality can occur (Wygant 1940; Safranyik et al. 1974). For example, if -30°C were to occur in mid winter, little mortality would be expected. However, if this temperature were to occur at the end of October, or in the middle of March, then nearly 100% mortality can be expected (see Fig. 14). Interestingly, in 1984 and 1985 a major outbreak in the Chilcotin region of central British Columbia collapsed due to a series of days during which temperatures dropped below -30°C in late October and early November, respectively (Safranyik and Linton 1991). The mortality due to unseasonable cold temperatures during the winter of 1984-85 was so severe that surviving brood were restricted to the lower 0.5 m of the bole (below the snowline), and comprised only 10% of the numbers required for replacement of the parent generation.

The effects of cold exposure are normally exerted within the first two to four hours of exposure (Wygant 1940; Yuill 1941; Somme 1964). However, many factors can moderate the effects of low temperatures on mountain pine beetle mortality. Thick bark and deep snow will insulate beetle broods from declining ambient temperatures (Wygant 1940; Safranyik et al. 1974). Also, the rate of decline of subcortical temperatures is slower for large-diameter versus small-diameter trees due to the greater capacity of large objects to store heat (Safranyik and Linton 1998). Beetle attack characteristics will also affect the potential for mortality due to cold. As temperatures approach lethal lows, mortality is negatively related to attack,

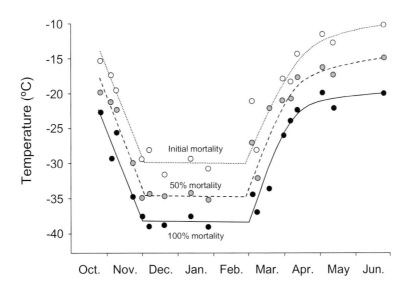

Figure 14. Temperature thresholds at which initial, 50% and 100% mortality of third and fourth instar mountain pine beetle larvae occurs in relation to time of year. Larvae were exposed to low temperatures for 2.5 hours. Adapted from Wygant (1940).

brood and egg gallery densities, due to the insulating effects of air pockets created by gallery construction (Safranyik and Linton 1998). Consequently, for cold weather events to impose significant mortality upon a mountain pine beetle population, temperatures must decline and remain low for several days to ensure that subcortical temperatures reach lethal levels.

Synchrony and phenology

The potential for mountain pine beetle populations to establish and persist within habitats with suitable host trees is largely dependent upon the phenology and synchrony of populations within and among seasons. However, unlike many insects in seasonal environments, the mountain pine beetle does not have a diapause (i.e., an obligatory winter torpor) to functionally synchronize populations with critical phenological events (Logan and Bentz 1999). Development is under direct temperature control, suggesting that in environments with temperature regimes outside a narrow optimal range, population synchrony would degrade over time. Interestingly, the high mortality associated with asynchrony has selected for adaptations that ensure adult emergence is temporally coincident, thereby maximizing chances for successful mass attacks (Raffa and Berryman 1987), and phenologically timed to enable broods to mature to cold-tolerant life stages before winter (Logan and Bentz 1999; Logan and Powell 2001).

Adult emergence is synchronized by stage-specific responses to temperature (Bentz et al. 1991). Late instar larvae have higher temperature thresholds for development than early instars, preventing progression to cold-susceptible advanced life stages before the onset of winter. Due to their lower developmental thresholds, early instars originating from late-hatching eggs are able to "catch up" and become synchronous with the rest of the population after temperatures have become too cool for late instar larval development (Bentz et al. 1991). To ensure that populations maintain their phenological timing, the mountain pine beetle has also evolved regional differences in its developmental rate. Given the large differences in heat accumulation in the northern versus southern portions of its range, populations of the mountain pine beetle in the north have evolved to develop faster for a given input of temperature than beetles from the south (Bentz et al. 2001). These two adaptations ensure that populations can maintain a synchronous univoltine life cycle that is phenologically coincident with critical seasonal events over an extremely broad range of climatic conditions.

In cooler environments, such as those that occur at high elevations and near the northern edges of its range, heat accumulation is often insufficient for completion of the typical univoltine life cycle and mountain pine beetle populations become semivoltine (Fig. 15). Stretching the life cycle over two years results in severe mortality since the beetles will be forced to overwinter twice, often in cold-susceptible stages, and exposed to natural enemies for a longer period (Amman 1973; Safranyik 1978). Moreover, a two-year life cycle slows the beetle's physiological clock in relation to the chronological clock, prolonging critical life history events such as adult emergence and dispersal (Logan et al. 1995; Logan and Powell 2001). This will significantly reduce colonization success since the mountain pine beetle relies on mass attack to overcome host resistance.

Generally, in areas where mountain pine beetle populations can maintain a univoltine life cycle, the frequency of adverse weather conditions is not great enough to prevent development of outbreaks or to reduce populations to low, endemic levels. By contrast, in semivoltine populations climate becomes a dominant factor affecting both the distribution and abundance of mountain pine beetle (Safranyik 1978).

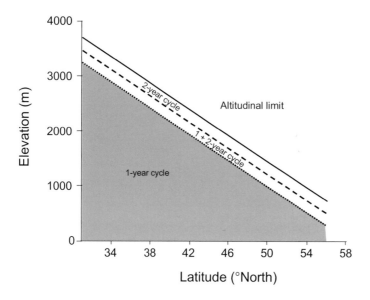

Figure 15. Historic distribution of mountain pine beetle life cycle duration in relation to elevation and latitude. Adapted from Amman (1973).

Population dynamics

Several authors have modelled the dynamics of mountain pine beetle populations (Berryman 1976; Cole et al. 1985; Raffa and Berryman 1986; Polymenopoulos and Long 1990; Safranyik et al. 1999a). It is not our intention to review modelling techniques. Instead we will address the independent and interacting effects of the various aspects of mountain pine beetle life history that determine its population dynamics (i.e., the fluctuation of populations in time and space), some of which may have been included in various modelling efforts.

Mating and oviposition

Prior to mating, females construct the initial 1 to 5 cm of the egg gallery in the phloem tissue across the grain of the wood of their host tree, keeping it clear of boring dust (Reid 1962b). The male joins the female and mating takes place in the lower end of the egg gallery. Nearly all mating occurs after initiation of the egg gallery. Indeed, only 1% or 2% of females are mated prior to emergence and dispersal (Reid 1958a; McCambridge 1970). After mating, males assist females with gallery construction by removing debris, plugging the entrance hole and packing boring dust at the lower end of the gallery. They also guard against the intrusion of other males (McGhehey 1968; Ryker and Rudinsky 1976) and may continue to produce anti-aggregation pheromones (Pureswaran and Borden 2003b). Males often die in the egg gallery and are sealed in by the female as she continues packing the lower end of the gallery with debris. However, males may leave galleries to seek additional females. The quantity of spermatozoa produced by males increases for several days after emergence (Cerezke 1964).

Male mountain pine beetles are polygynous and multiple mating is the norm; however, mating frequency is much reduced after females commence egg laying (Reid 1962b). In nature the male:female sex ratio is near 1:2, but under laboratory conditions, a ratio a low as 1:4 did not affect mating success (Reid 1958a). Sperm remains viable in the spermatheca for at least one year so that re-emerged females do not have to mate again to produce viable eggs.

Within the host tree, the behaviour of female adults in relation to egg gallery construction, egg laying and flight preparation are determined to a large extent by moisture and temperature conditions (Reid 1962b). Oviposition ceases when the moisture content of the phloem and outer sapwood falls below 105% and 60% of oven dry weight, respectively. Under drier conditions than these, the female beetle ceases egg laying, builds up its flight muscles, and re-emerges to make a second flight and attack. The lower temperature threshold for boring and oviposition activity is between 2° and 7°C, depending on the vigour of the individual beetle. The rate of egg gallery construction, egg density, and the numbers of eggs laid per day all increase with temperature above the lower threshold in a curvilinear fashion (Amman 1972a). The upper temperature limits for boring and oviposition have not been investigated. However, for the closely related Douglas-fir beetle, *Dendroctonus pseudotsugae* Hopkins, Rudinsky and Vité (1956) reported that egg gallery construction continued at 32°C, but restlessness and excessive activity hindered organized boring.

Under favourable conditions of moisture, temperature, and attack density, individual beetles can construct egg galleries up to 1.5 m in length and lay over 200 eggs (Reid 1962b). Generally, however, egg galleries are less than 30 cm long and contain fewer than 75 eggs. Large beetles lay more eggs and construct longer egg galleries than small beetles (Reid 1962b; McGhehey 1971; Amman 1973). The number of eggs per centimetre of egg gallery length (egg density) is independent of female size except for the smaller beetles that construct shorter egg galleries (McGhehey 1971). In three populations from southern British Columbia, egg density ranged from 2.4 to 4.2 eggs/cm (Richmond 1935; Reid 1962b; McGhehey 1971). Since fewer numbers of eggs are laid at the beginning and at the end of egg galleries, average egg density is less in short versus long egg galleries. Egg density is also affected by the proximity of adjacent egg galleries. The number of eggs per centimetre of gallery increases to a plateau once egg galleries are at least 2.5 cm apart (Amman and Cole 1983).

Survival and development

Temperature and moisture are the two most important abiotic factors affecting brood development and survival (Safranyik 1978). The physiological effects of temperature are important in a) delimiting growth and development, b) setting growth and development rates, c) regulating cold-hardiness, and d) determining survival. Temperature and moisture also affect brood development and survival indirectly through effects on host quality and host resistance. Other important mortality factors are competition for food and space, host quality and host defenses, and natural enemies. The relative importance of these factors varies with the state of the population (i.e., infestation size and age) and brood stage.

Eggs

The minimum and maximum temperatures for egg hatch are near 1.7° and 35°C, respectively (Reid and Gates 1970). However, only a few eggs hatch below 4.4°C. At constant 10°C and 20°C, Amman and Cole (1983) reported average hatching times of 36.6 and 8.4 days, respectively, for beetles from the intermountain region of the western United States. The corresponding values obtained by Safranyik and Whitney (1985) from the central interior of British Columbia, 34.0 and 7.4 days, agree reasonably well with those reported by Amman and Cole (1983), considering the differences in experimental methods and the wide geographic separation of beetle populations used for obtaining eggs.

The time required for mountain pine beetle eggs to hatch decreases with temperature in a curvilinear fashion (Safranyik and Whitney 1985; Logan and Amman 1986). Within the temperature limits for development, the rate of egg hatch per day is a curvilinear function of temperature with a maximum around 24° – 27°C (Safranyik and Whitney 1985; Bentz et al. 1991; Logan and Powell 2001). Under field conditions in southern British Columbia, an average of 118.4 degree-days were required above a threshold temperature of 4.4°C for half of the eggs to hatch (Reid and Gates 1970). The mean daily temperature during the study period was 15.4°C. At constant 15°C, these authors estimated that 127.2 degree-days were required above 4.4°C for half of the eggs to hatch. Similarly, Safranyik and Whitney (1985) found that 134.0 degree-days were required for half of the eggs to hatch for beetles originating from central British Columbia at the same constant temperature and temperature threshold reported in Reid and Gates (1970). The difference in the reported heat unit requirements for egg hatch based on constant temperatures in the laboratory versus field conditions may be explained in part by a non-linear rate of development above a lower temperature threshold. Differences in the degree-day requirements for egg hatch at constant temperatures may be due to differences in response to temperature among subpopulations.

Eggs of the mountain pine beetle are very susceptible to cold temperatures. Even when conditioned at -5°C, eggs freeze at an average temperature of -18°C whereas eggs not conditioned freeze at -17°C (Reid and Gates 1970). Eggs stored at -5°C for one month suffered 75% mortality. Interestingly, eggs in the first two stages of development were more susceptible to cold temperatures than older stages (Reid and Gates 1970). Since freezing temperatures are the norm in most areas where mountain pine beetles occur, and temperatures lower than the maximum supercooling point (i.e., -18°C) are common, overwintering eggs typically suffer complete mortality.

Conditions associated with the host tree will also affect eggs. Successful embryogenesis and egg hatch requires at least 90% relative humidity beneath the bark (Reid 1969). Furthermore, volatiles originating from defensive resin have only minimal impact (i.e., 3% mortality) on eggs, but coating the eggs with resin causes complete mortality (Reid and Gates 1970). On individual trees Reid (1963) found that up to 32% of the egg galleries were rendered non-productive by resin soaking.

The role of predation, parasitism and disease in the population dynamics of the mountain pine beetle is not well known. In theory, each factor may regulate low populations (McCambridge and Trostle 1972). A large number of predators and parasites are associated with the mountain pine beetle; comprehensive lists are given in DeLeon (1934) and Amman and Cole (1983). Rasmussen (1976) published a field guide to the most abundant insect parasites and predators of the mountain pine beetle in lodgepole pine. Other major references on natural enemies of bark beetles are Bushing (1965), Dahlsten (1982), and Moeck and Safranyik (1984). In general, the abundance of natural enemies varies considerably among stands as well as within and between trees within stands.

Medetera aldrichii Wheeler (Diptera: Dolichopodidae) is considered one of the most effective egg predators of mountain pine beetle as it may destroy up to 50% of eggs in some situations (DeLeon 1935b). Adult flies (Fig. 16a) feed on small insects and mites on the bark surface of trees. Larvae forage within beetle galleries (Fig. 16b). In ponderosa pine, Schmid (1971) found that *M. aldrichii* was most common within the first 10 cm of mountain pine beetle galleries located between 1.5 m and 3 m in height on the bole. The density of *M. aldrichii* larvae averaged 30 to 40 per m² bark, and each larva consumed 15 to 25 mountain pine beetle eggs. However, in a laboratory study of egg mortality in lodgepole pine spanning four seasons, Amman and Cole (1983) found that *M. aldrichii* consumed only 2.5% to 6.5% of mountain pine beetle eggs.

Amman and Cole also found that up to 4.1% of egg mortality was caused by nematode worms, and 0.8%-1.8% was attributed to unidentified fungi. Lesser amounts of mortality were caused by cannibalism, unknown factors, and infertility.

Larvae

Most of the mountain pine beetle life cycle is spent in the larval stage. Consequently, many biotic and abiotic factors have the potential to act alone or in concert to influence survival and development.

Figure 16. Common predators and parasitoids of the mountain pine beetle: *Medetera aldrichii* Wheeler (Diptera: Dolichopodidae) adult (a) and larva (b); *Thanasimus undatulus* Say (Coleoptera: Cleridae) adult (with a mountain pine beetle) (c) and its larva (d); and *Coeloides dendroctoni* Cushman (Hymenoptera:Braconidae) adults (e) and a larva parasitizing a late instar mountain pine beetle larva (f).

The lowest temperature threshold for larval development is near 2.2°C (McCambridge 1974). However, to ensure populations develop synchronously, the threshold temperature for development increases with successive larval instars (Amman and Cole 1983; Bentz et al. 1991; Logan et al. 1995; Logan and Powell 2001 [see Synchrony and Phenology]). The survival of larvae increases with increasing temperatures to a peak of 24°C, after which survival declines precipitously (Safranyik and Whitney 1985). Beetles are significantly smaller when reared at a constant 25°C compared to those reared at 15°C or 20°C (Amman and Cole 1983; Safranyik and Whitney 1985). At temperatures between 30°C and 35°C larvae will die within 10 days of hatching, still in the first instar.

The average number of degree-days at constant temperatures required for beetle development from egg to adult above a threshold of 5.6°C ranged from 478.3 at 27°C, to 546.6 at 18°C, the lowest temperature at which development was completed (Safranyik and Whitney 1985). As with the egg stage, the differences in degree-day accumulation requirements at different constant temperatures suggest a non-linear development rate above a threshold. Rearing of beetles from the egg to the adult stage was unsuccessful at 10°C and 15°C; at the latter temperature the larvae completed development, turned creamy white, stopped feeding and died 167 – 217 days after the start of incubation. Interestingly, Amman and Cole (1983) were successful in rearing mountain pine beetle from the egg to the adult stage at a constant 15°C, suggesting regional differences in beetle subpopulations.

Competition among mountain pine beetle larvae is the principal density-dependent mortality factor that regulates beetle populations. The significance of intraspecific competition to beetle populations is evidenced by the extremely effective system of anti-aggregation pheromones that has evolved to regulate attack density during colonization. Competition for food and space has a complex effect on brood survival. In general, larval survival is inversely related to attack and egg gallery density. The nature of this relationship is affected by a number of host factors such as tree resistance, diameter, phloem thickness and moisture content. Consequently, under a given set of climatic conditions, low attack densities in non-resistant trees with thick phloem tend to produce high brood per parent ratios (e.g., Reid 1963; Amman and Pace 1976; Berryman 1976).

The effect of larval density on mountain pine beetle fitness is instar dependent. Cole (1973) found that, with increasing larval density, in artificial medium both initial feeding and survival rates increased, and duration between moults of the first two instars decreased. On the other hand, crowding increased the duration of the last two larval instars, and prolonged high larval densities decreased survival to the adult stage. Crowding increases the frequency of encounters, especially among late instar larvae, and frequently results in death from cannibalism or injury (Amman and Cole 1983). Ultimately, the fecundity of surviving females is negatively related to the level of crowding during the larval stages (Cole 1973).

Impacts of phloem thickness are also partly instar dependent. Initially, the rate of mining by larvae in thin phloem is faster than that in thick phloem, and this results in significantly larger individuals (determined by head capsule widths) during the second and third instars (Cole 1973; Amman and Cole 1983). Higher initial feeding rates in thin versus thick phloem may be due to the need to consume a greater quantity of a less-nutritional substrate to obtain sufficient resources for development. However, by the end of the larval period, individuals developing in thick phloem are much larger than those from thin phloem, due to a combination of overall better nutrition and faster feeding rates during the third and fourth instars.

The production of defensive resin by the tree acts directly on larvae as a physical impediment to feeding, and indirectly by soaking otherwise nutritionally adequate phloem (Shrimpton 1978; Raffa and Berryman 1983a). Defensive resin is also antagonistic to the blue stain fungi (e.g., Smith 1972; Reid et al. 1967) that the beetle depends upon to complete development (see Insect-Host Interactions). Moreover, low larval survival has been associated with high densities of resin blisters in the bark (Berryman 1976) and resin soaking within the egg galleries (Reid 1963). As a consequence of the diminishing impacts of host resistance and increasing impacts of intraspecific interactions with increasing attack density, brood survival is a hump-back function of attack density (Reid 1963; Amman and Pace 1976; Berryman 1976; Raffa and Berryman 1983b [Fig. 17]).

Excessive drying of the phloem and outer sapwood is detrimental to larval feeding and survival. Under very dry conditions the larvae will desiccate and die. The depth of sapwood in even-aged trees tends to be directly related to tree diameter and since the sapwood contains more moisture than the heartwood (Reid 1961), the greater rate of drying of small-diameter trees is assumed to be related to reduced sapwood depth (Amman 1978). Under laboratory conditions, the phloem of young trees can produce large brood densities (Amman and Cole 1983). However, brood production in the field is generally poor, mainly because of the high resin content in the bark of young trees and excessive drying of the sapwood and phloem following attacks.

Interspecific competition is also an important factor affecting the development and survival of mountain pine beetle brood. Over fifty species of scolytid bark beetles breed in the subcortical tissues of lodgepole pine in Canada (Bright 1976). The vast majority of these species do not infest healthy, large-diameter trees, and are therefore referred to as "secondary" species. Depending on host requirements and geographic distribution, only a subset of these species is expected to be present in any given stand of lodgepole pine. Interestingly, in a multi-year study of the interaction of mountain pine beetle with other bark beetle species, the authors (unpublished data) found that throughout central British Columbia endemic mountain pine beetle populations (see Epidemiology) were consistently associated with six or seven secondary species that inhabit the lower bole of lodgepole pine trees (Table 1).

Table 1. Bark beetle (Coleoptera: Scolytidae) species commonly found inhabiting the lower bole of lodgepole pine trees in direct association with endemic mountain pine beetle populations in British Columbia.

Species	Common name
Pseudips mexicanus (Hopkins)	Monterey pine beetle
Ips latidens (LeConte)	-
I. pini (Say)	pine engraver
Hylurgops porosus (LeConte)	-
H. rugipennis (Mannerheim)	-
Dendroctonus murrayanae (Hopkins)	lodgepole pine beetle
D. valens (LeConte)	red turpentine beetle

Secondary bark beetle species may influence both the establishment and survival of mountain pine beetle broods (Safranyik et al. 1999b). For example, the aggregation pheromones utilized by the pine engraver, *Ips pini* Say, reduce the number of attacks by mountain pine beetles, and their larvae compete directly for food and space with mountain pine beetle larvae (Rankin 1988; Safranyik et al.1996). In general, secondary beetles typically have higher attack densities, and are often bivoltine (i.e., two generations within one year), attacking early in the season before mountain pine beetles emerge, producing a brood that completes development and emerges to attack again, often at the same time mountain pine beetles initiate their attacks. Thus, they can interact with mountain pine beetle in two ways: by pre-empting breeding space and by direct competition for food and space.

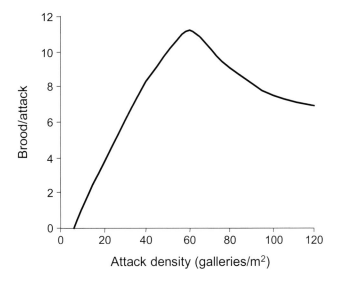

Figure 17. Relationship between brood production (number of pupae formed per attacking female) and attack density. Adapted from Raffa and Berryman (1983b).

Medetera aldrichii is considered the most effective predator of mountain pine beetle larvae (DeLeon 1935b; Amman and Cole 1983). In lodgepole pine in southeastern British Columbia, the highest densities of *M. aldrichii* larvae were found during mountain pine beetle development on the north aspects of trees (Reid 1963) and in the lower 2 m of the bole. *Medetera aldrichii* larvae (Fig. 16b) are able to move through the bark to find their prey, and may kill and feed on several mountain pine beetle larvae during their development (Schmid 1971). In laboratory tests, *M. aldrichii* larvae required 6 to 15 mountain pine beetle larvae to complete development, depending on the size of the beetle prey offered (Nagel and Fitzgerald 1975). *Medetera aldrichii* appears to respond to mountain pine beetle populations in a density-dependent fashion (i.e., predation increases as the density of beetles increases), a behaviour that can potentially increase the impact of predation on population dynamics (see Epidemiology). However, *M. aldrichii* larvae are generalists and will feed on the immature stages of most subcortical insects, including their own (DeLeon 1935b). This behaviour tends to reduce their effectiveness as predators, especially in situations where mountain pine beetle broods are intermingled with those of other subcortical insects.

The clerid beetles (Coleoptera: Cleridae) *Enoclerus sphegeus* Fabricius and *Thanasimus undatulus* Say prey both as adults (Fig. 16c) and larvae (Fig. 16d) on the adults and larvae of various bark beetle species, including the mountain pine beetle. They tend to be more numerous on the north aspect and the lower portions of the bole of lodgepole pine (Reid 1963). Clerid larvae are generalist predators in the bark of infested trees and are able to mine through subcortical tissues to find their prey. In laboratory tests, *E. sphegeus* larvae consumed on average 16 large or 38 small mountain pine beetle larvae during their development (Amman 1970), and larvae of *T. undatulus* larvae consumed an average of 18 large or 35 small mountain pine beetle larvae (Amman 1972c). Clerid larvae are cannibalistic, a behaviour that tends to limit their larval densities (Berryman 1967).

Coeloides dendroctoni Cushman (Hymenoptera: Braconidae) is considered the most important parasite (DeLeon 1935a; Reid 1963) of mountain pine beetle (Fig. 16e,f). *Coeloides dendroctoni* may use either temperature or vibration to locate its host, at which point it pierces the bark with its ovipositor (Fig. 16e) and lays an egg on a larva feeding in the subcortical tissue (Dahlsten 1982). Reid (1963) found *C. dendroctoni* was by far the most abundant parasite attacking mountain pine beetle. It was more numerous on the north and east aspects of lodgepole pine trees, and its density was inversely related to bark thickness. *Coeloides dendroctoni* preferentially parasitizes late instar mountain pine beetle larvae. If beetle larvae develop to this stage and avoid parasitism they have a high probability of reaching the adult stage (DeLeon 1935a). Parasitism appears to be highly spatially variable. DeLeon (1935a) reported average parasitism rates of 4% to 32% from lodgepole pine in eastern Idaho and Montana, whereas Amman (1984) found rates of parasitism between 0.02% and 1.7% in southeastern Idaho and northern Utah. Furthermore, *C. dendroctoni* is more abundant in older, established mountain pine beetle infestations and is relatively scarce in recent, isolated infestations. *Coeloides dendroctoni* has the potential to be a more effective natural enemy than *M. aldrichii* because many of the mountain pine beetle larvae destroyed by the latter in the fall, when prey and predator are most abundant, would have died from other sources prior to

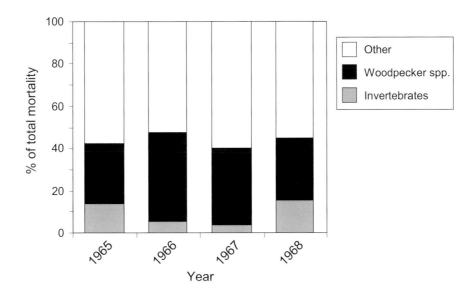

Figure 18. Percentage of total mortality of mountain pine beetle brood caused by invertebrate predators and parasitoids, woodpeckers and other mortality agents over four years in an incipient infestation located in southeastern British Columbia.

reaching the adult stage. Assuming that each parasitoid destroyed one host larva, Reid (1963) reported that parasitism reduced the mountain pine beetle population by 9% in southeastern British Columbia. However, there was no relationship between the density of mountain pine beetle egg galleries and the density of parasites, suggesting that *C. dendroctoni* does not respond to changes in its host abundance in a density dependent manner. Furthermore, peak emergence of *C. dendroctoni* in southeastern British Columbia precedes that of the mountain pine beetle by approximately two weeks (Reid 1963). Hence, there is often a scarcity of late instar mountain pine beetle larvae for parasitism, forcing *C. dendroctoni* to attack advanced larval stages of other bark beetle species such as *Ips pini*. In addition, Amman (1984) suggested that the dispersal capacity of *C. dendroctoni* is much less than that of mountain pine beetle, thereby limiting impacts of parasitism on beetle populations, especially during suboutbreak periods when populations are widely dispersed.

Woodpecker species are considered to be important mortality agents of bark beetles (Dahlsten 1982; Fayt et al. 2005), including the mountain pine beetle (Blackman 1931). They can consume large numbers of larvae, pupae and adults, and they indirectly destroy many more by creating openings in the bark and by chipping away the bark and reducing its thickness thereby promoting larval desiccation (Amman and Cole 1983). Parasitism and predation by the beetle's natural enemies may also increase due to reduced bark thickness as a consequence of woodpecker activity (Otvos 1965). In a four-year study of an incipient-epidemic mountain pine beetle population in southeastern British Columbia, the authors (unpublished data) found that in bark where woodpecker predation was not excluded by wire cages at four heights on the bole, average larval survival was only about half of that in adjacent portions of the bole protected from woodpeckers (Fig. 18). Woodpeckers concentrate feeding on trees containing high densities of large larvae and tend to avoid trees containing small larvae (Koplin and Baldwin 1970). However, even though it is generally accepted that woodpecker predation may have important impacts on low beetle populations, the magnitude of the impact is inversely related to beetle population size (Berryman 1973; Korol 1985). This inverse density dependence is due, in part, to the territorial behaviour of woodpeckers during nesting season which limits their density within forests.

Pupae

The pupal stage is relatively brief for the mountain pine beetle. Under field conditions, pupation normally requires two to four weeks. Safranyik and Whitney (1985) determined that 100 degree-days above a base temperature of 5.6°C were required to develop to young adults when pupae were reared at constant 24°C. With the exception of host resistance, the natural mortality factors are generally the same as those listed for the larvae. Occasionally, pupae suffer high mortality from desiccation and woodpecker predation. On average, however, mortality in this stage is much reduced compared to the larvae (Amman and Cole 1983).

Adults

At constant temperatures in the laboratory, mountain pine beetle adults matured after 6.4 days at 24°C and 11 days at 18°C. At the higher temperature, this required 118 degree-days, while at the lower temperature 136.5 degree-days were required above 5.6°C for maturation (Safranyik and Whitney 1985), suggesting that the rate of development above a lower threshold may be non-linear just as in the earlier life stages.

In nature, mountain pine beetle populations are consistently female-biased (see Mating and Oviposition), but the extent of this bias varies among populations and among years. Laboratory studies have reported some broods that consist entirely of females (McGhehey 1969). Apparently, factors that cause stress in a population such as crowding, cold exposure, adverse rearing temperatures, and phloem degradation will reduce male survival. It is possible that differential survival of the X and Y sperm are involved, or a lethal cytoplasmic factor that causes the death of male embryos (Lanier and Wood 1968).

A variety of natural enemies are associated with mountain pine beetle adults. Reid (1958c) found seven species of entomophilic nematodes within a beetle population from southeastern British Columbia. Several species inhabited the thorax, abdomen, digestive tract, and the reproductive organs of female beetles. The most common species, *Sphaerularia hasta* Khan (Nematoda: Tylenchida), infested 27.5% of the female adults and caused an average 32.5% reduction in the number of eggs laid (Reid 1958c). Nematodes also cause adult mortality and reduction in dispersal capacity.

Clerid beetles prey on mountain pine beetle adults (Fig. 16c). Adult clerids are attracted by the pheromones emitted by bark beetles during the attack phase (Dahlsten 1982) and so aggregate on trees with abundant prey. This is an effective numerical response by the predator to the prey, but it lasts only as long as the pheromones are emitted. The impact of predation by adult clerids on adult mountain pine beetle populations is not known. In a laboratory test, Schmid (1970) found that *E. sphegeus* adults killed one mountain pine beetle per individual per day. He estimated that in natural populations of the mountain pine beetle, mortality caused by *E. sphegeus* would be less than 1%.

Occasionally, localized high levels of mountain pine beetle mortality can be caused by diseases (MacCambridge and Trostle 1972) such as that caused by the fungal pathogen *Beauveria bassiana* (Balasmo) Villemin (Euascomycetes: Clavicipitales) (Safranyik et al. 2001). In addition, during dispersal birds may consume many flying beetles. Amman and Cole (1983) reported that within a localized mountain pine beetle infestation, nighthawks (Aves: Caprimulgidae) were collected with an average of 76 beetles/bird in their stomachs. In general, however, the mortality of adult beetles caused by natural enemies does not have a significant effect on population fluctuations.

Epidemiology[1]

We recognize four phases in the population cycle of the mountain pine beetle: endemic, incipient-epidemic, epidemic (i.e., outbreak) and post-epidemic (i.e., declining) populations. The endemic and incipient-epidemic phases represent distinct population states regarding interactions with host trees and the assemblage of bole-infesting secondary bark beetle species, whereas the other two population phases mainly represent differences in population size and spatial extent. There is also some suggestion of changes in mountain pine beetle population behaviour among the different phases, as with other species of *Dendroctonus* bark beetles (Wallin and Raffa 2004). However, this aspect of beetle biology is insufficiently understood and needs further research.

Endemic populations

Following the collapse of outbreaks during the post-epidemic phase, and before populations increase as incipient epidemics, the mountain pine beetle is considered to be in the endemic phase. Amman (1984) defined the endemic state as one where populations are so small that they are capable of mass attacking no more than one large-diameter tree within 40.5 ha of forest. In a multi-year study of the dynamics of low-level mountain pine beetle populations across south-central British Columbia, the authors (unpublished data) have determined that endemic populations exist at even lower densities. Indeed, an endemic population can be defined as one with insufficient beetles to overcome even a single large-diameter tree within a stand. Beetles in this population phase are restricted to low-quality host trees with little or no defensive capacity.

---

[1] Based in part on: Safranyik, L. 2004. Epidemiology. Pages 33-40 *in* T.L. Shore; J.E. Brooks; J.E. Stone (eds). Proceedings of the mountain pine beetle symposium: challenges and solutions. Canadian Forest Service, Pacific Forestry Centre, Victoria. Information Report BC-X-399. 298 p.

In lodgepole pine, resistance to the mountain pine beetle increases with age, approximately in parallel with increases in current annual increment (CAI) (Safranyik et al. 1974, 1975). Resistance peaks at an age when natural stands attain maximum stocking on all physiographic sites (Horton 1956 [see Fig. 13]). Near the culmination of CAI, on at least the more productive sites, many trees are of sufficient size and density to sustain a large mountain pine beetle population. However, due to high tree resistance and low beetle numbers, these trees are unavailable to endemic populations. The only host trees available to endemic beetles are those largely incapable of a resistance response as a consequence of the stresses associated with among-tree competition (i.e., suppression), pathogens, soil compaction, fluctuations in the water table, or other forms of biotic or abiotic injury. Since the culmination of CAI on fully stocked sites also corresponds to the point at which crown closure begins for lodgepole pine (e.g., Farnden 1996), there is generally a steady supply of low-vigour, suppressed trees as maturing stands begin the process of self-thinning (Yoda et al. 1963). Therefore, after the peak CAI, most lodgepole pine stands will maintain a consistent assemblage of bole-infesting bark beetles, including endemic mountain pine beetles.

Our study of endemic populations has revealed that the mountain pine beetle in this population phase generally infests suppressed trees that have been partially attacked, either during the previous season(s) or earlier in the same season, by other bole-infesting bark beetle species (see Table 1). Within mature lodgepole pine stands, three to six trees/ha/year had mountain pine beetle galleries. Attacks occurred at very low densities (two or three per tree), and the mountain pine beetle galleries were either intermingled with those of co-attacking secondary species or occurred in strips within the uncolonized portions of the boles of trees attacked in previous years (unpublished data). Subsequent to mountain pine beetle attack, the infested trees frequently sustained additional attacks during the same year, (and in the subsequent years if sufficient green phloem persisted) by one or more of the secondary bark beetle species listed in Table 1. Interspecific competition appears to be an important mortality factor during this population phase of the mountain pine beetle and may be largely responsible for the regulation of population fluctuations. The activity of secondary beetles may affect endemic mountain pine beetle populations in several ways. Exploitation of the limited resource of low-vigour trees through attacks during previous seasons or earlier in the same season will preempt mountain pine beetle breeding space. Furthermore, since many of the bole-infesting bark beetles are bivoltine, their second broods often compete directly with mountain pine beetle for phloem.

Based upon the above discussion, an endemic population can be characterized as follows.

- The diameter of attacked trees is less than the stand average (although occasional large-diameter trees are attacked following sudden, near-lethal stress such as lightning or windthrow).

- Attack densities are very low; often only two or three galleries per tree.

- Attacks are preceded in the current or previous season(s) by attacks from secondary, bole-infesting bark beetle species (see Table 1).

• Currently attacked trees are not located near brood trees.

• Yearly tree mortality is less than yearly volume growth within a stand.

Another important characteristic of endemic populations is that they are in a dynamic balance with their environment so that, over a number of generations, there is no significant change in population size. For populations to maintain this balance (i.e,. to remain more or less static) in time and space for a number of generations, they must suffer very high levels of generation mortality. Given an average number of eggs per female (*E*) and an average female ratio (*R*), the relationship between generation mortality (*M*) and potential change in population size (*P*) is as follows:

$$P = ER(1 - M)$$ [1]

where *M* is expressed as a proportion.

To maintain static population levels among generations, *P* = 1. Therefore, the corresponding generation mortality $M = 1-1/ER$. Since female mountain pine beetles lay on average 60 eggs, about two-thirds of which will be females (Reid 1962b), the beetle population has to suffer a generation mortality in the order of *M* = 97.5% to remain static (Fig. 19).

Under endemic conditions a large number of factors may interact to limit beetle populations from increasing. However, given that endemic beetle populations are relatively small, host availability (the scarcity and patchy distribution of suitable trees to attack), host quality and interspecific competition are thought to be the most important factors. Since endemic populations exist mainly in suppressed and otherwise weakened trees, stand hygiene (i.e., the removal of suppressed and damaged trees) may be an effective means of limiting the localized build-up of mountain pine beetle populations.

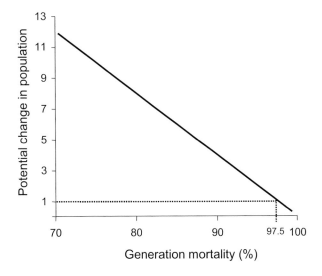

Figure 19. Relationship between the yearly potential change in populations and generation mortality of mountain pine beetle populations, assuming that populations are two-thirds females with a mean fecundity of 60 eggs/female. The dotted line indicates the level of generation mortality (97.5%) required for populations to remain static (i.e., potential rate of change = 1).

Incipient-epidemic populations

We define this phase as one where mountain pine beetle populations have grown to a minimum size sufficient to successfully mass attack a single large-diameter tree within a stand. Because large-diameter trees tend to be the most resistant within stands (Shrimpton 1973a), the main factors that permit the populations to escape the endemic phase are those that cause either a decline in tree resistance or an increase in beetle population size. The decline in tree resistance can be either temporary, such as following a period of drought, or it could be a permanent consequence of senility, disease or damage. A number of consecutive years with warm and dry weather during the flight and dispersal periods, combined with mild winters, has been associated with sustained increases in beetle populations (e.g., Safranyik et al. 1974, 1975). Hence, a decline in host resistance combined with favourable conditions for beetle establishment and survival are thought to be the main factors for the development of incipient infestations.

Berryman (1982b) defined the minimum beetle population size necessary for colonizing the larger-diameter components in a stand as the epidemic threshold. The concept of the epidemic threshold in relation to beetle population size and stand resistance is illustrated in Figure 20. In most situations, incipient-epidemic populations are the beginning stages of epidemics. However, where stands suffer from temporary weakening, such as short-term drought in younger stands, incipient populations usually decline back to the endemic state once the stands have recovered (Fig. 20). In addition, during the early stages of the incipient-epidemic phase, attack densities may be relatively low, allowing overlapping attacks by secondary bark beetle species such as *I. pini* (Hopping 1961; Wood 1982; Amman and Safranyik 1985). Reduced brood production associated with interspecific interactions may also return a mountain pine beetle population to the endemic state. Similarly, increased impacts by natural enemies, especially woodpeckers, may act to hold localized mountain pine beetles below the epidemic threshold.

The tenuous nature of the incipient-epidemic phase is illustrated in Figure 21. For a mountain pine beetle population with a generation mortality sufficient to maintain a static population (i.e., 0.975; see Fig. 19), the probability of extinction, as defined by Bartlett (1956), remains extremely high unless populations are reasonably large (Fig. 21). However, if conditions are ideal for mountain pine beetle survival and generation mortality declines, for example to 0.850 [equivalent to a yearly six-fold increase in populations (Fig. 19)], the probability of extinction diminishes to zero even with very small populations (Fig. 21).

Incipient-epidemic populations are distinct from endemic populations in several ways. Based upon the pattern of trees infested, they have the following characteristics.

• Most of the infested trees have larger diameters.

• Clumps of infested trees are scattered and confined to parts of individual stands.

• The groups of infested trees vary considerably in size and number from year to year but tend to grow over time.

• Perhaps as a consequence of localized pockets of tree stress, groups of infested trees are frequently associated with draws and gullies, edges of swamps or other places with wide fluctuation in the water table, places where lodgepole pine is growing among patches of aspen (possibly indicating the presence of root disease), and areas on dry, south-facing and west-facing slopes.

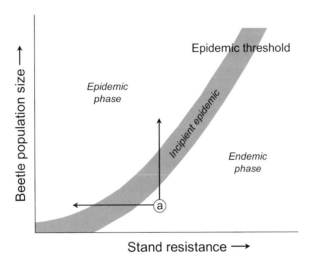

Figure 20. Conceptual representation of the threshold nature of mountain pine beetle population states. Populations in the endemic phase (a) may cross the threshold to the epidemic phase through reductions in stand resistance and/or increases in beetle numbers (as indicated by arrows). Beetles may reach the intermediate incipient-epidemic phase (shaded area) and return to the endemic state if reduced stand resistance is ephemeral and/or the magnitude of the increase in beetle numbers is insufficient to maintain an increasing population. Modified from Berryman (1982b).

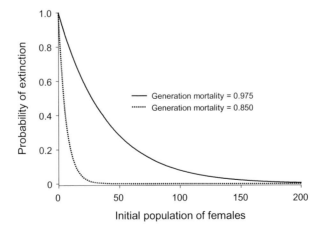

Figure 21. Probability of extinction (Bartlett 1956) for a mountain pine beetle population versus the initial population of females where generation mortality is either 0.975 (solid line) or 0.850 (dotted line). Extinction probability was calculated as $(D/B)F$; where D = death rate, B = birth rate; and F = initial female population (Bartlett 1956). See also Fig. 19.

During and following the development of incipient-epidemic populations, there is a strong positive linear relationship between mortality and tree diameter. Expressed in terms of the number of trees killed in a diameter class (i.e., dbh) in a given area (N_k), the relationship between mortality and dbh (D_c) is as follows:

$$N_k = 0, \; D_c < a/r \qquad\qquad\qquad [2]$$

$$N_k = N_c(rD_c - a), \; a/r \leq D_c \leq (1 + a)/r \qquad [3]$$

$$N_k = N_c, \; D_c > (1 + a)/r \qquad\qquad\qquad [4]$$

where N_c is the number of trees in dbh class D_c, a is a constant such that the minimum dbh for killed trees is a/r, and r is the mortality rate per unit dbh above a/r. In this form the relationship indicates that tree mortality is a function of both tree diameter and the number of live trees in that dbh class. Interestingly, the same relationship can be derived based on an assumption of random search by the attacking beetles and the probability of landing being proportional to the silhouette (i.e., dbh) of trees above a minimum size (Safranyik et al. 2004).

Generally, incipient-epidemic populations grow relatively slowly at first. Indeed, averaged over a number of generations the rate of increase may not exceed two. As a consequence, there may not be much noticeable change in infestation levels for up to five or more years. Eventually, however, as long as populations do not fall back below the epidemic threshold there will be a sustained yearly growth in beetle population size with corresponding increases in size and number of infested spots. Spot infestations will coalesce into larger patches and new infested spots may develop in several adjacent stands (see Fig. 6). This situation marks the beginning of the onset of epidemic-level infestations.

Epidemic populations

As a consequence of the growth and expansion of local incipient-epidemic populations combined with long-range dispersal, epidemic populations exist at the landscape level. If large areas of susceptible host, such as mature lodgepole pine, coincide with sustained favourable weather conditions for beetle establishment, development, and survival, outbreaks may spread over many thousands of hectares.

Epidemic populations have the following characteristics.
• They are resilient to proportionally large losses in their numbers. This generally means that the larger the population size (and the infested area) the less likelihood of collapse from adverse factors such as unseasonably cold temperatures.

• Generation mortality is usually in the range of 80% to 95%, corresponding to potential rates of population increase of approximately two- to eightfold each year (see Fig. 19). The usual annual rate of increase, however, is two- to fourfold taken over the entire area of the epidemic.

• Infestations are widespread and exist at the landscape level.

• There are usually large annual increases in both infested areas and numbers of infested trees.

Outbreaks tend to be synchronized over much of the distribution of the mountain pine beetle. This may be due to the Moran effect (Moran 1953; Royama 1992). This theory states that if regional populations are under the influence of the same density-dependent factors, they will be correlated under the influence of density-independent factors such as climate and weather that function over large areas.

The following factors are the main determinants of yearly changes in population and damage levels during outbreaks: i) size of the parent beetle population; ii) stand characteristics such as species composition, density, age and diameter distribution; iii) the spatial distribution of stands of different susceptibility; iv) weather events; and v) intraspecific competition. Natural enemies are thought to be of minor importance to epidemic populations due to their inability to respond in a density-dependent manner. Similarly, interspecific competition has little impact compared with the endemic and incipient-epidemic phases because much of the infested bark area is fully colonized by the mountain pine beetle (Berryman 1976).

During epidemics, tree mortality is usually proportional to tree diameter above a certain minimum value. The minimum dbh where little or no mortality occur varies somewhat with stand characteristics and infestation intensity, but is usually close to 10 cm (Safranyik et al. 1974). The expected rate of mortality above this minimum diameter is in the range of 1.5% to 4.0% with each centimetre increase in dbh (Fig. 22). As a consequence of this pattern of mortality, trees in the larger diameter classes are often severely depleted. Although some stands may sustain nearly complete mortality, average mortality in mature stands over the landscape will be much less, normally in the range of 30% to 45% of trees. However, because proportionately more of the larger-diameter trees are killed, the volume of killed trees will be proportionately much greater. At the landscape level, the relative severity of mortality in the various stands will generally reflect tree and stand susceptibility as defined in Shore and Safranyik (1992).

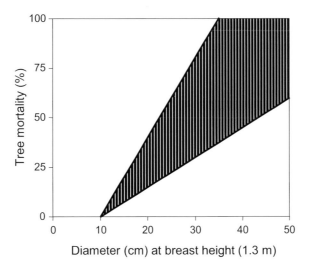

Figure 22. Relationship between tree mortality within stands and diameter above a threshold of 10 cm during a mountain pine beetle epidemic. Above the diameter threshold, the rate of mortality ranges from 1.5% (lower line) to 4% (upper line) with each centimetre increase in diameter.

Outbreak populations collapse primarily from one or a combination of the following two factors: i) unseasonably cold weather conditions during the late fall to early spring period; ii) the large-diameter susceptible host components of stands have been killed. In the final stages of population decline, increased mortality from natural enemies, inter- and intraspecific competition may also have an impact.

Post-epidemic populations

Depending primarily on the cause of epidemic collapse, the size distribution of trees attacked by post-epidemic populations may be different from that attacked during epidemics. For example, following sudden major declines in beetle numbers as a consequence of lethal low temperatures, the residual beetle population generally breeds in the same type of trees that were attacked prior to the decline. However, as there are far fewer beetles, many trees may only be partially attacked. As well, the rate of accumulation of attacks may be reduced. Consequently, brood survival will be reduced due to the expression of host resistance resulting from an insufficient mass attack. Another consequence of reduced beetle numbers is that interspecific competition for food and space (Safranyik et al. 1999b), as well as predation and parasitism, once again may become important factors affecting populations. By contrast, when the collapse of epidemics is primarily due to local depletion of suitable hosts, subsequent generations of beetles are forced to breed in trees of reduced nutritional quality or increased resistance and will likely suffer mortalities of similar magnitude as those occurring in endemic populations.

During outbreaks, large populations of some secondary bark beetle species such as *I. pini* will build up in portions of the bole not utilized by mountain pine beetle [e.g., high on the stem where the phloem becomes thin (Amman and Safranyik 1985)]. For one to three years following the collapse of mountain pine beetle outbreaks, these secondary species may kill large numbers of pine trees, mainly in the lower diameter classes (Safranyik et al. 1974).

In western Canada, the average duration of epidemics has been about10 years. Most persist for more than five years, while the longest recorded epidemic continued for about 18 years (Safranyik et al. 1974). Based on the assumptions that (*i*) mean outbreak duration in the region is 10 years, (*ii*) minimum duration is five years, (*iii*) outbreak-terminating events follow a geometric temporal distribution, and (*iv*) the future will repeat the past, predictions of the probability of outbreak collapse as a function of years since initiation are possible. Based on a fixed expected probability of outbreak collapse in year *i*, for years 6 to 18 given that it has not collapsed prior to year *i*, then:

$$Y_i = \sum_{j=1}^{n} P(1 - P)^{(j-1)} \qquad [5]$$

where Y_i = the cumulative distribution of the probability of outbreak collapse as a function of the number of years since the start of the outbreak (Y_i = 0 when $i \leq 5$); $n = i - 5$; P = expected (average) probability of outbreak collapse (1/(10-5) = 0.20) for years 6 – 18. If the expected probability of collapse increases with years after year 6, then the equation changes to become:

$$Y_i = \sum_{j=1}^{n} \left[\left\{ \prod_{k=1}^{j} (1 - P_{k-1}) \right\} P_j \right] \qquad [6]$$

where P_j = the probability of outbreak collapse in year j given that it has not occurred in previous years, and the symbol Π designates a mathematical product. P_j is calculated as the product of the average probability of outbreak collapse (P in equation 5) and the ratio $(m+1-i)/(m-1)$, where m = maximum observed outbreak duration (i.e., 18 years).

Figure 23 is a graphical representation of the two models. If the probability of epidemic collapse increases with time since outbreak initiation (equation 6), then the probability of outbreak termination (Y_i) after 10 and 15 years is 75% and 98%, respectively. These probabilities are approximately 12% higher than the corresponding estimates of Y_i based on a fixed probability of outbreak collapse (equation 5; Fig. 23). While these two models are useful for projecting the potential impacts of outbreaks, it should be noted that changing climatic conditions may alter the course of future epidemics (Carroll et al. 2004).

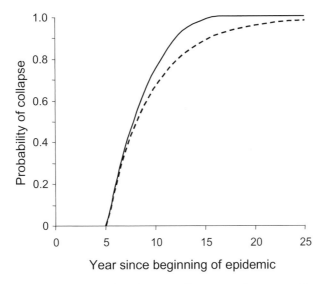

Figure 23. Predicted probability of epidemic collapse as a function of years since outbreak initiation based upon an increasing probability of collapse (solid line) and a fixed probability of collapse (dashed line). See text for details.

Population regulation

Regulation is a stabilizing process characterized by negative feedback and is caused by factors whose intensity of action is related to population density (e.g., Royama 1992). These are called density-dependent factors. The effects of food (availability, quantity, quality), habitat and parasitism/predation often (but not always) are density-dependent factors. Weather and edaphic conditions are examples of density-independent factors. Regulation in the sense described above does not necessarily prevent population eruptions; population density is determined by the interaction of density-dependent and density-independent factors (see Royama 1992).

Amman and Cole (1983) and Amman (1984) showed that for mountain pine beetle populations from the southern Rocky Mountains, the density-independent effects of temperature extremes caused the greatest amount of mortality overall. Phloem drying, a factor that becomes increasingly important with increasing brood density, was the second most important factor in epidemic and post-epidemic infestations. Of the insect's natural enemies, *Medetera aldrichii* (Fig. 16a,b) was the only one that showed a consistent density-dependent response over time. Mortality from woodpeckers showed a weak density-dependent response, especially in pre-epidemic infestations when the birds concentrated on the few available infested trees. In general, the relative effects of mortality factors varied by the size of trees and the state of the mountain pine beetle infestation.

It is generally accepted that, for a localized mountain pine beetle population, host availability is the primary density-dependent factor affecting the epidemic population state. Indeed, even at the landscape level, in the absence of a widespread density-independent mortality event such as extreme unseasonable cold, epidemic populations will persist until they deplete the host resource (e.g., Safranyik et al. 1975). As epidemic beetle populations increase, the largest trees in a stand will be attacked first. With each successive generation, as the large-diameter hosts are depleted, beetles are forced into smaller and smaller trees and the resultant increasingly deleterious effects of intraspecific competition will ultimately cause populations to collapse. For example, high attack densities in small-diameter trees leads to increased mortality due to phloem drying (Amman and Cole 1983). Moreover, the thinner, less nutritious phloem of increasingly smaller host trees leads to smaller adult females and lower fecundity (Amman and Pace 1976; Amman and Cole 1983).

Host availability is also the primary factor regulating endemic mountain pine beetle populations. Locally, there may be many potential host trees, but because of host resistance only those with severely impaired vitalities are available to endemic populations. These trees are often in short supply and are widely scattered over the landscape. Hence, mortality during dispersal and host finding is likely one of the main factors determining the rates of population change in endemic populations.

In a recent study of endemic mountain pine beetle populations, the authors (unpublished data) have found that, in the absence of significant emigration from neighbouring populations, interactions among competitors, host resistance and the mountain pine beetle may be the primary factor limiting the transition from the endemic to incipient-epidemic state. In pine forests, bole-infesting secondary bark beetles have specialized to attack suppressed and damaged trees. In contrast, mountain pine beetle fitness is low in these trees due to their thin phloem. However, endemic populations comprise too few beetles to mass attack a healthy, thick-phloem tree, and therefore, are restricted to suboptimal trees in direct competition with secondary beetles. As discussed above, secondary beetles can restrict endemic mountain pine beetles through both exploitation (i.e., preempting potential breeding space) and interference (i.e., direct competitive interactions) competition. The form of this interaction is shown in Figure 24a. Stress events, such as among-tree competition, or biotic or abiotic damage, will reduce the vigour of some trees in a stand, thereby increasing the number of trees susceptible to bark beetles. This will have a positive influence on the amount of food available to both secondary and endemic mountain pine beetles. The increased food available to secondary bark beetles will increase their brood production, which in turn will exploit the resource (thereby reducing their own food availability). At the same time, the increased resource will have a positive influence on food availability to mountain pine beetle brood (who also reduce their own food availability); however, the rapid and effective exploitation of these trees by secondary beetles will reduce the food available to mountain pine beetle (Fig. 24a), thereby restricting their numbers.

It requires only a subtle shift for this interaction to change and allow mountain pine beetles to escape to the incipient-epidemic phase (Fig. 24b). If the stress within a stand increases (as a result of drought, for example), then the number of susceptible trees and the amount of food available to the bole-infesting bark beetle assemblage, including the mountain pine beetle, will increase. If the increase is sufficient for the mountain pine beetle population to gain access to an average, large-diameter tree within a stand, it may breach the endemic-epidemic threshold and enter the incipient-epidemic phase (Fig. 20). In general, the secondary bark beetle assemblage cannot tolerate tree resistance to the same extent as the mountain pine beetle. Thus, the mountain pine beetle can escape the constraint of interspecific competition that limits endemic populations. Furthermore, the beetle no longer strictly depends on a stress event to gain access to hosts. Provided the stand has sufficient large-diameter trees and weather conditions remain amenable to beetle survival, the dramatic increase in populations associated with brood production in larger trees (Fig. 25) effectively means that in the incipient-epidemic phase most trees in a stand are susceptible to attack. Thus, a short-term positive feedback loop is formed (Fig. 24b), and populations may grow to the epidemic phase.

The relationship with secondary beetles changes dramatically with the transition from the endemic to the incipient-epidemic state. Primary attacks of healthy trees by the mountain pine beetle often increase the amount of food available to secondary species (Fig. 24b), and those secondary species will attack unexploited portions of the phloem of dying trees early the next season. Thus, mountain pine beetle populations may regulate the bole-infesting secondary bark beetle assemblage during the incipient-epidemic and epidemic phases.

An epidemic forms as localized infestations coalesce over the landscape. This entails emigration of mountain pine beetles from the localized points of increase into neighbouring stands, thereby facilitating the endemic – incipient epidemic transition of resident populations. During the epidemic phase, since the mountain pine beetle is the first to initiate attacks in relatively resistant trees, it is able to largely escape competitive interactions with the rest of the bole-infesting bark beetle assemblage (Fig. 24c). However, the rapid increase in populations often quickly depletes the host resource and the positive feedback loop that developed in the incipient-epidemic phase begins to locally break down (Fig. 24c).

Within individual stands, the collapse of populations during the post epidemic phase is precipitated largely by the depletion of susceptible trees. In addition, it is common for large populations of secondary bark beetle species that have built up in the unexploited portions of mountain pine beetle-killed trees during the epidemic phase to once again exert significant competitive pressure and exacerbate the collapse (Fig. 24d). The renewed interspecific interactions manifest as both interference competition where secondary beetle species, notably *Ips pini* (Safranyik et al. 1999b), attack amongst the declining density of mountain pine beetles, and exploitation competition where the elevated secondary populations are capable of attacking any residual healthy larger-diameter trees remaining in the stand. At the landscape level, epidemics will continue until the losses from mortality factors within trees and from dispersal exceed beetle production in the available trees.

There is compelling evidence that endemic mountain pine beetle populations are limited by interactions among the secondary bark beetle assemblage and host tree resistance. In a four-year study in which every stem within six mature lodgepole pine stands (three at each of two sites; mean ($\pm$ SE) stand size = 14.9 $\pm$ 0.96 ha) in south-central British Columbia was assessed at four-week intervals for the presence of bole-infesting bark beetles (see Table 1), three stands transitioned from endemic to incipient-epidemic phases as defined above, without detectable mountain pine beetle emigration (unpublished data). In each case, the escape by mountain pine beetle populations from the endemic state was preceded by a drought event followed by one or two years of elevated secondary bark beetle activity (Fig. 25). The increase in attacks by the bole-infesting bark beetle assemblage (including endemic mountain pine beetles) as a consequence of a localized increase in stress facilitated an increase in the endemic mountain pine beetle past the endemic-epidemic threshold (see Figs. 20 and 24b).

The escape from competitive interactions with the secondary bole-infesting bark beetle assemblage is characterized in Figure 26 (unpublished data). During the endemic phase, beetles colonized trees in diameter classes not significantly different than the stand averages (19.9 – 21.9 cm), but as the assemblage of beetles increased in stands (Fig. 25), and the mountain pine beetle populations entered the incipient-epidemic phase, the diameter of successfully attacked trees increased by nearly 40% (Fig. 26a). In gaining access to the relatively resistant, larger-diameter trees within a stand, the mountain pine beetle effectively eludes the remainder of the bole-infesting beetle assemblage. Indeed, during the endemic to incipient epidemic transition, the percentage of trees colonized by the mountain pine beetle that were previously attacked by other bark beetle species declined from approximately 70% to less than 5% (Fig. 26b).

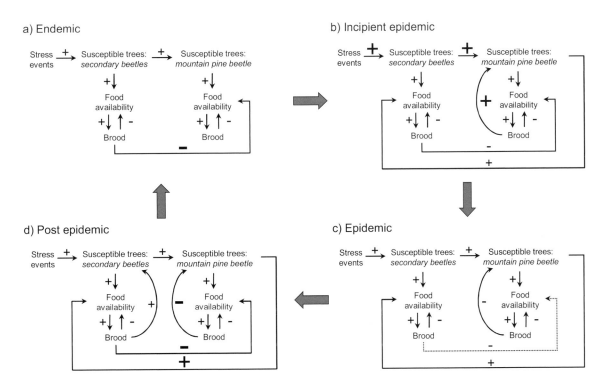

Figure 24. A schematic representation of the interaction among lodgepole pine, secondary bark beetle species, and the mountain pine beetle as its populations cycle through the endemic (a), incipient-epidemic (b), epidemic (c), and post-epidemic (d) phases. Arrows accompanied by '+' and '−' indicate positive and negative effects, respectively, whereas the size of the symbols represent the strength of the interaction. Arrows with a dotted line represent a very weak or insignificant interaction. See text for details.

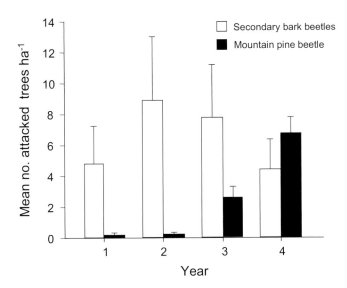

Figure 25. Mean (± standard error) number of trees per hectare either mass attacked by the mountain pine beetle (black bars) or infested by secondary bark beetle species (white bars) in three mature lodgepole pine stands in southern British Columbia over four years as mountain pine beetle populations increased from the endemic to the incipient-epidemic state. See text for description of population states.

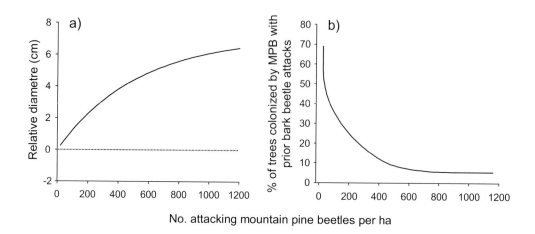

Figure 26. Relationships between the relative diameter (attacked – stand average) of trees attacked by mountain pine beetle (MPB) (a), and the percentage of trees it colonized that were attacked previously (in the same season, or in previous years) by other bole-infesting bark beetle species (b), versus the number of attacking mountain pine beetles per hectare in three mature lodgepole pine stands in southern British Columbia.

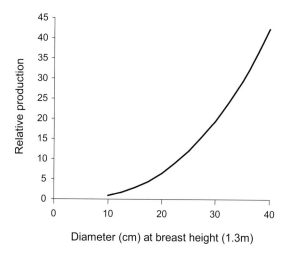

Figure 27. Mountain pine beetle brood production in lodgepole pine trees of different diameters in relation to a 10-cm-diameter tree. Based on Safranyik et al. (1975) and Safranyik (1988).

The critical nature of the endemic to incipient epidemic transition to mountain pine beetle populations can be seen in Figure 27. Until the beetle can gain access to large-diameter trees, the potential rate of increase is very small. In fact, roughly 40 times the number of beetles will emerge from a 40-cm tree when compared with a 10-cm tree (Fig. 27). The constraints imposed by interspecific competition for suppressed and damaged trees may have selected for the "aggressive" attack of healthy, resistant trees by mountain pine beetle.

Summary and conclusions

The potential for mountain pine beetle populations to establish, persist and ultimately increase to epidemic levels in lodgepole pine forests depends on the coincidence of large amounts of susceptible hosts on the landscape, several years with weather that is conducive to beetle survival, and the complex interaction of an intricate suite of life-history traits. The critical aspects of mountain pine beetle life history are:

• An efficient host-selection behaviour that enables beetles to discover even sparsely distributed patches of suitable host trees;

• A significant dispersal capacity that enables beetles to move over short (i.e., hundreds of metres) and long (i.e., hundreds of kilometres) distances;

• A highly evolved mutualistic relationship with ophiostomoid "blue stain" fungi that facilitates access to trees that are otherwise too resistant to successfully colonize;

• A semiochemical communication system that mediates "mass attacks" of highly resistant host trees while at the same time minimizing intraspecific competition by regulation of attack density;

• Stage-specific developmental thresholds that ensure synchrony of development with the growing season, increase the chance that the most cold tolerant stages (the larvae) will over-winter, and lead to temporally coincident emergence of adults to facilitate mass attacks; and

• Subpopulation-based development rates to ensure synchronous univoltine development over a large part of the distributional range.

Based upon the nature of their interactions with host trees and the assemblage of bole-infesting secondary bark beetle species, there are four distinct phases in the population cycle of the mountain pine beetle: endemic, incipient-epidemic, epidemic (i.e., outbreak) and post-epidemic (i.e., declining) populations. Endemic populations are defined as those with insufficient beetles to overcome a single large-diameter tree within a stand. A complex of factors interact to cause sufficient generation mortality in endemic populations (≈97%) such that, on average, their yearly rate of increase equals unity (i.e., populations are stable). Because endemic beetles are restricted to suppressed or damaged trees in direct competition with an assemblage of "secondary" bark beetle species that have evolved as specialists on such a resource, interspecific competition is one of the primary factors limiting endemic populations. As a consequence of increasing stress within lodgepole pine stands, secondary beetles and mountain pine beetles may increase in concert such that the latter may escape the endemic phase and attack a large-diameter, high-quality host tree. This is the incipient-epidemic phase which may expand to the epidemic phase if conditions remain conducive to beetle survival and there are sufficient large-diameter trees within stands. Access to large-diameter trees is critical to mountain pine beetle populations; brood production is more than 40 times greater in a 40-cm versus a 10-cm-diameter tree. Epidemic populations occur on the landscape and, due to their sheer size, extent and potential rate of increase (two - to eightfold, yearly), they are highly resilient to losses. In the absence of a widespread extreme weather event, epidemics will normally continue until most of the large-diameter trees on the landscape are depleted, at which point intraspecific interactions within a host resource of diminishing quality will cause populations to collapse. During the post-epidemic phase, large populations of some secondary bark beetle species such as *Ips pini* will build up in portions of the bole not utilized by mountain pine beetle and for several years following the collapse of mountain pine beetle outbreaks, they may kill large numbers of pine trees, mainly in the lower diameter classes.

From our review of the biology and epidemiology of the mountain pine beetle, several management implications emerge.

1) Given the large contiguous forests of lodgepole pine that dominate much of northwestern North America, and evidence for a warming climate (see Carroll et al. 2004), future large-scale mountain pine beetle outbreaks are highly probable and will necessitate new, efficient control strategies and tactics.

2) Mountain pine beetle populations have a significant capacity to erupt and rapidly coalesce over vast landscapes. Consequently, effective control programs must be based on early detection and implementation, and a continuous commitment of resources.

3) Since past forest management has shifted the age-class structure of most pine forests in western Canada into the range where they are highly susceptible to mountain pine beetle (Taylor and Carroll 2004), the most viable means of mitigating future impacts in the long term is to shift the management focus from the beetle to strategies for managing lodgepole pine age-classes, host vigour and stand resistance on the landscape.

References

Amman, G.D. 1969. Mountain pine beetle emergence in relation to depth of lodgepole pine bark. USDA Forest Service, Intermountain Forest and Range Experiment Station, Ogden, UT, Research Note INT-96.

Amman, G.D. 1970. Prey consumption and variations in larval biology of *Enoclerus sphegeus* (Coleoptera: Cleridae). The Canadian Entomologist 102:1374-1379.

Amman, G.D. 1972a. Some factors affecting oviposition behavior of the mountain pine beetle. Environmental Entomology 1:691-695.

Amman, G.D. 1972b. Mountain pine beetle brood production in relation to thickness of lodgepole pine phloem. Journal of Economic Entomology 65(1):138-140.

Amman, G.D. 1972c. Prey consumption and development of *Enoclerus undatulus*, a predator of the mountain pine beetle. Environmental Entomologist 4:528-530.

Amman, G.D. 1973. Population changes of the mountain pine beetle in relation to elevation. Environmental Entomology 2:541-547.

Amman, G.D. 1975. Abandoned mountain pine beetle galleries in lodgepole pine. USDA Forest Service, Intermountain Forest and Range Experiment Station, Ogden, UT, Research Note INT-97. 6 p.

Amman, G.D. 1978. Biology, ecology, and causes of outbreaks of the mountain pine beetle in lodgepole pine forests. Pages 39-53 *in* A. Berryman, G.D. Amman and R.W. Stark, tech. eds. Theory and practice of mountain pine beetle management in lodgepole pine forests. Symposium proceedings, April 25-27, 1978, Pullman WA., Moscow, ID. University of Idaho, Forest, Wildlife and Range Experiment Station.

Amman, G.D. 1980. Incidence of mountain pine beetle abandoned galleries in lodgepole pine. USDA Forest Service, Intermountain Forest and Range Experiment Station, Ogden, UT, Research Note INT-284. 6 p.

Amman, G.D. 1982. Characteristics of mountain pine beetles reared in four pine hosts. Environmental Entomology 11:590-593.

Amman, G.D. 1984. Mountain pine beetle (Coleoptera: Scolytidae) mortality in three types of infestations. Environmental Entomology 13:184-191.

Amman, G.D.; Pace, V.E. 1976. Optimum egg gallery densities for the mountain pine beetle in relation to lodgepole pine phloem thickness. USDA Forest Service, Intermountain Forest and Range Experiment Station, Ogden, UT, Research Note INT-209. 8 p.

Amman, G.D.; Cole, W.E. 1983. Mountain pine beetle dynamics in lodgepole pine forests. Part II: population dynamics. USDA Forest Service, Intermountain Forest and Range Experiment Station, General Technical Report INT-145. 59 p.

Amman, G.D.; Safranyik, L. 1985. Insects of lodgepole pine: Impacts and control. Pages 107-124 *in* D.M. Baumgartner, R.A. Krebill, J.T. Arnott and G.F. Weetman, eds. Lodgepole pine, the species and its management. Symposium proceedings, May 8-10, 1984, Spokane, Washington; May 14-16, 1984, Vancouver, British Columbia. Washington State University, Pullman, WA. 381 p.

Ballard, R.G.; Walsh, M.A.; Cole, W.E. 1982. Blue-stain fungi in xylem of lodgepole pine: a light-microscope study on extent of hyphal distribution. Canadian Journal of Botany 60:2334-2341.

Bartlett, M.S. 1956. An introduction to stochastic processes with special reference to methods of application. Cambridge University Press. 312 p.

Bentz, B.J.; Mullin, D.E. 1999. Ecology of mountain pine beetle (Coleoptera: Scolytidae) cold hardening in the Intermountain West. Environmental Entomology 28:577-587.

Bentz, B.J.; Logan J.A.; Amman G.D. 1991. Temperature-dependent development of the mountain pine beetle (Coleoptera: Scolytidae) and simulation of its phenology. The Canadian Entomologist 123:1083-1094.

Bentz, B.J.; Powell J.A.; Logan, J.A. 1996. Localized spatial and temporal attack dynamics of the mountain pine beetle in lodgepole pine. USDA Forest Service, Intermountain Forest and Range Experiment Station, Ogden, UT, Research Paper INT-RP-494. 8 p.

Bentz, B.J.; Logan J.A.; Vandygriff, J.C. 2001. Latitudinal variation in *Dendroctonus ponderosae* (Coleoptera: Scolytidae) development time and adult size. The Canadian Entomologist 133:375-387.

Berryman, A.A. 1967. Preservation and augmentation of insect predators of the western pine beetle. Journal of Forestry 65:260-262.

Berryman, A.A. 1972. Resistance of conifers to invasion by bark beetle-fungal associations. BioScience 22:598-602.

Berryman, A.A. 1973. Management of mountain pine beetle populations in lodgepole pine ecosystems. Pages 627-650 *in* D. Baumgartner, ed. Management of lodgepole pine ecosystems – a symposium, October 9-11, 1973. Washington State University Cooperative Extension Service.

Berryman, A.A. 1976. Theoretical explanation of mountain pine beetle dynamics in lodgepole pine forests. Environmental Entomology 5:1225-1233.

Berryman, A.A. 1982a. Mountain pine beetle outbreaks in Rocky Mountain lodgepole pine forests. Journal of Forestry 80:410-419.

Berryman, A.A. 1982b. Population dynamic of bark beetles. Pages 264-314 *in* J. B. Mitton and K.B. Sturgeon, eds. Bark beetles in North American conifers: a system for the study of evolutionary biology. University of Texas Press, Austin, TX. 527 p.

Berryman, A.A.; Raffa, K.F.; Millstein, J.A.; Stenseth, N.C. 1989. Interaction dynamics of bark beetle aggregation and conifer defense rates. Oikos 56:256-263.

Billings, R.F.; Gara, R.I. 1975. Rhythmic emergence of *Dendroctonus ponderosae* (Coleoptera: Scolytidae) from two host species. Annals of the Entomological Society of America 68:1033-1036.

Billings, R.F.; Gara R.I.; Hrutfiord, B.F. 1976. Influence of ponderosa pine resin on response of *Dendroctonus ponderosae* to synthetic trans-verbenol. Environmental Entomology 5:171-179.

Blackman, M.W. 1931. The Black Hills beetle (*Dendroctonus ponderosae* Hopk.). Syracuse University, New York State College of Forestry, Syracuse, New York, Technical Publication Number 36. 97 p.

Borden, J.H. 1982. Aggregation pheromones. Pages 74-139 *in* J.B. Mitton and K.B. Sturgeon, eds. Bark beetles in North American conifers: a system for the study of evolutionary biology. University of Texas Press, Austin, TX. 527 p.

Borden, J.H.; Chong, L.J.; Fuchs, M.C. 1983a. Application of semiochemicals in post-logging manipulation of the mountain pine beetle, *Dendroctonus ponderosae* (Coleoptera: Scolytidae). Journal of Economic Entomology 76:1428-1432.

Borden, J.H.; Chong, L.J.; Pratt, K.E.G.; Gray, D.R. 1983b. The application of behaviour-modifying chemicals to contain infestations of the mountain pine beetle, *Dendroctonus ponderosae.* Forestry Chronicle 59:235-239.

Borden, J.H.; Ryker, L.C. Chong, L.J.; Pierce, H.D., Jr.; Johnston, B.D.; Oeschlager, A.C. 1987. Response of the mountain pine beetle, *Dendroctonus ponderosae* Hopkins (Coleoptera: Scolytidae), to five semiochemicals in British Columbia lodgepole pine forests. Canadian Journal of Forest Research 17:118-128.

Bright, D.E., Jr. 1976. The bark beetles of Canada and Alaska. Coleoptera: Scolytidae. Canada Department of Agriculture, Biosystematics Research Institute, Research Branch, Ottawa, ON, Publication 1576. 241 p.

Burnell, D.G. 1977. A dispersal-aggregation model for mountain pine beetle in lodgepole pine stands. Researches on Population Ecology 19:99-106.

Bushing, R.W. 1965. A synoptic list of the parasites of Scolytidae (Coleoptera) in North America north of Mexico. The Canadian Entomologist 97:449-492.

Byers, J.A. 1999. Effects of attraction radius and flight paths on catch of scolytid beetles dispersing outward through rings of pheromone traps. Journal of Chemical Ecology 25:985-1005.

Carlson, R.W.; Cole W.E. 1965. A technique for sampling populations of the mountain pine beetle. USDA Forest Service, Intermountain Forest and Range experiment Station, Ogden, UT, Research Paper INT-20, 13 p.

Carroll, A.L.; Safranyik, L. 2004. The bionomics of the mountain pine beetle in lodgepole pine forests: establishing a context. Pages 21-32 *in* T.L. Shore, J.E. Brooks and J.E. Stone, eds. Proceedings of the mountain pine beetle symposium: challenges and solutions, October 30-31, 2003, Kelowna, British Columbia, Canada. Natural Resources Canada, Canadian Forest Service, Pacific Forestry Centre, Victoria, BC. Information Report BC-X-399. 298 p.

Carroll, A.L.; Taylor S.W.; Régnière J.; Safranyik, L. 2004. Effects of climate and climate change on the mountain pine beetle. Pages 223-232 *in* T.L. Shore, J.E. Brooks and J.E. Stone, eds. Proceedings of the mountain pine beetle symposium: challenges and solutions, October 30-31, 2003, Kelowna, British Columbia, Canada. Natural Resources Canada, Canadian Forest Service, Pacific Forestry Centre, Victoria, BC. Information Report BC-X-399. 298 p.

Cerezke, H.F. 1964. Morphology and functions of the reproductive systems of *Dendroctonus monticolae* Hopk. (Coleoptera: Scolytidae). The Canadian Entomologist 96:477-500.

Cerezke, H.F. 1989. Mountain pine beetle aggregation semiochemical use in Alberta and Saskatchewan, 1983-1987. Page 113 *in* G. D. Amman, Compiler. Proceedings-Symposium on the management of lodgepole pine to minimize losses to the mountain pine beetle, July 12-14, 1988, Kalispell, Montana. USDA Forest Service, Intermountain Research Station, Ogden, UT. General Technical Report INT-262. 117 p.

Chapman, J.A. 1967. Response behaviour of scolytid beetles and odour meteorology. The Canadian Entomologist 99:1132-1137.

Cole, W.E. 1973. Crowding effects among single-age larvae of the mountain pine beetle, *Dendroctonus ponderosae* (Coleoptera: Scolytidae). Environmental Entomologist 2:285-293.

Cole, W.E. 1981. Some risks and causes of mortality in mountain pine beetle populations: a long-term analysis. Researches on Population Ecology 23:116-144.

Cole, W.E.; Amman, G.D. 1969. Mountain pine beetle infestations in relation to lodgepole pine diameters. USDA Forest Service, Intermountain Forest and Range Experiment Station, Research paper INT-96.

Cole, W.E.; Amman, G.D.; Jensen, C.E. 1985. Mountain pine beetle dynamics in lodgepole pine forests. Part III: Sampling and modelling of mountain pine beetle populations. USDA Forest Service, Intermountain Forest and Range Experiment Station, Ogden, UT. General Technical Report INT-188. 46 p.

Conn, J.E.; Borden, J.H.; Scott, B.E.; Friske, L.M.; Pierce, H.D.; Oehlschlager, A.C. 1983. Semiochemicals for the mountain pine beetle in British Columbia: field trapping studies. Canadian Journal of Forest Research 13:320-324.

Coster, J.E.; Gara, R.I. 1968. Studies on the attack behaviour of the southern pine beetle. II. Response to attractive host material. Contributions of the Boyce Thompson Institute 24:69-75.

Dahlsten, D.L.1982. Relationships between bark beetles and their natural enemies. Pages 140-182 *in* J.B. Mitton and K.B. Sturgeon, eds. Bark Beetles in North American conifers – a system for the study of evolutionary biology. University of Texas Press, Austin.

DeLeon, D. 1934. An annotated list of the parasites, predators, and other associated fauna of the mountain pine beetle in western white pine and lodgepole pine. The Canadian Entomologist 66:51-61.

DeLeon, D. 1935a. The biology of *Coeloides dendroctoni* Cushman (Hymenoptera: Braconidae), an important parasite of the mountain pine beetle (*Dendroctonus monticolae* Hopk.). Annals of the Entomological Society of America 28:411-424.

DeLeon, D. 1935b. A study of *Medetera aldrichii* Wh. (Diptera: Dolichopodidae), a predator of the mountain pine beetle (*Dendroctonus monticolae* Hopk., Coleo.-Scolytidae). Entomologica Americana 15:59-89.

Elkin, C.M.; Reid, M.L. 2005. Low energy reserves and energy allocation decisions affect reproduction by mountain pine beetles, *Dendroctonus ponderosae*. Functional Ecology 19:102-109.

Evenden, J.C.; Bedard, W.D.; Struble, G.R. 1943. The mountain pine beetle, an important enemy of western pines. USDA, Washington, DC, Circular No. 664. 25 p.

Farnden, C. 1996. Stand density management diagrams for lodgepole pine, white spruce and interior Douglas-fir. Natural Resources Canada, Canadian Forest Serve, Pacific Forestry Centre, Victoria, BC. Information Report BC-X-360. 41 p.

Fayt, P.; Machmer, M.M.; Steeger, C. 2005. Regulation of spruce bark beetles by woodpeckers – a literature review. Forest Ecology and Management 206:1-14.

Furniss, M.M.; Furniss, R.L. 1972. Scolytids (Coleoptera) on snowfields above timberline in Oregon and Washington. The Canadian Entomologist 104:1471-1478.

Gara, R.I.; Geiszler, D.R.; Littke, W.R. 1984. Primary attraction of the mountain pine beetle to lodgepole pine in Oregon. Annals of the Entomological Society of America 77:333-334.

Geiszler, D.R.; Gara, R.I. 1978. Mountain pine beetle attack dynamics in lodgepole pine. Pages 182-187 *in* A.A. Berryman, G.D. Amman and R.W. Stark, tech. eds. Theory and practice of mountain pine beetle management in lodgepole pine forests. Symposium proceedings, April 25-27, 1978, Pullman WA., Moscow, ID. University of Idaho, Forest, Wildlife and Range Experiment Station.

Geiszler,D.R.; Gallucci, V.F.; Gara, R.I. 1980. Modelling the dynamics of mountain pine beetle aggregation in a lodgepole pine stand. Oecologia 46:244-253.

Gibson, K.E.; Schmitz, R.F.; Amman, G.D.; Oakes, R.D. 1991. Mountain pine beetle response to different verbenone dosages in pine stands of western Montana. USDA Forest Service, Intermountain Research Station, Research Paper INT-444. 11 p.

Gray, B.; Billings, R.F.; Gara, R.I.; Johnsey, R.L. 1972. On the emergence and initial flight behaviour of the mountain pine beetle, *Dendroctonus ponderosae*, in eastern Washington. Zeitschrift Fur Angewandte Entomologie 71:250-259.

Gray, D.R.; Borden, J.H. 1989. Containment and concentration of mountain pine beetle (Coleoptera: Scolytidae) infestations with semiochemicals: validation by sampling of baited and surrounding zones. Journal of Economic Entomology 82(5):1399-1495.

Hay, C.J. 1956. Experimental crossing of mountain pine beetle with Black Hills beetle. Annals of the Entomological Society of America 49:567-571.

Hopkins, A.D. 1902. Insect enemies of pine in the Black Hills forest reserve. USDA, Division of Entomology, Washington, DC, Bulletin 32 (new series). 24 p.

Hopkins, A.D. 1905.The Black Hills beetle. USDA, Bureau of Entomology, Washington, DC, Bulletin 56. 24 p.

Hopkins, A.D. 1909. Practical information on the scolytid beetles of North American forests. I. Bark beetles of the genus *Dendroctonus.* USDA, Bureau of Entomology, Washington, DC, Bulletin 83, part I. 169 p.

Hopping, G.R. 1961. Insects injurious to lodgepole pine in the Canadian Rocky Mountain region. Pages 77-87 *in* L.A. Smithers, ed. Lodgepole pine in Alberta. Department of Forestry, Canada, Bulletin 127.

Hopping, G.R.; Beall, G. 1948. The relation of diameter of lodgepole pine to incidence of attack by the bark beetle *Dendroctonus monticolae* Hopkins. Forestry Chronicle 24:141-145.

Horton, K.W. 1956. The ecology of lodgepole pine in Alberta and its role in forest succession. Canada Department of Northern Affairs and National Resources, Forestry Branch, Forest Research Division Technical Note No. 45.

Hughes, P.R. 1973. Effect of α-pinene exposure on *trans*-verbenol synthesis in *Dendroctonus ponderosae* Hopk. Naturwissenschaften 60:261-262.

Hunt, D.W.A.; Borden, J.H. 1989. Terpene alcohol pheromone production by *Dendroctonus ponderosae* and *Ips paraconfusus* (Coleoptera: Scolytidae) in the absence of readily culturable microorganisms. Journal of Chemical Ecology 15:1433-1463.

Hunt, D.W.A.; Borden, J.H. 1990. Conversion of verbenols to verbenone by yeasts isolated from the *Dendroctonus ponderosae* (Coleoptera: Scolytidae). Journal of Chemical Ecology 16:1385-1397.

Hynum, B.G.; Berryman A.A. 1980. *Dendroctonus ponderosae* (Coleoptera: Scolytidae): pre-aggregation landing and gallery initiation on lodgepole pine. The Canadian Entomologist 112:185-191.

Kim, J.J.; Allen E.A.; Humble, L.M.; Breuil, C. 2005. Ophiostomatoid and basidiomycetous fungi associated with green, red, and grey lodgepole pines after mountain pine beetle (*Dendroctonus ponderosae*) infestation. Canadian Journal of Forest Research 35:274-284.

Knight, F.B. 1959. Partial life tables for the Black Hills beetle. Journal of Economic Entomology 52(6):1199-1202.

Koplin, J.R.; Baldwin, P.H. 1970. Woodpecker predation on an endemic population of Engelmann spruce beetles. American Midland Naturalist 83:510-515.

Korol, J.J. 1985. A simulation of predation by non-game birds on the mountain pine beetle (*Dendroctonus ponderosae* Hopkins). M.Sc. Thesis, Department of Forestry, University of British Columbia, Vancouver. 174 p.

Langor, D.W. 1989. Host effects on phenology, development, and mortality of field populations of the mountain pine beetle, *Dendroctonus ponderosae* Hopkins (Coleoptera: Scolytidae). The Canadian Entomologist 121:149-157.

Lanier, G.N.; Wood, D.L. 1968. Controlled mating, caryology, morphology and sex ratio in the *Dendroctonus ponderosae* complex. Annals of the Entomological Society of America 61:517-526.

Libbey, L.M.; Ryker, L.C.; Yandell, K.L. 1985. Laboratory and field studies of volatiles released by *Dendroctonus ponderosae* Hopkins (Coleoptera, Scolytidae). Zeitschrift fur Angewandte Entomologie 100:381-392.

Logan, J.A.; Amman, G.D. 1986. A distribution model for egg development in mountain pine beetle. The Canadian Entomologist 118:361-372.

Logan, J.A.; Bentz, B.J. 1999. Model analysis of mountain pine beetle (Coleoptera: Scolytidae) seasonality. Environmental Entomology 28:924-934.

Logan, J.A.; Powell, J.A. 2001. Ghost forests, global warming, and the mountain pine beetle (Coleoptera:Scolytidae). American Entomologist 47:60-173.

Logan, J.A.; Bolstad, P.V.; Bentz, B.J.; Perkins, D.L. 1995. Assessing the effects of changing climate on mountain pine beetle dynamics. Pages 92-105 *in* R.W. Tinus, ed. Proceedings of the Interior west global change workshop, April 25-27, 1995, Fort Collins, Colorado, USDA Forest Service, Rocky Mountain Forest and Range Experiment Station, General Technical Report RM-GTR-262.

Logan, J.A.; White, P.; Bentz, B.A.; Powell, J.A. 1998. Model analysis of spatial patterns in mountain pine beetle outbreaks. Theoretical Population Biology 53:236-255.

Lyon, R.L. 1958. A useful secondary sex character in *Dendroctonus* bark beetles. The Canadian Entomologist 90:582-584.

Mathre, D.E. 1964. Pathogenicity of *Ceratocystis ips* and *Ceratocystis minor* to *Pinus ponderosa*. Contributions of the Boyce Thompson Institute 22:363-388.

McCambridge, W.F. 1970. Spermatozoa in unemerged female mountain pine beetles, *Dendroctonus ponderosae* Hopkins. Proceedings of the Entomological Society of Ontario 100:168-170.

McCambridge, F.W. 1971. Temperature limits of flight of the mountain pine beetle, *Dendroctonus ponderosae*. Annals of the Entomological Society of America 64:534-535.

McCambridge, W.F. 1974. Influence of low temperatures on attack, oviposition and larval development of mountain pine beetle, *Dendroctonus ponderosae* (Coleoptera: Scolytidae). The Canadian Entomologist 106:979-984.

McCambridge, W.F.; Trostle, G.C. 1972. The mountain pine beetle. USDA Forest Service, Washington, DC, Forest Pest Leaflet 2. 6 p.

McGhehey, J.H. 1968. Territorial behaviour of bark beetle males. The Canadian Entomologist 100:1153

McGhehey, J.H. 1969. Sex ratios of individual brood of the mountain pine beetle. Department of Fisheries and Forestry, Bi-Monthly Research Notes 25:1.

McGhehey, J.H. 1971. Female size and egg production of the mountain pine beetle, *Dendroctonus ponderosae* Hopkins. Canadian Forest Service, Northern Forest Research Centre, Information Report NOR-X-9. 18 p.

McGregor, M.D. 1985. The conflict between people and the beetle. Pages 16-23 *in* R.C. Loomis, S. Tucker and T.H. Hoffacker, eds. Insect and disease conditions in the United States. USDA Forest Service, General Report WO-46.

Meyer, H.J.; Norris, D.M. 1973. A mathematical relation to describe the influence of wind on the initial flight dispersal of *Scolytus multistriatus* (Coleoptera: Scolytidae). Annals of the Entomological Society of America 66:505-508.

Michael, R.R.; Rudinsky. J.A. 1972. Sound production in Scolytidae: specificity in male *Dendroctonus* beetles. Journal of Insect Physiology 18:2189-2201.

Mitchell, R.G.; Preisler, H.K. 1991. Analysis of spatial patterns of lodgepole pine attacked by outbreak populations of the mountain pine beetle. Forest Science 37:1390-1408.

Moeck, H.A.; Safranyik L. 1984. Assessment of predator and parasitoid control of bark beetles. Environment Canada, Canadian Forestry Service, Pacific Forestry Centre, Victoria, BC, Information Report BC-X-248. 24 p.

Moeck, H.A.; Simmons, C.S. 1991. Primary attraction of mountain pine beetle, *Dendroctonus ponderosae* Hopk. (Coleoptera: Scolytidae), to bolts of lodgepole pine. The Canadian Entomologist 123:299-304.

Moran, P.A.P. 1953. Statistical analysis of the Canadian lynx cycle. II. Synchronization and Meteorology. Australian Journal of Zoology 1:291-98.

Nagel, W.P.; Fitzgerard, T.D. 1975. *Medetera aldrichii* larval feeding behavior and prey consumption (Dipt.: Dolichopodidae). Entomophaga 20:121-127.

Otvos, I.S. 1965. Studies on avian predators of *Dendroctonus brevicomis* LeConte (Coleoptera: Scolytidae) with special reference to Picidae. The Canadian Entomologist 97:1184-1199.

Paine, T.D.; Raffa, K.F.; Harrington, T.C. 1997. Interactions among scolytid bark beetles, their associated fungi, and live host conifers. Annual Review of Entomology 42:179-206.

Pitman, G.B.; Vité, J.P. 1969. Aggregation behaviour of *Dendroctonus ponderosae* (Coleoptera: Scolytidae) in response to chemical messengers. The Canadian Entomologist 101:143-149.

Pitman, G.B.; Vite, J.P.; Kinzer, G.W.; Fentiman, A.F. 1968. Bark beetle attractants: *trans-*verbenol isolated from *Dendroctonus*. Nature 218:168-169.

Polymenopoulos, A.D.; Long, G. 1990. Estimation and evaluation methods for population growth models with spatial diffusion: dynamics of mountain pine beetle. Ecological Modelling 51:97-121.

Powell, J.; Tams, J.; Bentz, B.; Logan, J. 1998. Theoretical analysis of "switching" in a localized model of mountain pine beetle attack. Journal of Theoretical Biology 194:49-63.

Preisler, H.K.; Mitchell R.G. 1993. Colonization patterns of the mountain pine beetle in thinned and unthinned lodgepole pine stands. Forest Science 39:528-545.

Pureswaran, D.S.; Borden, J.H. 2003a. Test of semiochemical mediated host specificity in four species of tree killing bark beetles (Coleoptera: Scolytidae). Environmental Entomology 32:963-969.

Pureswaran, D.S.; Borden, J.H. 2003b. Is bigger better? Size and pheromone production in the mountain pine beetle, *Dendroctonus ponderosae* Hopkins (Coleoptera: Scolytidae). Journal of Insect Behavior 16:765-782.

Pureswaran, D.S.; Gries, R.; Borden, J.H.; Pierce, H.D., Jr. 2000. Dynamics of pheromone production and communication in the mountain pine beetle, *Dendroctonus ponderosae* Hopkins, and the pine engraver, *Ips pini* (Say) (Coleoptera: Scolytidae). Chemoecology 10:153-168.

Pureswaran, D.S.; Borden, J.H. 2004. New repellent semiochemicals for three species of *Dendroctonus* (Coleoptera: Scolytidae). Chemoecology 14:67-75.

Raffa, K.F.; Berryman, A.A. 1980. Flight responses and host selection by bark beetles. Pages 213-233 *in* A.A. Berryman and L. Safranyik, eds. Proceedings of the 2nd IUFRO conference on dispersal of forest insects: evaluation, theory and management implications. Cooperative Extension Service, Washington State University, Pullman, WA.

Raffa, K.F.; Berryman, A.A. 1982a. Gustatory cues in the orientation of *Dendroctonus ponderosae* (Coleoptera: Scolytidae) to host trees. The Canadian Entomologist 114:97-104.

Raffa, K.F.; Berryman, A.A. 1982b. Physiological differences between lodgepole pines resistant and susceptible to the mountain pine beetle and associated microorganisms. Environmental Entomology 11:486-492.

Raffa, K.F.; Berryman, A.A. 1983a. Physiological aspects of lodgepole pine wound responses to a fungal symbiont of the mountain pine beetle, *Dendroctonus ponderosae* (Coleoptera: Scolytidae). The Canadian Entomologist 115:723-734.

Raffa, K.F.; Berryman, A.A. 1983b. The role of host plant resistance in the colonization behavior and ecology of bark beetles (Coleoptera: Scolytidae). Ecological Monographs 53:27-49.

Raffa, K.F.; Berryman, A.A. 1986. A mechanistic computer model of mountain pine beetle populations interacting with lodgepole pine stands and its implications for forest managers. Forest Science 32:789-805.

Raffa, K.F.; Berryman, A.A. 1987. Interacting selective pressures in conifer-bark beetle systems: a basis for reciprocal adaptations? The American Naturalist 129:234-3-262.

Rankin, L.J. 1988. Competitive interactions between the mountain pine beetle and the pine engraver in lodgepole pine. Master of Pest Management Professional Paper. Simon Fraser University, Burnaby, British Columbia. 33 p.

Rasmussen, L.A. 1974. Flight and attack behaviour of mountain pine beetles in lodgepole pine of northern Utah and southern Idaho. USDA Forest Service, Intermountain Forest and Range Experiment Station, Ogden, UT, Research Note INT-180. 7 p.

Rasmussen, L.A. 1976. Keys to common parasites and predators of the mountain pine beetle. USDA Forest Service, Intermountain Forest and Range Experiment Station, Ogden, UT, General Technical Report INT-29. 4 p.

Reid, R.W. 1958a. The behaviour of the mountain pine beetle, *Dendroctonus monticolae* Hopk., during mating, egg laying and gallery construction. The Canadian Entomologist 90:505-509.

Reid, R.W. 1958b. Internal changes in the female mountain pine beetle, *Dendrocronus monticalae* Hopk., associated with egg laying and flight. The Canadian Entomologist 90:464-468.

Reid, R.W. 1958c. Nematodes associated with the mountain pine beetle (*Dendroctonus monticolae*). Division of Forest Biology, Department of Agriculture, Canada, Bimonthly Progress Reports. 14 (1, 3).

Reid, R.W. 1960. Studies on the biology of the mountain pine beetle *Dendroctonus monticolae* Hopkins (Coleoptra: Scolytidae). Ph.D. Thesis, Montana State College, Bozeman, Montana. 98 p.

Reid, R.W. 1961. Moisture changes in lodgepole pine before and after attack by mountain pine beetle. The Forestry Chronicle 37:368-375, 403.

Reid, R.W. 1962a. Biology of the mountain pine beetle, *Dendroctonus monticolae* Hopkins, in the east Kootenay region of British Columbia. I. Life cycle, brood development and flight periods. The Canadian Entomologist 94:531-538.

Reid, R.W. 1962b. Biology of the mountain pine beetle, *Dendroctonus monticolae* Hopkins, in the east Kootenay region of British Columbia. II. Behaviour in the host, fecundity, and internal changes in the female. The Canadian Entomologist 94:605-613.

Reid, R.W. 1963. Biology of the mountain pine beetle, *Dendroctonus monticolae* Hopkins, in the east Kootenay region of British Columbia. III. Interaction between the beetle and its host, with emphasis on brood mortality and survival. The Canadian Entomologist 95:225-238.

Reid, R.W. 1969. The influence of humidity on incubating bark beetle eggs. The Canadian Entomologist 101:182-183.

Reid, R.W.; Gates, H. 1970. Effect of temperature and resin on hatch of eggs of the mountain pine beetle (*Dendroctonus ponderosae*). The Canadian Entomologist 102:617-622.

Reid, R.W.; Whitney, H.S.; Watson, J.A. 1967. Reaction of lodgepole pine to attack by *Dendroctonus ponderosae* Hopkins and blue stain fungi. Canadian Journal of Botany 45:1115-1126.

Renwick, J.A.A; Vité, J.P. 1970. Systems of chemical communications in *Dendroctonus*. Contributions of the Boyce Thompson Institute 24:283-292.

Renwick, J.A.A.; Pitman, G.B. 1979. An attractant isolated from female Jeffrey pine beetles, *Dendroctonus jeffreyi*. Environmental Entomology 8:40-41.

Richmond, H.A. 1935. Morphological study of the bark beetle *Dendroctonus monticolae* Hopk. M.Sc. Thesis, McGill University, Montreal, Quebec.

Royama, T. 1992. Analytical population dynamics. Chapman and Hall, New York. 380 p.

Rudinsky, J.A.; Vité, J.P. 1956. Effects of temperature upon the activity and behaviour of the Douglas-fir beetle. Forest Science 2:258-267.

Rudinsky, J.A. 1963. Response of *Dendroctonus pseudotsugae* Hopkins to volatile attractants. Contributions of the Boyce Thompson Institute 22:22-38.

Ryker, L.C.; Rudinsky, J.A. 1976. Sound production in Scolytidae: aggressive and mating behavior of the mountain pine beetle. Annals of the Entomological Society of America 69:677-680.

Ryker, L.C.; Rudinsky, J.A. 1982. Field bio-assay of *exo-* and *endo*-brevicomin with *Dendroctonus ponderosae* in lodgepole pine. Journal of Chemical Ecology 8:701-707.

Ryker, L.C.; Libbey, L.M. 1982. Frontalin in the male mountain pine beetle. Journal of Chemical Ecology 8:1399-1409.

Ryker, L.C.; Yandell, K.L. 1983. Effect of verbenone on aggregation of *Dendroctonus ponderosae* Hopkins (Coleoptera: Scolytidae) to synthetic attractant. Zeitschrift Fur Angewandte Entomologie 96:452-459.

Safranyik, L. 1968. Development of a technique for sampling mountain pine beetles in lodgepole pine. Ph.D. thesis, University of British Columbia, Vancouver, BC. 195 p.

Safranyik, L. 1971. Some characteristics of the spatial arrangement of attacks by the mountain pine beetle, *Dendroctonus ponderosae* (Coleoptera: Scolytidae) on lodgepole pine. The Canadian Entomologist 103:1607-1625.

Safranyik, L. 1978. Effects of climate and weather on mountain pine beetle populations. Pages 77-84 *in* D.L. Kibbee, A.A. Berryman, G.D. Amman and R.W. Stark, eds. Theory and practice of mountain pine beetle management in lodgepole pine forests. Symposium Proceedings, University of Idaho, Moscow, ID.

Safranyik, L. 1988. Estimating attack and brood totals and densities of the mountain pine beetle in individual lodgepole pine trees. The Canadian Entomologist 120:323-331.

Safranyik, L.; Jahren, R. 1970. Emergence patterns of the mountain pine beetle from lodgepole pine. Canadian Forest Service, Bi-monthly Research Notes 26:11,19.

Safranyik, L.; Linton, D.A. 1982. Survival and development of mountain pine beetle broods in jack pine bolts from Ontario. Canadian Forestry Service, Research Notes 2:17-18.

Safranyik, L.; Linton, D.A. 1983. Brood production by three species of *Dendroctonus* (Coleoptera: Scolytidae) in bolts from host and non-host trees. Journal of the Entomological Society of British Columbia 80:10-13.

Safranyik, L.; Linton, D.A. 1985. The relationship between the density of emerged *Dendroctonus ponderosae* (Coleoptera: Scolytidae) and density of exit holes in lodgepole pine. The Canadian Entomologist 85:267-275.

Safranyik, L.; Linton, D.A. 1991. Unseasonably low fall and winter temperatures affecting mountain pine beetle and pine engraver beetle populations and damage in the British Columbia Chilcotin Region. Journal of the Entomological Society of British Columbia 88:17-21.

Safranyik, L.; Linton, D.A. 1998. Mortality of mountain pine beetle larvae, *Dendroctonus ponderosae* (Coleoptera: Scolytidae) in logs of lodgepole pine (*Pinus contorta* var. *latifolia*) at constant low temperatures. Journal of the Entomological Society of British Columbia 95:81-87.

Safranyik, L.; Whitney, H.S. 1985. Development and survival of axenically reared mountain pine beetles, *Dendroctonus ponderosae* (Coleoptera: Scolytidae), at constant temperatures. The Canadian Entomologist 117:185-192.

Safranyik, L.; Shrimpton, D.M.; Whitney, H.S. 1974. Management of lodgepole pine to reduce losses from the mountain pine beetle. Environment Canada, Canadian Forestry Service, Pacific Forest Research Centre, Victoria, BC. Forestry Technical Report 1. 24 p.

Safranyik, L.; Shrimpton, D.M.; Whitney, H.S. 1975. An interpretation of the interaction between lodgepole pine, the mountain pine beetle and its associated blue stain fungi in western Canada. Pages 406-428 *in* D.M. Baumgartner, ed. Management of lodgepole pine ecosystems. Washington State University Cooperative Extension Service, Pullman, WA.

Safranyik, L.; Shore, T.L.; Linton, D.A. 1996. Ipsdienol and lanierone increase *Ips pini* Say (Coleoptera: Scolytidae) attack and brood density in lodgepole pine infested by mountain pine beetle. The Canadian Entomologist 128:199-207.

Safranyik, L.; Shore, T.L.; Linton, D.A. 2004. Measuring trap efficiency for bark beetles. Journal of Applied Entomology 128:337-341.

Safranyik, L.; Silversides, R.; McMullen, L.H.; Linton, D.A. 1989. An empirical approach to modelling the dispersal of the mountain pine beetle (*Dendroctonus ponderosae* Hopk.) (Col., Scolytidae) in relation to sources of attraction, wind direction and speed. Journal of Applied Entomology 108:498-511.

Safranyik, L.; Linton, D.A.; Silversides, R.; McMullen, L.H. 1992. Dispersal of released mountain pine beetles under the canopy of a mature lodgepole pine stand. Journal of Applied Entomology 113:441-450.

Safranyik, L.; Barclay, H.; Thomson, A.; Riel, W.G. 1999a. A population dynamics model for the mountain pine beetle, *Dendroctonus ponderosae* Hopk. (Coleoptera: Scolytidae). Natural Resources Canada, Canadian Forest Service, Pacific Forestry Centre, Victoria, BC, Information Report BC-X-386. 35 p.

Safranyik, L.; Shore, T.L.; Linton, D.A.; Rankin L. 1999b. Effects of induced competitive interactions with secondary bark beetle species on establishment and survival of mountain pine beetle broods. Natural Resources Canada, Canadian Forest Service, Pacific Forestry Centre, Victoria, BC, Information Report BC-X-384. 33 p.

Safranyik, L.; Shore, T. L.; Moeck, H. A.; Whitney, H. F. 2001. *Dendroctonus ponderosae* Hopkins, Mountain Pine Beetle (Coleoptera: Scolytidae). Chapter 21, pages 104-109 *in* P.G. Mason, and J.T. Huber, eds. Biological control programmes in Canada, 1981-2000. CBI Publishing, Wallingford, UK, New York. 583 p.

Safranyik, L.; Shore, T.L.; Linton, D.A. 2004. Measuring trap efficiency for bark beetles (Col., Scolytidae). Journal of Applied Entomology 128:337-341.

Schmid, J.M. 1970. *Enoclerus spheges* (Coleoptera :Cleridae), a predator of *Dendroctonus ponderosae* (Coleoptera: Scolytidae) in the Black Hills. The Canadian Entomologist 102:969-977.

Schmid, J.M. 1971. *Medetera aldrichii* (Diptera: Dolochopodidae) in the Black Hills. II. Biology and densities of immature stages. The Canadian Entomologist 103:848-853.

Schmid, J.M. 1972. Emergence, attack densities and seasonal trends of mountain pine beetle (*Dendroctonus ponderosae*) in the Black Hills. USDA Forest Service, Rocky Mountain Forest and Range Experiment Station, Ft. Collins, CO, Research Note RM-211. 7 p.

Schmitz, R.F.; McGregor, M.D.; Amman, G.D. 1980. Mountain pine beetle response to lodgepole pine stands of different characteristics. Pages 234-243 *in* A.A. Berryman and L. Safranyik, eds. Proceedings of the 2nd IUFRO Conference on Dispersal of Forest Insects: Evaluation, Theory and Management Implications. Aug. 27-31, Sandpoint, ID. Cooperative Extension Service, Washington State University, Pullman, WA.

Schofer, G.A.; Lanier, G.N. 1970. A sexual character in pupae of *Dendroctonus* (Coleoptera: Scolytidae) The Canadian Entomologist 102:1487-1488.

Seybert, J.P.; Gara, R.I. 1970. Notes on flight and host-selection behavior of the pine engraver *Ips pini* (Coleoptera: Scolytidae). Annals of the Entomological Society of America 63:947-950.

Shepherd, R.F. 1965. Distribution of attacks by *Dendroctonus ponderosae* Hopk. on *Pinus contorta* Dougl. var. *latifolia* Engelm. The Canadian Entomologist 97:207-215.

Shepherd, R.F. 1966. Factors influencing the orientation and rates of activity of *Dendroctonus ponderosae* Hopkins (Coleoptera: Scolytidae). The Canadian Entomologist 98:507-518.

Shore, T.L.; Safranyik L. 1992. Susceptibility and risk rating systems for the mountain pine beetle in lodgepole pine stands. Forestry Canada, Pacific and Yukon Region, Information Report BC-X 336. 12 p.

Shrifrine, M.; Phaff, H.J. 1956. The association of yeasts with certain bark beetles. Mycologia 48:41-55.

Shrimpton, D.M. 1973a. Age- and size-related response of lodgepole pine to inoculation with *Europhium clavigerum*. Canadian Journal of Botany 51:1155-1160.

Shrimpton, D.M. 1973b. Extractives associated with the wound response of lodgepole pine attacked by the mountain pine beetle and associated microorganisms. Canadian Journal of Botany 51:527-534.

Shrimpton, D.M. 1978. Effects of lodgepole pine resistance on mountain pine beetle populations. Pages 64-76 *in* A.A.Berryman, G.D. Amman and R.W. Stark, tech. eds. Theory and practice of mountain pine beetle management in lodgepole pine forests, Symposium proceedings, April 25-27, 1978, Pullman WA., Moscow, ID. University of Idaho, Forest, Wildlife and Range Experiment Station.

Shrimpton, D.M.; Thomson, A.J. 1985. Relationship between phloem thickness and lodgepole pine growth characteristics. Canadian Journal of Forest Research 15:1004-1008.

Shrimpton, D.M.; Whitney, H.S. 1968. Inhibition of growth of blue stain fungi by wood extractives. Canadian Journal of Botany 46:757-761.

Six, D.L. 2003. A comparison of mycangial and phoretic fungi of individual mountain pine beetles. Canadian Journal of Forest Research 33:1331-1334.

Six, D.L.; Paine, T.D. 1998. Effects of mycangial fungi and host tree species on progeny survival and emergence of *Dendroctonus ponderosae* (Coleoptera: Scolytidae). Environmental Entomology 27:1393-1401.

Six, D.L.; Paine, T.D. 1999. Phylogenetic comparison of ascomycete mycangial fungi and *Dendroctonus* bark beetles (Coleoptera: Scolytidae). Annals of the Entomological Society of America 92:159-166.

Six, D.L.; Klepzig, K.D. 2004. *Dendroctonus* bark beetles as model systems for the study of symbiosis. Symbiosis 37:207-232.

Smith, R.H. 1963. Toxicity of pine resin vapors to three species of *Dendroctonus* bark beetles. Journal of Economic Entomology 56:827-831.

Smith, R.H. 1972. Xylem resin in the resistance of the *Pineaceae* to bark beetles. USDA Forest Service, Pacific Southwest Forest and Range Experiment Station, General Technical Report PSW-1. 7 p.

Solheim, H. 1995. Early stages of blue stain fungus invasion of lodgepole pine sapwood following mountain pine beetle attack. Canadian Journal of Botany 73:70-74.

Somme, L. 1964. Effects of glycerol on cold hardiness in insects. Canadian Journal of Zoology 42:87-101.

Stock, M.W.; Amman, G.D. 1980. Genetic differentiation between mountain pine beetle populations from lodgepole pine and ponderosa pine in northeast Utah. Annals of the Entomological Society of America 3:472-478.

Stock, M.W.; Guenter, J.D. 1979. Isozyme variation among mountain pine beetle (*Dendroctonus ponderosae*) populations in the Pacific Northwest. Environmental Entomology 8:889-893.

Stock, M.W.; Guenter, J.D.; Pitman. G.B. 1978. Implications of genetic differences between mountain pine beetle populations to integrated pest management. Pages 197-201 *in* A.A. Berryman, G.D. Amman and R.W. Stark, tech. eds. Theory and practice of mountain pine beetle management in lodgepole pine forests, symposium proceedings, April 25-27, 1978, Pullman, Washington, Moscow, Idaho. University of Idaho, Forest, Wildlife and Range Experiment Station.

Taylor, S.W.; Carroll, A.L. 2004. Disturbance, forest age, and mountain pine beetle outbreak dynamics in BC: A historical perspective. Pages 41-51 *in* T.L. Shore, J.E. Brooks and J.E. Stone, eds. Proceedings of the Mountain Pine Beetle Symposium: Challenges and Solutions, October 30-31, 2003, Kelowna, British Columbia. Natural Resources Canada, Canadian Forest Service, Pacific Forestry Centre, Victoria, BC, Information Report BC-X-399. 298 p.

Unger, L. 1993. Mountain pine beetle. Forest Pest Leaflet 76. Forestry Canada, Pacific Forestry Centre, Victoria, BC. 7 p.

Wallin, K.F.; Raffa, K.F. 2004. Feedback between individual host selection behavior and population dynamics in an eruptive herbivore. Ecological Monographs 74:101-116.

Watson, J.A. 1970. Rhythmic emergence patterns of the mountain pine beetle *Dendroctonus ponderosae* (Coleoptera: Scolytidae). The Canadian Entomologist 102:1054-1056.

Whitney, H.S. 1971. Association of *Dendroctonus ponderosae* (Coleoptera: Scolytidae) with blue stain fungi and yeasts during brood development in lodgepole pine. The Canadian Entomologist 103:1495-1503.

Whitney, H.S.; Farris, S.H. 1970. Maxillary mycangium in the mountain pine beetle. Science 167:54-55.

Whitney, H.S.; Blauel, R.A. 1972. Ascospore dispersion in Ceartocystis spp. and *Europheum clavigerum* in conifer resin. Mycologia 64:410-414.

Wood, D.L. 1982. The role of pheromones, kairomones and allomones in the host selection and colonization behavior of bark beetles. Annual Review of Entomology 27:411-446.

Wood, S.L. 1963. A revision of bark beetle genus *Dendroctonus* Erichson (Coleoptera: Scolytidae). Great Basin Naturalist 23:1-117.

Wood, S.L. 1982. The bark and ambrosia beetles of North and Central America (Coleoptera: Scolytidae), a taxonomic monograph. Great Basin Naturalist Memoirs No. 6, Brigham Young University, Provo, UT. 135 p.

Wygant, N.D. 1940. Effects of low temperature on the Black Hills beetle (*Dendroctonus ponderosae*) Hopkins. Ph.D. dissertation summary, State University of New York, College of Environmental Science and Forestry, Syracuse, NY. 57 p.

Yoda, K., Kira, T., Ogawa, H.; Hozumi, K. 1963. Self-thinning in overcrowded pure stands under cultivated and natural conditions. Journal of Biology 14:107-129.

Yuill, J. S. 1941. Cold hardiness of two species of bark beetles in California forests. Journal of Economic Entomology 34:702-709.

Zúniga, G., Cisneros, R., Hayes, J.L.; Macias-Samano, J. 2002. Karyology, geographic distribution, and origin of the genus *Dendroctonus* (Coleoptera: Scolytidae). Annals of the Entomological Society of America 95:267-275.

Chapter 2

Forest, Climate and Mountain Pine Beetle Outbreak Dynamics in Western Canada

Steve W. Taylor, Allan L. Carroll, Rene I. Alfaro, and Les Safranyik

Natural Resources Canada, Canadian Forest Service, Pacific Forestry Centre, 506 West Burnside Road, Victoria, British Columbia, V8Z 1M5

Abstract

Mountain pine beetle (*Dendroctonus ponderosae* Hopk. [Coleoptera: Scolytidae]) outbreaks have been observed in all pine species in western Canada. However, they have occurred principally in lodgepole pine (*Pinus contorta* Dougl. ex Loud. var. latifolia) in the southern half of British Columbia and the extreme south-western portion of Alberta, with one outbreak recorded in the Cypress Hills at the southern junction of the Alberta–Saskatchewan border. At least four large-scale outbreaks have occurred in western Canada in the past 120 years, as documented in forest survey records or detected as growth releases in tree rings. The Chilcotin Plateau in central interior British Columbia has sustained the most years of outbreak. Dendrochronological evidence suggests an outbreak periodicity of about 40 years in this region.

The size of mountain pine beetle infestations varies with short-term changes in weather and long-term changes in host availability. Retrospective modelling suggests that both the amount of susceptible mature lodgepole pine and the area with favourable climate have increased during the past century. An age-class projection model using contemporary forest inventory data in combination with wildfire and harvesting statistics suggests that during the early 1900s, approximately 17% of pine stands were in age-classes susceptible to mountain pine beetle attack. Forest age-class structure is controlled by the disturbance regime. In unmanaged lodgepole pine forests, wildfire was the primary disturbance agent. With fire-return cycles of 40 - 200 years, the long-term average susceptibility to mountain pine beetle would be about 17% - 25% over large areas. However, during the past 80 years the amount of area burned by wildfire in pine forests in British Columbia has significantly decreased. While harvesting has also increased during this same period, the net disturbance rate is believed to have decreased. The reduction in disturbance rate has resulted in an increase in the average age of pine stands such that approximately 55% of pine forests are presently in age-classes considered susceptible to mountain pine beetle. Analysis and modelling of the historical distribution of a climatic suitability index and of outbreaks suggests that over the past 40 years the range of mountain pine beetle has expanded, as has the area that is climatically favourable for it. Thus, an increase in both the amount of susceptible-aged host and range expansion due to a more favourable climate have created ideal conditions for the development of an extensive mountain pine beetle epidemic. A better understanding of the effect of forest dynamics and climatic variation on mountain pine beetle populations and outbreak development will allow for management of lodgepole pine with regard to disturbance risk.

Résumé

Bien que le dendroctone du pin ponderosa (*Dendroctonus ponderosae* Hopk. [Coleoptera: Scolytidae]) s'attaque à toutes les espèces de pins dans l'Ouest canadien, le pin tordu latifolié (*Pinus contorta* Dougl. ex Loud. var. latifolia) est sa cible de prédilection dans la moitié méridionale de la Colombie-Britannique et l'extrême sud-ouest de l'Alberta. Une infestation a également été signalée dans les collines Cypress, à la jonction sud de la frontière Alberta-Saskatchewan. Les données d'inventaires forestiers ou les anneaux de croissance des arbres indiquent que l'Ouest canadien a connu au moins quatre graves infestations au cours des 120 dernières années. La région des plateaux Chilcotin, située dans l'Intérieur centre de la Colombie-Britannique, a pour sa part subi le plus grand nombre d'années d'infestation. Les données dendrochronologiques indiquent que les infestations se répètent environ tous les 40 ans dans la région.

L'ampleur des infestations varie en fonction des fluctuations à court terme des conditions météorologiques et de la variation à long terme de la disponibilité des hôtes. Des modèles rétrospectifs donnent à penser que le nombre de pins tordus latifoliés mûrs vulnérables et la superficie du territoire exposé à des conditions climatiques favorables ont augmenté au cours du siècle dernier. Selon un modèle de projection structuré en fonction des classes d'âge fondé sur des données d'inventaires forestiers contemporaines ainsi que des statistiques sur les incendies de forêt et l'exploitation forestière, la proportion de pinèdes appartenant à des classes d'âge vulnérables au dendroctone du pin ponderosa s'établissait à environ 17 % au début des années 1900. La structure des classes d'âge des forêts est déterminée par le régime des perturbations. Dans les forêts de pins tordus latifoliés non aménagées, le feu était le principal agent de perturbation. En présence d'intervalles de récurrence des feux de 40 à 200 ans, la vulnérabilité moyenne à long terme au dendroctone du pin ponderosa à l'échelle de vastes territoires s'établirait à environ 17 à 25 %. La superficie brûlée, dans les pinèdes, a cependant considérablement diminué en Colombie-Britannique au cours des 80 dernières années. Même si l'exploitation forestière s'est intensifiée durant cette même période, il semble que le taux net de perturbation ait diminué. Cette réduction s'est traduite par une augmentation de l'âge moyen des peuplements de pins, de telle sorte qu'environ 55 % des forêts de pins appartiennent aujourd'hui à des classes d'âge vulnérables au ravageur. L'analyse et la modélisation de la répartition historique des régions présentant des conditions climatiques favorables ainsi que des infestations laissent penser qu'au cours des 40 dernières années, l'aire de répartition du dendroctone du pin ponderosa s'est accrue, tout comme la superficie du territoire où le climat lui est favorable. L'augmentation du nombre d'hôtes appartenant à des classes d'âge vulnérables et l'expansion de l'aire du ravageur résultant de conditions climatiques plus favorables ont donc engendré des conditions idéales pour qu'une épidémie majeure se déclenche. Une meilleure compréhension des effets de la dynamique des forêts ainsi que des variations climatiques sur les populations de dendroctones du pin ponderosa et le déclenchement des infestations permettra d'aménager les peuplements de pins tordus latifoliés en fonction du risque lié aux perturbations.

Introduction

Mountain pine beetle *Dendroctonus ponderosae* Hopk. (Coleoptera: Scolytidae) infestations have been documented in western Canada for over 85 years. The first Dominion of Canada entomologist, J.M. Swaine, observed mountain pine beetle and other bark beetle outbreaks during field surveys in western Canada in the early 1900s (Swaine 1918). Following the establishment of the Dominion Forest Biology Lab in Vernon, British Columbia in 1919, significant outbreaks occurring in the southern part of the province continued to be recorded. From 1959 to 1996, the Canadian Forest Service, Forest Insect and Disease Survey (FIDS), in cooperation with provincial agencies, conducted annual systematic province-wide aerial overview surveys of forest insect outbreaks. During these surveys, boundaries of infestations were recorded on topographic maps and infestations were classified into "low", "moderate" and "high" severity classes corresponding to <10%, 10%-30% and >30% attacked (i.e., red) trees, respectively (for details see Van Sickle et al. 2001). Photographs of spot (i.e., low), moderate, and high severity infestations are shown in Figure 1. After 1996, provincial governments took over insect and disease surveys in western Canada. The British Columbia Ministry of Forests has carried out annual overview forest health surveys since 1999. Powell (1966), and Wood and Unger (1996), reviewed the historical distribution of outbreaks in British Columbia from insect survey records. However, recent digitization of the historic insect outbreak maps has allowed for new spatial analyses of outbreak dynamics.

Tree rings maintain a record of the canopy disturbance history for a locality, and therefore have been used to determine past outbreaks of bark beetles (Stuart et al. 1989; Heath and Alfaro 1990; Veblen et al. 1991a, 1991b; Zhang et al. 1999; Eisenhart and Veblen 2000) and defoliating insects (e.g., Swetnam and Lynch 1993; Zhang and Alfaro 2002, 2003). Because mountain pine beetle outbreaks do not normally kill all trees in a stand, non-host and surviving host trees experience extended periods of increased growth that is visible in tree ring series. Thus, release from competition can be used as a proxy for canopy disturbance by mountain pine beetle. However, the release is not precisely simultaneous among all trees in the stand because not all host trees are attacked nor die in the same year (Eisenhart and Veblen 2000). Therefore, the method relies on stand averages to date an outbreak. Partial or unsuccessful attacks by mountain pine beetles often leave lesions on surviving trees (Fig. 2). These scars can be dated with dendrochronological methods and provide further confirmation of beetle infestations. Although partial or unsuccessful attacks are most prevalent during outbreaks, they may also occur at sub-outbreak levels. These investigations are providing new insights into temporal outbreak patterns predating the survey period.

In this chapter we review the history of mountain pine beetle infestations in western Canada, and examine the effects of forest age dynamics and climate on these outbreaks. A better understanding of the influence of forest dynamics and climatic variation on the development of mountain pine beetle outbreaks may help to direct longer-term management strategies.

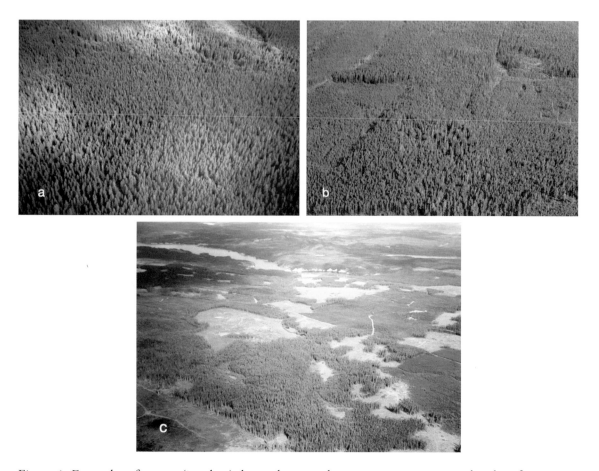

Figure 1. Examples of a. spot (i.e., low), b. moderate and c. severe mountain pine beetle infestations (Photos: J. Westfall).

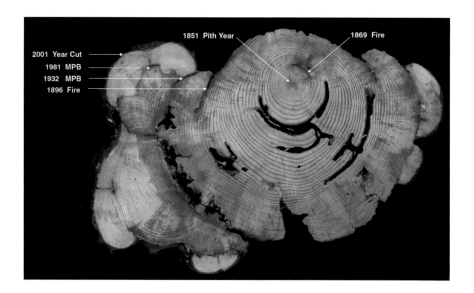

Figure 2. Tree disc showing presumed fire (1869, 1896) and mountain beetle (1932, 1981) scarring cut from a lodgepole pine stand on the Chilcotin Plateau in 2001.

Mountain pine beetle infestations in western Canada

The geographic and elevational range of mountain pine beetle, as with many bark beetles, is determined by the distribution of suitable host trees and by climate (Swaine 1925). Mountain pine beetle occurs in most native and exotic pine species in western North America (McCambridge et al. 1979). Of these, lodgepole, western white, whitebark and limber pine occur in Canada. Occasionally, non-host trees such as Engelmann spruce (*Picea engelmannii* Parry) are attacked, but beetle populations do not persist in these occasional hosts (Unger 1993). In western North America, despite the broad host range of mountain pine beetle, lodgepole pine is considered the main host species.

The mountain pine beetle occurs from northern Mexico (latitude 30°N), north through 12 American states, and into central British Columbia (latitude 56°N); from the Pacific Ocean in the west, to North Dakota; and from sea level to over 2000 m in elevation (Safranyik 2001). In Canada, mountain pine beetle occurs principally in the southern half of British Columbia and the extreme southwestern portion of Alberta with one outbreak recorded in the Cypress Hills at the southern junction of the Alberta – Saskatchewan border. The range of mountain pine beetle appears to be limited mainly by the occurrence of 40° C temperatures within the distribution of host species (Safranyik et al. 1975), temperatures at which all life stages of the beetle suffer extensive mortality (Safranyik and Linton 1998; see Chapter 1 of this book).

Recently, digitization of historical insect survey maps has allowed for re-analysis of mountain pine beetle outbreak patterns in British Columbia. The cumulative area infested by mountain pine beetle by decade since 1920 is plotted in Figure 3 over the distribution of forest stands in which pine species predominate (derived from the 1994 Forest, Range, and Recreation Resource Analysis [British Columbia Ministry of Forests 1995]). Significant outbreaks in lodgepole and ponderosa pine in the 1920s were recorded around Aspen Grove and in the Kettle Valley (Fig. 3a). In the 1930s, a large outbreak was examined in the Chilcotin in west-central British Columbia (Fig. 3b). During the 1940s, significant mountain pine beetle-caused mortality was recorded in Kootenay and Banff National Parks (Fig. 3c); smaller infestations were recorded in western white pine in the Shuswap region and in coastal British Columbia. During the 1950s and 1960s, one of the longest duration outbreaks ever recorded (18 years) was observed around Babine Lake and Stuart Lake in north-central British Columbia (Figs. 3d and 3e). A smaller infestation was observed on shore pine and western white pine on Vancouver Island and the Sunshine Coast during the 1960s. Major infestations developed in the 1970s and 1980s on the Chilcotin plateau and in southeastern British Columbia (Figs. 3f and 3g). Small infestations were also noted in southwestern Alberta and in the Cypress Hills of Alberta and Saskatchewan during the 1980s. The present outbreak began to develop in north central British Columbia during the 1990s, and is the largest recorded outbreak to date (Fig. 3h). The cumulative area affected is shown in Figure 4.

The sum of the annual areas infested by mountain pine beetle (between 1960-2004) was approximately 16.8 million hectares. Of this, 52%, 24%, and 23% of the infested area fell in low, moderate, and high severity classes, respectively. However, the cumulative area infested between 1959 and 2004 was about 9.8 million hectares (Fig. 4). There appears to be a higher proportion of low and moderate severity area affected in the current (1995-2004) outbreak than in the previous (1970s-1980s) major outbreak, possibly because more mixed stands of pine and spruce are being affected in the current outbreak (Fig. 5a).

The digital outbreak maps were intersected with forest inventory records to determine the historical distribution of outbreaks by stand type in British Columbia (Fig. 5b). Between 1959-2002, of the approximately 6 million ha of outbreak for which inventory records were available, 63% of outbreaks occurred in pine-dominated stands (>50% pine species by volume), which represents about 22% of the approximately 14 million ha of pine-dominated forests in British Columbia (British Columbia Ministry of Forests 1995). Pine-dominated stand types sustained the majority of high-severity outbreaks. However, about 70% of affected forests (i.e., all attack severities) had a significant component of non-host tree species, principally white (*Picea glauca*) or Engelmann spruce, Douglas-fir (*Pseudotsuga menziesii*), trembling aspen (*Populus tremuloides*), western larch (*Larix occidentalis*) or subalpine fir (*Abies lasiocarpa*) (Fig. 5b).

The distribution of mountain pine beetle outbreaks was also examined across biogeoclimatic zones (Meidinger and Pojar 1991) in British Columbia. Lodgepole pine is ubiquitous in British Columbia, occurring in all biogeoclimatic zones from sea level to alpine tundra and from rainforest to semi-desert. The majority of mountain pine beetle outbreaks occurred in the Sub Boreal Spruce (SBS) zone, followed by the Sub-Boreal Pine Spruce (SBPS), Interior Douglas-Fir (IDF), and Engelmann Spruce Subalpine Fir (ESSF), Montane Spruce (MS), and Interior Cedar Hemlock (ICH) zones (Table 1 and Fig. 5c). Minor outbreaks have occurred in other zones. Outbreaks in mixed stands of pine and spruce have predominated in the SBS and ESSF zones and in mixed stands of pine and Douglas-fir in the IDF zone. Lodgepole pine is a seral species in these zones and mountain pine beetle outbreaks in mixed stands hasten the successional process to non-host species. Outbreaks in pure lodgepole pine stands have occurred predominantly in the SBS and MS zones. Lodgepole pine is considered a persistent fire-climax species in the SBPS zone, and succession to spruce would be very slow (Steen and Demarchi 1991) because there is little spruce in the understory or as a seed source. The residual stand following mountain pine beetle outbreaks in the SBPS is primarily smaller diameter lodgepole pine. Outbreaks have not occurred to any great extent in the Boreal White and Black Spruce (BWBS) and Spruce Willow Birch (SWB) zones in northern British Columbia despite a relative abundance of host because these zones experience extreme winter temperatures.

The majority of mountain pine beetle outbreaks have occurred between 800 and 1400 m in elevation (Fig. 5d) in British Columbia, with the mean elevation decreasing from about 1400 m at 49° to 1000 m at 55° N. Outbreak severity appears to have been less at lower elevations (400-800 m), possibly because of a higher prevalence of mixed stands of Douglas-fir and lodgepole pine. There also appears to be a higher proportion of low- and moderate-severity outbreaks north from 53° N, possibly because of a higher proportion of mixed stands of lodgepole pine, spruce and subalpine fir.

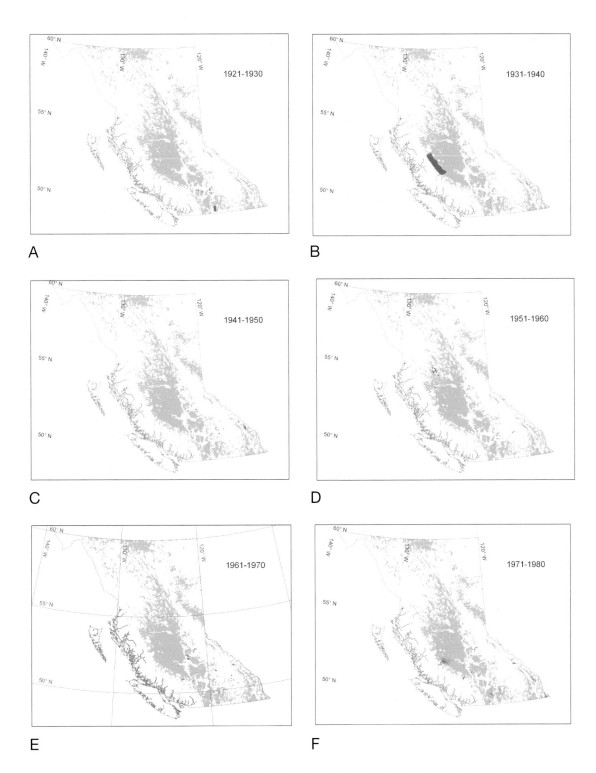

Figure 3. Distribution of mountain pine beetle outbreaks (red) by decade and the distribution of pine-leading stands (green) in British Columbia for 1920-2004. (See following page for Figures G, H, and I.)

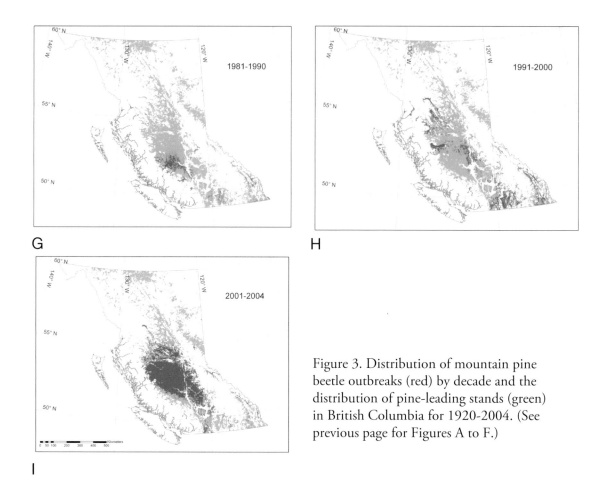

G

H

I

Figure 3. Distribution of mountain pine beetle outbreaks (red) by decade and the distribution of pine-leading stands (green) in British Columbia for 1920-2004. (See previous page for Figures A to F.)

The Chilcotin Plateau in south-central British Columbia (SBPS zone) sustained the most years of consecutive outbreaks (approximately 52° N, 124° W - see Fig. 4) during 1920-2004. Alfaro et al. (2004) used dendrochronological methods to further investigate the history of canopy disturbances indicative of potential past mountain beetle outbreaks at 15 locations in this area. An example of a standardized chronology for one of the stands showing two periods of release from competition is shown in Figure 6. Of the 15 chronologies, 30% of the stands showed release periods in the 1890s, and 75% showed release in the 1940s and the 1980s (Fig. 7). Each of the three release periods lasted, on average, 13.8 years (Range 5–23) and recurred every 42 years (Range 28–53), counted from the start of one release to the start of the next release. The dendrochronology record still does not show potential release due to the current outbreak (ongoing in 2006). The releases in the 1940s and 1980s are consistent with insect outbreak survey records, but the occurrence in the 1890s predates the surveys. Because of a delay in tree growth response to thinning, the release is not precisely simultaneous (Eisenhart and Veblen 2000). Heath and Alfaro (1990) indicated that the thinning response of lodgepole pine, expressed as a significant increase in ring growth, began 2 to 6 years after the start of a severe beetle outbreak and peaked 5 to 9 years after. Therefore, the outbreak episodes indicated by the dendrochronological assessment may have began nearly a decade earlier (i.e., 1880s, 1930s, 1970s), a premise supported by the survey records of the latter two outbreaks (see Figs. 3 and 5).

Table 1. Distribution of pine-leading stands and mountain pine beetle (MPB) outbreaks by biogeoclimatic zone in British Columbia

Biogeoclimatic zone	Elevation (m) [1]	Mean annual temp. (°C) [1]	Mean annual precip. (mm) [1]	Area of lodgepole pine - leading stands (ha) [2]				Cumulative 1960-2002 MPB outbreak area (ha) [3]
				< 80 years	80 - 140 years	140 + years	Total	
AT - Alpine tundra	1000 + 2250+	-4 - 0	700 -3000	17 840	36 839	26 284	80 964	38 138
BG - Bunchgrass	-1000	-	-	17	120	44	181	2 178
BWBS - Boreal White and Black Spruce	230 -1300	- 2.9 - 2.0	330 - 570	1 131 427	1 365 306	110 239	2 606 973	3 221
CDF - Coastal Douglas-Fir	0 - 150	9.2 - 10.5	647 -1263	319	171	0	490	0
CWH - Coastal Western Hemlock	0 -900	5.2 - 10.5	1000 -4400	29 717	48 918	149 625	228 260	67 472
ESSF - Engelmann Spruce Subalpine Fir	900 - 2300	-2.0 - 2.0	400 - 2200	679 045	1 119 162	376 275	2 174 482	670 880
ICH - Interior Cedar Hemlock	400 - 1500	2.0 - 8.7	500 - 1200	322 297	235 449	9 769	567 516	342 949
IDF - Interior Douglas-Fir	350 - 1450	1.6 - 9.5	300 - 750	400 828	534 547	55 348	990 723	1 077 803
MH - Mountain Hemlock	400 - 1800	0.0 - 5.0	1700 - 5000	262	1380	2 681	4323	8 674
MS - Montane Spruce	1100 - 1500	0.5 - 4.7	380 - 900	620 785	866 169	271 538	1 758 492	531 732
PP - Ponderosa Pine	335 - 900	4.8 - 10.0	280 - 500	490	536	0	1 026	4 258
SBPS - SubBoreal Pine Spruce	850 - 1300	0.3 - 2.7	335 - 580	567 610	984 488	187 917	1 740 015	1 354 126
SBS - SubBoreal Spruce	1100 - 1300	1.7 - 5.0	440 - 900	1 166 322	2 154 913	483 587	3 804 822	1 846 115
SWB - Spruce Willow Birch	900 -1700	-0.7 - 3.0	46 - 700	281 388	434 431	130 691	846 511	1
Total				5 218 349	7 782 430	1803 998	14 804 777	5 947 547

[1] Meidinger and Pojar (1991)
[2] Adapted from B.C. Seamless Forest Inventory - does not include private land, national parks, some provincial parks, and some tree farm licences.
[3] Canadian Forest Service and British Columbia Ministry of Forests insect survey records.

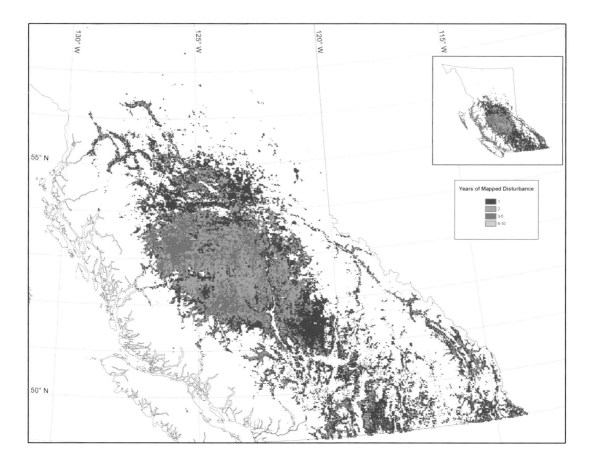

Figure 4. Cumulative area of mountain pine beetle outbreak in British Columbia during 1920-2004 showing number of years of attack.

The combined forest insect survey and dendrochronological records indicate that there have been four significant outbreak periods in British Columbia during the last 120 years and that outbreaks may recur in some areas as surviving trees in the residual stand grow to susceptible size. The records also suggest that outbreak size has been increasing over time. However, infestations have not yet occurred throughout the full range of the beetle's primary host—lodgepole pine (see Fig. 1). Despite its significant distribution, the current latitudinal and elevational range of mountain pine beetle in western Canada is not restricted by the availability of suitable host trees—lodgepole pine extends north into the southern Yukon and Northwest Territories, and east across much of Alberta, beyond the contemporary range of mountain pine beetle.

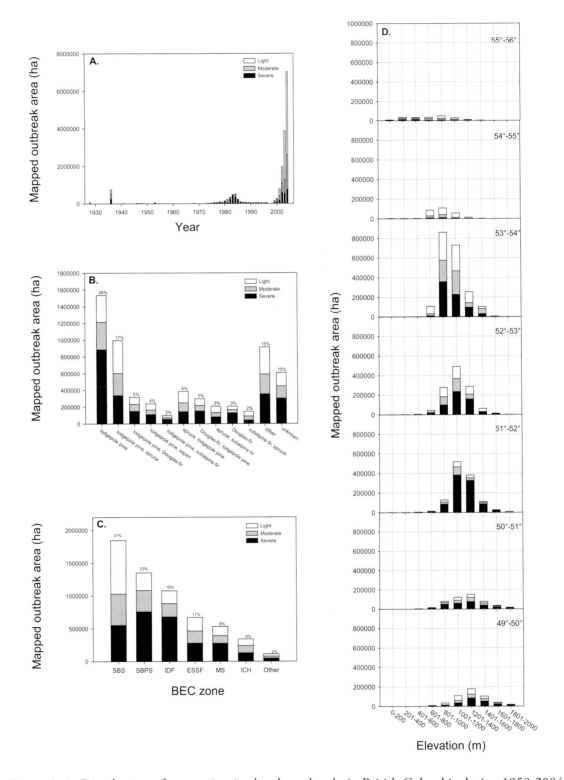

Figure 5. A. Distribution of mountain pine beetle outbreaks in British Columbia during 1959-2004 by severity class. B. Distribution of mountain pine beetle outbreaks in British Columbia during 1959-2002 by forest inventory type group and severity class. C. Distribution of mountain pine beetle outbreaks in British Columbia during 1959-2002 by biogeoclimatic zone and forest type. D. Distribution of mountain pine beetle outbreaks in British Columbia during 1959-2002 by elevation, latitude and severity class.

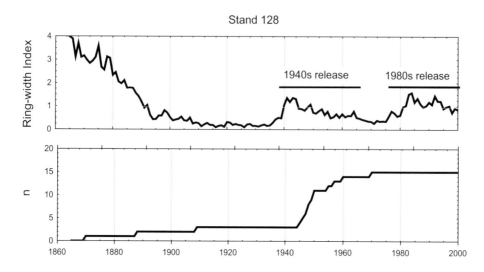

Figure 6. Example of tree ring chronology (top) and sample size for the chronology (bottom). Ring width indices for this stand clearly show two release periods (1940s and 1980s) attributable to canopy disturbances consistent with outbreaks of the mountain pine beetle beginning in the 1930s and 1970s.

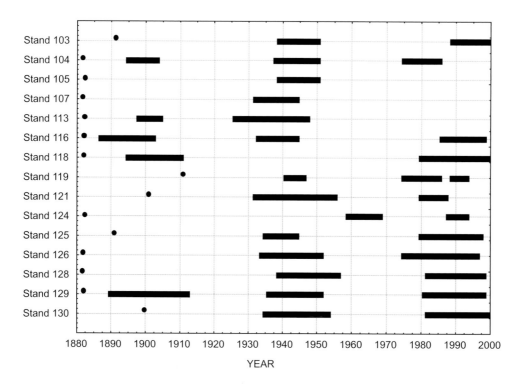

Figure 7. Release periods attributable to mountain pine beetle outbreaks in Chilcotin Plateau of British Columbia inferred from tree ring chronologies. Dot indicates start year for the chronology.

Mountain pine beetle outbreak requirements

For a mountain pine beetle outbreak to develop, two conditions must be satisfied. The first is an abundance of susceptible host trees (Safranyik 1978). Since mountain pine beetle larvae develop within the phloem of their hosts, large-diameter trees with thick phloem are the optimal resource for the beetle (e.g., Amman 1972). Senescing or suppressed trees tend to have thinner phloem and are thereby less suitable to mountain pine beetle (Berryman 1982). Accordingly, mountain pine beetle outbreaks generally occur in stands that are more than 80 years old, containing many trees of large diameter (Safranyik et al. 1974; Shore and Safranyik 1992). Thus, forest composition and age-class structure are the primary factors influencing host susceptibility and outbreak severity. The second condition comprises a sustained period of favourable weather over several years (Safranyik 1978). Insect development and activity are dependent upon temperature and seasonal weather conditions. Specifically, summer heat accumulation must be sufficient to allow development and reproduction followed by winter minimum temperatures that do not fall below thresholds that cause significant mortality (Carroll et al. 2004). Weather conditions during the dispersal period and water deficit have been found to influence mountain pine beetle populations directly through impacting survival of beetle adults, and/or indirectly through influencing host-tree resistance (Safranyik et al. 1975; Carroll et al. 2004). The following sections address these outbreak requirements with regard to the history of mountain pine beetle epidemics.

Lodgepole pine forest dynamics

Lodgepole pine is considered a fire dependent species (Lotan et al. 1985), and most first-growth lodgepole pine stands are of fire origin. During the heat of crown fires (when the majority of trees are killed), seeds are released from serotinous cones resulting in the re-establishment of virtually even-aged pine stands within a few years. The average frequency of fires at a particular location varies throughout the range of lodgepole pine from less than 100 years to over 500 years (Brown 1975). Based on an analysis of forest inventory data, Smith (1981) suggested that the natural fire-cycle in lodgepole pine forests in British Columbia was about 60 years.

In forests originating from stand-replacing disturbance processes such as wildfire, the rate of disturbance is the key determinant of forest age dynamics. Where fires occur randomly in space at a more or less constant rate, and all stands have an equal probability of burning irrespective of age and location, forest age structure will reach a steady state approximated by the negative exponential distribution (Van Wagner 1978; Li and Barclay 2001) where the average stand age is approximately equal to the fire cycle length. Before fire and timber management were applied in western North America, lodgepole pine forest age dynamics, and so their susceptibility to mountain pine beetle, would have been largely influenced by the forest fire regime, principally the fire cycle length, including the influence of burning by aboriginal peoples.

Taylor and Carroll (2004) examined the landscape-level age-related susceptibility to mountain pine beetle associated with negative exponential age distributions resulting from fire cycle lengths between 40 and 240 years and susceptibility in "normal" fully-regulated forests[1] with rotation lengths between 40 and 240 years, assuming that 80 – 160 year-old stands were most susceptible. They found that the proportion of the landscape susceptible to mountain pine beetle varied in a narrow range between about 12% – 25% for fire cycles of 40 – 240 years; susceptibility increased with fire cycle length to a maximum of 25% with a 120-year fire-return cycle, and then gradually declined (Fig. 8). In the "normal" forest, susceptiblity increased with rotation length to a maximum of 50% at 160 years (Fig. 8b). Examples of age distributions for 60- and 100-year fire-return cycles and a "normal" fully regulated forest with a 100-year rotation length are shown in Figure 9. The proportion of susceptible stands may vary through a greater range on a regional basis where there is deviation from the negative exponential age-class distribution because of spatial and temporal auto-correlation in wildfire occurrence (Boychuk and Perara 1997), or if older stands are susceptible. Where the rate of burning varies in space and time, variation in susceptibility will be greater in increasingly smaller landscapes as the ratio between average fire size and landscape size increases. However, in general, there are more younger stands than older stands in crown fire-dominated landscapes.

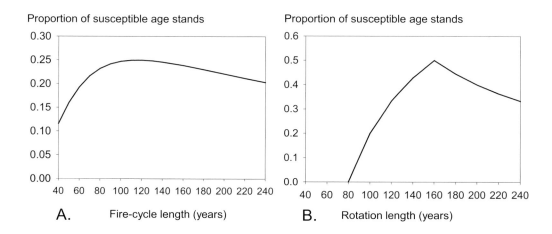

Figure 8. A.) Relationship between fire-cycle length and the proportion of stands susceptible to mountain pine beetle in forests with a negative exponential age-class distribution. B.) Relationship between rotation length and the proportion of stands susceptible to mountain pine beetle in forests with a uniform rectangular distribution.

[1] The "normal" forest is one with an equal amount of area by age class to a fixed rotation age, that is, a rectangular distribution. While rarely achieved, it is the most simple and fully regulated condition and a useful model for comparison.

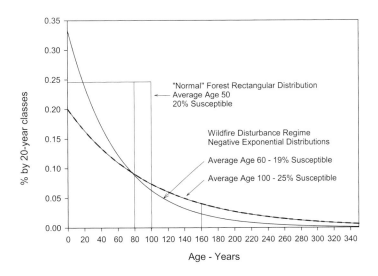

Figure 9. Theoretical distribution of age-classes susceptible to mountain pine beetle in a normal forest with a 100-year rotation, and in forests with 60- and 100-year fire cycles.

Barclay et al. (2005) used the term traversability to describe the presence of a spanning cluster of susceptible host stands that would provide a continuous path for mountain pine beetle to spread across a forested landscape, which they suggest is important to incipient mountain pine beetle outbreak development. The probability of such spanning clusters occurring depends on the proportion of susceptible aged/sized stands as well as patch size distribution. In a wildfire-dominated disturbance regime, patchiness is related to fire size distribution as well as fire cycle length. Using simulation modelling, Barclay et al. (2005) found that landscape traversability decreased as fire (patch) size increased. Barclay et al. (2005) also examined traversability of pine stands across British Columbia using contemporary forest inventory data. They found that traversability was highest in west-central British Columbia, in an area roughly coincident with the extent of the current outbreak. Presumably, this is because of a high proportion of lodgepole pine in these forests, as well as the development of relatively homogenous landscape patterns created by large fires in the region in the late 1800s and early 1900s.

Forest fire suppression began in western Canada approximately 100 years ago. The effective-ness of fire suppression has steadily increased, especially with greater availability of aircraft since the 1950s. This effectiveness is evident in the decreasing trend of area burned in pine-dominated forests in British Columbia between 1920 and 2002 (Taylor and Carroll 2004) (Fig. 10). While logging of lodgepole pine for railway ties also began about 100 years ago, large-scale exploitation of lodgepole pine for lumber and pulp did not occur until the 1960s. Consequently, the stand replacing disturbance rate across the vast pine forests of western Canada was, until recently, greatly reduced from the pre-management level. Using proxy 20-year age-class data from the British Columbia provincial forest inventory, Taylor and Carroll (2004) estimated that the total stand-replacement disturbance rate declined by two-thirds from about 1% during 1911-1930 to 0.31% during 1971-1991.

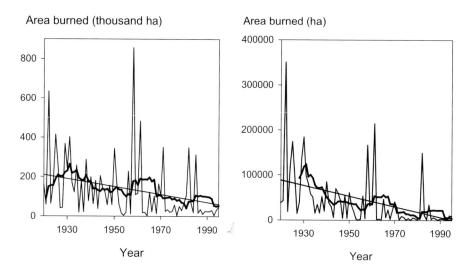

Figure 10. Area burned by forest fires during 1920-1995 in pine-dominated forests in British Columbia. Annual area burned (solid line), ten-year running average (bold line) and linear regression model (straight line).

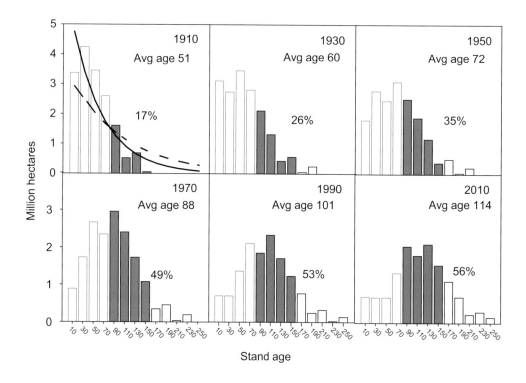

Figure 11. Age-class distribution of pine forests in British Columbia projected from 1990 inventory data. Age-classes susceptible to mountain pine beetle are shaded (percentage of total provided). The theoretical age distribution resulting from a 60-(solid line) and 100-year (dashed line) fire cycle is shown in the 1910 plot.

Combining disturbance data with provincial scale forest inventory data in a simple age-class projection model, Taylor and Carroll (2004) also reconstructed the area of pine by age-class in British Columbia during 1911-1991. Their results suggest that a large pine age cohort originated around 1880-1920, in an amount consistent with a 60-year fire-cycle. The burn rate may have been higher than would be predicted by a 60-year fire-cycle in this period due to fires resulting from mining exploration, land clearing, and railway activity (e.g., Leavitt 1915). With the introduction of fire management, a large proportion of the stands which regenerated after these fires have matured and entered the susceptible age-class for mountain pine beetle. The result is a threefold increase in the area of pine susceptible to mountain pine beetle during the 20th century (Fig. 11). Plotting the annual mountain pine beetle outbreak area alongside the area of susceptible pine by year suggests that the area increase of mountain pine beetle outbreaks since the 1970s are related to an increasing amount of susceptible pine (Fig. 12), although the outbreak area was apparently not limited by host availability on a provincial scale.

According to Clutter et al. (1983), if the rate of harvest in a fully-regulated forest is changed to a new level there are three possible outcomes: the forest structure will reach a new steady state, the forest will be totally depleted, or the forest will become unmanaged (the amount of timber lost to natural mortality exceeding harvesting). The same possible outcomes can be expected as a result of changing disturbance rates in forests that were historically regulated by natural disturbance. Currently, forest depletions by mountain pine beetle in British Columbia are greatly exceeding depletions by harvesting, making management of forest age structure through harvest regulation challenging.

Climatic Influences

Safranyik et al. (1975) developed a model of the influence of climate on the establishment and persistence of mountain pine beetle populations. They used an analysis of climatic variables measured at 42 locations for the period 1950 to 1971. The model combines six climatic variables believed to be important to beetle survival, attack, brood development, and host tree susceptibility (Table 1). The locations were chosen to represent the historic range of mountain pine beetle in British Columbia. The six variables were combined in an index of climatic suitability for mountain pine beetle (F):

$$F = P_i \overline{\big) X_1 \times X_2}$$

[1]

where: P_i is the number of years with the joint occurrence of variables P_1 through P_4 in runs of ≥ 2 consecutive years divided by the total number of years (see Table 2). The values of F range from 0 to 1. Climatic suitability classes (CSCs; Table 3) were created by comparing index values with the frequency of mountain pine beetle infestations across its historic range (Powell 1966). The climatic suitability index provides a means of examining the effect of temporal and spatial variation in climatic suitability on outbreaks.

Table 2. Description of climatic variables utilized to construct a model of climatic suitability of habitats to mountain pine beetle (MPB) populations (adapted from Safranyik et al. 1975).

Variable	Description	Rationale
P_1	> 305 degree-days above 5.5°C from Aug. 1 to end of growing season (Boughner 1964), and >833 degree-days from Aug. 1 to Jul. 31	A univoltine life cycle synchronized with critical seasonal events is essential for MPB survival (Logan and Powell 2001). Minimum heat requirement from peak flight to 50% egg hatch is 305 degree-days, and 833 degree-days is the minimum required for a population to be univoltine (adapted from Reid 1962).
P_2	Minimum winter temperatures >-40°C	Under-bark temperatures at or below -40°C causes 100% mortality within a population (Safranyik and Linton 1998).
P_3	Average maximum Aug. temperatures ≥18.3°C	The lower threshold for MPB flight is ≈18.3°C (McCambridge 1971). It is assumed that when the frequency of maximum daily temperatures is ≥18.3°C and ≤5% during August, the peak of MPB emergence and flight will be protracted and mass attack success reduced.
P_4	Total precipitation Apr. to Jun. < long-term average	Significant increases in MPB populations have been correlated with periods of two or more consecutive years of below-average precipitation over large areas of western Canada (Thomson and Shrimpton 1984).
X_1	Variability of growing season precipitation	Since P_4 is defined in terms of a deviation from average, the coefficient of variation of precipitation was included. Its numerical values were converted to a relative scale from 0 to 1 (see Safranyik et al. 1975).
X_2	Index of aridity[1]	Water deficit affects the resistance of lodgepole pine to MPB, as well as subsequent development and survival of larvae and associated blue stain fungi. An index of aridity (Ung et al. 2001) was used to approximate water deficit.

[1] The index of aridity replaces the water deficit approximation (National Atlas of Canada 1970) in the original model of Safranyik et al. (1975).

Table 3. Climatic suitability classes (CSCs) for mountain pine beetle derived from an index of climatic suitability (adapted from Safranyik et al. 1975).

Climatic suitability	Range of index (F)
Very low	0
Low	0.01 – 0.05
Moderate	0.06 – 0.15
High	0.16 – 0.35
Extreme	0.36+

Carroll et al. (2004) used historic weather and digital terrain data to model climatic suitability across British Columbia for the period 1930-2000. They found that during the latter half of the 20th century, there was a substantial shift in climatically benign habitats for mountain pine beetle northward and toward higher elevations. Areas suitable for mountain pine beetle (i.e., high and extreme CSCs) have expanded dramatically in south-central and south-eastern British Columbia (Fig. 13). The distribution of susceptible age pine by climatic suitability class is shown in Figure 14. As with climate suitability alone, there was an increase in the amount of susceptible age pine in moderate and high suitability classes in central British Columbia during 1950-1990. Furthermore, there was an increase in the amount of susceptible age pine in all climatic suitability classes since 1950 (Fig. 14b).

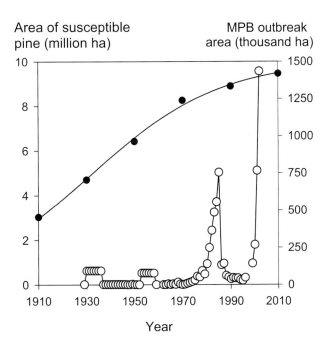

Figure 12. Estimated area of susceptible-aged pine (solid circles = million ha) and of mountain pine beetle (MPB) outbreaks (empty circles = thousand ha) in British Columbia during 1910-2010.

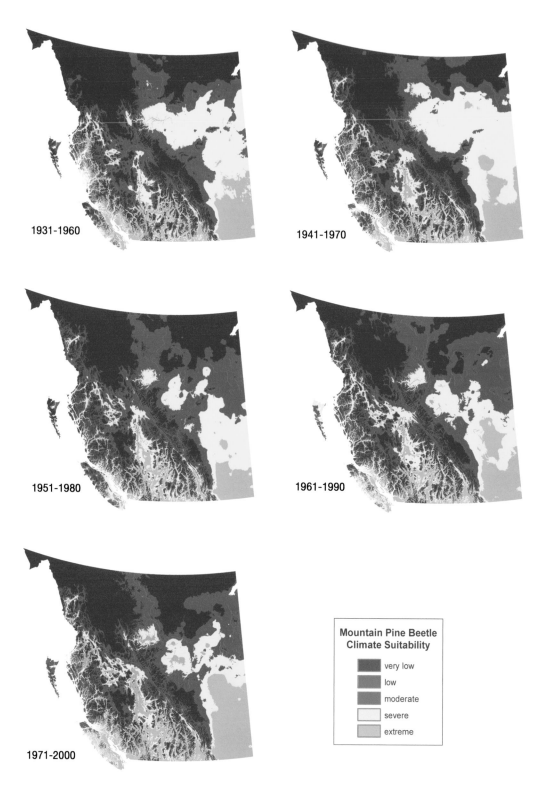

Figure 13. Historic distributions of climatic suitability classes (CSCs) derived from climate normals (30-year monthly means and extreme minima and maxima) for the mountain pine beetle in British Columbia and Alberta. "Very low" CSCs are habitats with climatic conditions unsuitable for mountain pine beetle whereas "extreme" CSCs are those considered climatically optimal.

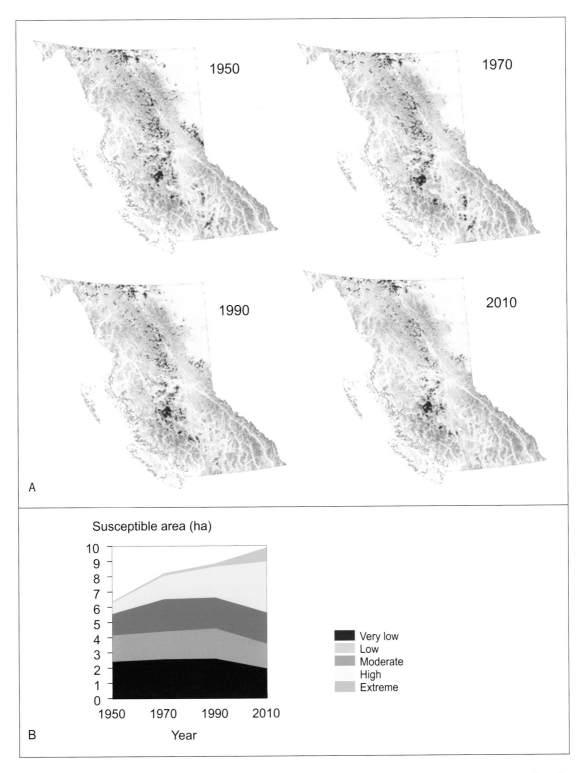

Figure 14. A. Historic and projected distribution of pine of susceptible age by mountain pine beetle climatic suitability class in British Columbia between 1950-2010. B. Area of pine of susceptible age by mountain pine beetle climatic suitability class (million ha) in British Columbia between 1950 - 2010.

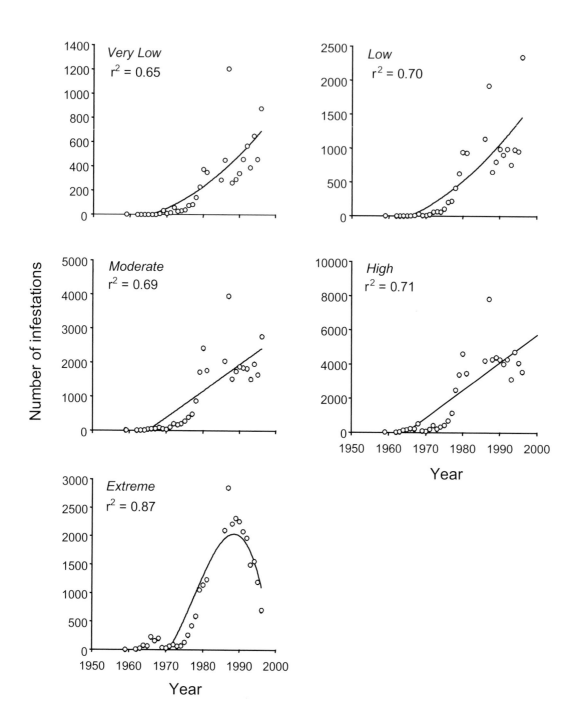

Fig. 15. Mountain pine beetle infestations (all severity classes) from 1998 to 2002 in areas of different climatic suitability classes in British Columbia. "Very low" CSCs are habitats with climatic conditions unsuitable for mountain pine beetle whereas "extreme" CSCs are those considered climatically optimal.

Carroll et al. (2004) also examined the distribution of mountain pine beetle outbreaks in British Columbia from historical survey data in relation to the CSCs. Mountain pine beetle populations have followed the apparent shift in climatically suitable habitats during the past three decades. Prior to 1968, no infestations had been recorded in areas with very low to low

CSCs (Safranyik et al. 1975). Since then, the increase (at an increasing rate) in the number of infestations in these areas of historically very low and low CSCs (Fig. 15) indicates that climate change in these habitats has allowed the establishment and persistence of mountain pine beetle populations in these formerly climatically unsuitable areas. Although temporal changes in the distribution of susceptible hosts (i.e., the amount of mature lodgepole pine) will affect the distribution of mountain pine beetle infestations, successful establishment of a beetle population is precluded unless the climatic conditions outlined in the climatic suitability model are met within a mature pine stand (Safranyik et al. 1975; Safranyik 1978).

By the mid-1980s, the number of infestations in habitats that were previously most suitable to mountain pine beetle (i.e., extreme CSC) declined dramatically (Fig. 15). There are at least two potential explanations for a decrease in the number of infestations in the formerly extreme CSC: (i) a reduction in the amount of susceptible pine in these habitat types due to previous disturbance (i.e., harvesting, fire, past mountain pine beetle outbreaks), or (ii) adverse effects of warmer temperatures on beetle populations. However, because there has been an apparent increase in the amount of pine in the extreme CSC (see Fig. 14b), the decline in infestations is most likely due to the adverse effects of warming climate. Studies by Logan and Bentz (1999) and Logan and Powell (2001) have shown that if heat accumulation during summer is sufficiently high, mountain pine beetle populations may be forced into partial multivoltinism (segments of the population having more than one generation per year) which will cause cold-susceptible stages (eggs, pupae, adults) to overwinter and interrupt flight synchrony, reducing mass attack success in the following year.

Historically, mountain pine beetle outbreaks in Canada have been most common in southern British Columbia. Non-forested prairies, the high elevations of the Rocky Mountains, and the extreme continental climate to the north and east have contributed to confining its range. However, it is hypothesized that as a consequence of global warming, environments that are climatically hostile to the mountain pine beetle will become climatically benign and allow a shift in the beetle's geographical distribution and changes in population behaviour (Logan and Powell 2001). Rapid ecological and genetic adaptation by insects in response to global warming has already been documented in Europe (Thomas et al. 2001). Indeed, with a conservative increase in average global temperature of 2.5°C associated with a doubling of atmospheric CO_2, as suggested by the Intergovernmental Panel on Climate Change as a plausible global warming scenario (Houghton et al. 1990), Logan and Powell (2001) predict a latitudinal shift of more than 7° N in the distribution of thermally benign habitats for mountain pine beetle. Perhaps as evidence of this shift, in recent years small but persistent mountain pine beetle populations have been detected along the northeastern slopes of the Rockies in British Columbia and Alberta at approximately 55° N – areas in which the beetle has not been previously recorded (Alberta Sustainable Resource Development 2003). These beetle populations are now in close proximity to the western range of jack pine, *Pinus banksiana* Lamb., a susceptible species (Cerezke 1995). In the absence of an unusual weather event (i.e., an unseasonable cold period or an extreme winter), expansion by the beetle into new habitats will provide it with a continual supply of mature pine, thereby maintaining populations at above-normal levels for decades into the future.

At the same time, areas with formerly extreme CSCs at southern and low-elevation regions may become less suitable for resident mountain pine beetle populations if further warming results in partial multivoltinism. If this was the case, the net effect would simply be a displacement of mountain pine beetle disturbance northward and areas of former suitability would be, in the future, less suitable. Unfortunately, a recent study (Bentz et al. 2001) has found a genetically-based latitudinal gradient in development rates for mountain pine beetle suggesting that there may be sufficient genetic variability in contiguous mountain pine beetle populations to match changes in the climatic environment within the present range of the species.

Summary

Mountain pine beetle outbreak development is influenced by host susceptibility, climatic suitability for mountain pine beetle, and forest management practices. Host susceptibility may in turn be influenced by the age, species composition, and contiguity of mature stands in the landscape, and by the occurrence of past outbreaks that degrade habitat quality for mountain pine beetle. Past disturbances, including harvesting, wildfire, wildfire suppression, and previous mountain pine beetle outbreaks, can have a profound influence on host susceptibility. Thus, where host susceptibility is age/size-dependent and trees are long-lived, and because it takes a number of years for smaller trees surviving an outbreak to reach a susceptible size, landscapes previously unaffected by outbreaks may be more susceptible than landscapes that have sustained relatively recent attacks.

In the lodgepole pine forests of western Canada, the disturbance regime is changing on a vast scale from an unmanaged state influenced by various natural disturbances to a managed condition in which natural disturbances are suppressed where possible, and forest harvesting is the predominant disturbance. Due to a reduction in the disturbance rate, a large cohort of lodgepole pine has reached an age/size susceptible to mountain pine beetle. This, combined with an increasingly favourable climate allowing for range expansion into previously unaffected forests, has created ideal conditions for an unprecedented mountain pine beetle outbreak. However, this susceptible pine cohort is a transitional phenomena - it is unlikely that such a large amount of susceptible pine will be seen again.

Safranyik (2004) suggested that, in the long-term, our focus should be on management of lodgepole pine, not on management of the mountain pine beetle. However, while management strategies should consider reducing landscape-scale susceptibility, it would take decades to hundreds of years to influence forest composition and age structure over the extensive pine forests in western Canada because large-scale disturbances impart an "ecological memory" to landscape patterns (Peterson 2002). In the short term, a better understanding of the effect of forest dynamics and climatic variation on mountain pine beetle outbreaks will allow for management of lodgepole pine forests with regard to disturbance risk.

Acknowledgements

This work was supported by Forest Renewal British Columbia, the British Columbia Forest Innovation Initiative, and the Government of Canada Mountain Pine Beetle Initiative. The cooperation of the British Columbia Ministry of Water, Land and Air Protection, and the British Columbia Ministry of Forests is gratefully acknowledged. Thanks go to Gurp Thandi, Bob Erickson, Patricia Perkins and Jamie MacDuff for technical assistance and to Vince Nealis for his thoughtful review of an earlier draft of the manuscript.

References

Alfaro, R.I.; Campbell, R.; Vera, P.; Hawkes, B.; Shore, T. 2004. Dendroecological reconstruction of mountain pine beetle outbreaks in the Chilcotin Plateau of British Columbia. Pages 245-256 *in* T.L. Shore, J.E. Brooks and J.E. Stone, eds. Challenges and Solutions: Proceedings of the Mountain Pine Beetle Symposium. Kelowna, British Columbia. October 30-31, 2003. Natural Resources Canada, Canadian Forest Service, Pacific Forestry Centre, Victoria, British Columbia, Information Report BC-X-399. 298 p.

Barclay, H.J.; Li, C.; Benson, L.; Taylor, S.; Shore, T. 2005. Effects of fire return rates on traversability of lodgepole pine forests for mountain pine beetle and the use of patch metrics to estimate traversability. The Canadian Entomologist. 137(5):566-583.

Bentz, B.J.; Logan, J.A.; Vandygriff, J.C. 2001. Latitudinal variation in *Dendroctonus ponderosae* (Coleoptera: Scolytidae) development time and adult size. The Canadian Entomologist 133:375-387.

Berryman, A.A. 1982. Mountain pine beetle outbreaks in Rocky Mountain lodgepole pine forests. Journal of Forestry 80:410-413, 419.

Boychuck, D.; Perera, A.H. 1997. Modelling temporal variability of boreal landscape age-classes under different fire disturbance regimes and spatial scales. Canadian Journal of Forest Research 27:1083-1094.

British Columbia Ministry of Forests. 1995. 1994 forest, recreation, and range resource analysis. British Columbia Ministry of Forests, Public Affairs Branch, Victoria, BC. 308 p.

Brown, J.K. 1975. Fire cycles and community dynamics in lodgepole pine forests. Pages 429-456 *in* D.M. Baumgartner, ed. Management of lodgepole pine ecosystems. Washington State University Cooperative Extension Service, Pullman, WA.

Carroll, A.L.; Taylor, S.W.; Régnière, J.; Safranyik, L. 2004. Effects of climate change on range expansion by the mountain pine beetle in British Columbia. Pages 223-232 *in* T.L. Shore, J.E. Brooks and J.E. Stone, eds. Challenges and Solutions: Proceedings of the Mountain Pine Beetle Symposium. Kelowna, British Columbia. October 30-31, 2003. Natural Resources Canada, Canadian Forest Service, Pacific Forestry Centre, Victoria, British Columbia, Information Report BC-X-399. 298 p.

Cerezke, H.F. 1995. Egg gallery, brood production, and adult characteristics of mountain pine beetle, *Dendroctonus ponderosae* Hopkins (Coleoptera: Scolytidae), in three pine hosts. The Canadian Entomologist 127:955-965.

Clutter, J.L.; Fortson, J.C.; Pienarr, L.V.; Brister, G.H.; Bailey, R.L. 1983. Timber management: a quantitative approach. Wiley, New York. 333 p.

Eisenhart, K.S.; Veblen, T.T. 2000. Dendroecological detection of spruce bark beetle outbreaks in northwestern Colorado. Canadian Journal of Forest Research 30:1788-1798.

Heath, R.; Alfaro, R.I. 1990. Growth response in a Douglas-fir/lodgepole pine stand after thinning of lodgepole pine by the mountain pine beetle: A case study. Journal of the Entomological Society of British Columbia 87:16-21.

Houghton, J.T.; Jenkins, G.J.; Ephraums, J.J., eds. 1990. Climate change: the IPCC scientific assessment. Cambridge University Press, Cambridge, UK.

Leavitt, C. 1915. Forest protection in Canada 1913-1914. Commission of Conservation Canada, Ottawa. 317 p.

Li, C.; Barclay, H.J. 2001. Fire disturbance patterns and forest age structure. Natural Resources Modelling 14:495-521.

Logan, J.A.; Bentz, B.J. 1999. Model analysis of mountain pine beetle (Coleoptera: Scolytidae) seasonality. Environmetal Entomology 28:924-934.

Logan, J.A.; Powell, J.A. 2001. Ghost forests, global warming and the mountain pine beetle (Coleoptera: Scolytidae). American Entomologist 47:160-173.

Lotan, J.E.; Brown, J.K.; Neuenschwander, L.F. 1985. Role of fire in lodgepole pine forests. Pages 133-152 *in* D.M. Baumgartner, R.G. Krebill, J.T. Arnott, and G.F. Weetman, eds. Proceedings of lodgepole pine: the species and its management. May 8-10 1984, Spokane Washington State University, Pullman, WA.

McCambridge, W.F.; Amman, G.D.; Trostle, G.C. 1979. Mountain pine beetle. USDA Forest Service, Forest Insect and Disease Leaflet 2. WA. 7 p.

McCambridge, W.F. 1971. Temperature limits of flight of the mountain pine beetle, *Dendroctonus ponderosae*. Annals of the Entomological Society of America 64:534-535.

Meidinger, D.; Pojar, J., eds. 1991. Ecosystems of British Columbia. British Columbia Ministry of Forests Special Report Series 6. 330 p.

Peterson, G.D. 2002. Contagious disturbance, ecological memory and the emergence of landscape pattern. Ecosystems 5:329-338.

Powell, J.M. 1966. Distribution and outbreaks of *Dendroctonus ponderosae* in forests of Western Canada. Canadian Department of Forestry, Information Report A-X-2, Forest Research Lab., Calgary, AB. 19 p.

Reid, R.W. 1962. Biology of the mountain pine beetle, *Dendroctonus monticolae* Hopkins, in the East Kootenay region of British Columbia. 1. Life Cycle, broad development and flight periods Canadian Entomology 94:531-538.

Safranyik, L. 1978. Effects of climate and weather on mountain pine beetle populations. Pages 77-84 *in* A.A. Berryman, G.D. Amman and R.W. Stark, eds. Theory and practice of mountain pine beetle management in lodgepole pine forests. Symposium Proceedings, April 25-27, 1978, Pullman, WA. University of Idaho, Moscow, ID.

Safranyik, L. 2001. Seasonality in the mountain pine beetle: Causes and effects on abundance. Pages 150-151 *in* Volney, W.J.A.; Spence, J.R.; Lefebvre, E.M., eds. Boreal Odyssey: Proceedings of the North American Forest Insect Work Conference, May 14-18, 2001, Edmonton, Alberta, Canada. Natural Resources Canada, Canadian Forest Service, Northern Forest Research Centre, Edmonton AB.

Safranyik, L. 2004. Pages 33-40 *in* T.L. Shore, J.E. Brooks and J.E. Stone, eds. Challenges and Solutions: Proceedings of the Mountain Pine Beetle Symposium. Kelowna, British Columbia. October 30-31, 2003. Natural Resources Canada, Canadian Forest Service, Pacific Forestry Centre, Victoria, British Columbia, Information Report BC-X-399. 298 p.

Safranyik, L.; Linton, D.A. 1998. Mortality of mountain pine beetle (Coleoptera: Scolytidae) in logs of lodgepole pine (*Pinus contorta var. latifolia*) at constant low temperatures. Journal of the Entomological Society of British Columbia 95:81-87.

Safranyik, L.; Shrimpton, D.M.; Whitney, H.S. 1974. Management of lodgepole pine to reduce losses from the mountain pine beetle. Canadian Forest Service Technical Report. 1, 24pp.

Safranyik, L.; Shrimpton D.M.; Whitney, H.S. 1975. An interpretation of the interaction between lodgepole pine, the mountain pine beetle and its associated blue stain fungi in western Canada. Pages 406-428 *in* D.M. Baumgartner, ed. Management of lodgepole pine ecosystems. Washington State University Cooperative Extension Service, Pullman, WA.

Shore, T.L.; Safranyik, L. 1992. Susceptibility and risk rating systems for the mountain pine beetle in lodgepole pine stands. Canadian Forest Service, Pacific Forestry Centre. Information Report. BC-X-336. 12 p.

Smith, J.H.G. 1981. Fire cycles and management alternatives. Pages 511-531 *in* Fire regimes and ecosystem properties. Proceedings of the conference, December 11-15, 1978. Honolulu, Hawaii. USDA Forest Service General Technical Report WO-26, Washington.

Steen, O.; Demarchi, D.A. 1991. Sub-Boreal Pine - Spruce Zone. Pages 195-207 *in* D. Meidinger and J. Pojar compilers, eds. Ecosystems of British Columbia. British Columbia Ministry of Forests Special Report Series 6.

Swaine, J.M. 1918. Insect injuries to forests in British Columbia. Pages 220-236 *in* H.N. Whitford, R. D. Craig. The Forests of British Columbia. Commission on Conservation Canada. Ottawa. 409 p.

Swaine, J.M. 1925. The factors determining the distribution of North American bark beetles. Canadian Entolologist LVII:261-266.

Swetnam, T.W.; Lynch A.M. 1993. Multicentury, regional-scale patterns of western spruce budworm outbreaks. Ecological Monographs 63:399-424.

Taylor, S.W.; Carroll, A.L. 2004. Disturbance, forest age, and mountain pine beetle outbreak dynamics in BC: A historical perspective. Pages 41-56 *in* T.L. Shore, J.E. Brooks and J.E. Stone, eds. Challenges and Solutions. Proceedings of the Mountain Pine Beetle Symposium. Kelowna, British Columbia. October 30-31, 2003. Natural Resources Canada, Canadian Forest Service, Pacific Forestry Centre, Victoria, British Columbia, Information Report BC-X-399. 298 p.

Thomas, C.D.; Bodsworth, E.J.; Wilson, R.J.; Simmons, A.D.; Davies, Z.G.; Musche, M.; Conradt, L. 2001. Ecological and evolutionary processes at expanding range margins. Nature 411:577-581.

Thompson, A.J.; Shrimpton, D.M. 1984. Weather associated with the start of mountain pine beetle outbreaks. Canadian Journal of Forest Research 14:255-258

Ung, C.H.; Bernier, P.Y.; Raulier, F.; Fournier, R.A.; Lambert, M.-C.; Régnière; J. 2001. Biophysical site indices for shade tolerant and intolerant boreal species. Forest Science 47:83-95.

Unger, L. 1993. Mountain pine beetle. Canadian Forest Service, Pacific Forestry Centre, Victoria, BC. Forest Pest Leaflet No. 76.

Van Sickle A.; Fiddick, R.L.; Wood, C.S. 2001. The forest insect and disease survey in the Pacific Region. Journal of the Entomological Society of British Columbia 98:169-176.

Van Wagner, C.E. 1978. Age-class distribution and the forest fire cycle. Canadian Journal of Forest Research 8:220-227.

Veblen, T.T.; Hadley, K.S.; Reid, M.S.; Rebertus, A.J. 1991a. Methods of detecting past spruce beetle outbreaks in Rocky Mountain subalpine forests. Canadian Journal of Forest Research 21:242-254.

Veblen, T.T.; Hadley, K.S.; Reid, M.S.; Rebertus, A.J. 1991b. The response of subalpine forests to spruce beetle outbreak in Colorado. Ecology 72:213-231.

Wood, C.S.; Unger, L.S. 1996. Mountain pine beetle. A history of outbreaks in pine forests in British Columbia, 1910 to 1995. Natural Resources Canada, Canadian Forest Service, Pacific Forestry Centre, Victoria, BC. 61 p.

Zhang, Qi-bin; Alfaro, R.I. 2002. Periodicity of two-year cycle spruce budworm outbreaks in central British Columbia: a cendro-ecological analysis. Forest Science 48:722-731.

Zhang, Qi-bin; Alfaro, R.I. 2003. Spatial synchrony of the two-year cycle budworm outbreaks in central British Columbia. Oikos 102:146-154.

Zhang, Qi-bin; Alfaro, R.I.; Hebda, R. 1999. Dendroecological studies of tree growth, climate and spruce beetle outbreaks in Central British Columbia. Forest Ecology and Management 121:215-225.

Chapter 3

Effects of the Mountain Pine Beetle on Lodgepole Pine Stand Structure and Dynamics

Terry L. Shore, Les Safranyik, Brad C. Hawkes, and Steve W. Taylor

Natural Resources Canada, Canadian Forest Service, Pacific Forestry Centre,
506 West Burnside Road, Victoria, British Columbia, V8Z 1M5

Abstract

This chapter reviews the ecology of lodgepole pine (*Pinus contorta* Dougl. ex Loud. var. *latifolia* Engelm.) in relation to interactions with fire and the mountain pine beetle (*Dendroctonus ponderosae* Hopk. [Coleoptera: Scolytidae]), with special reference to western Canada. Lodgepole pine has wide ecological amplitude. In western Canada, lodgepole pine is present in the majority of biogeographic zones in its distributional range and has four successional roles ranging from minor seral to climax. Although lodgepole pine can regenerate without fire disturbance, it is principally a fire-maintained species. The mean fire return period and mean fire size are the major determinants of age distribution of lodgepole pine types on the landscape, and hence the spatial and temporal extent of susceptible forests. Epidemics may heavily deplete the large diameter pine components of stands, thereby increasing the non-host overstory component of mixed stands. The surviving host and non-host trees will generally increase in growth. Post-epidemic development of forest types depends on a large number of factors such as fire disturbance, extent of stand depletion, advance regeneration, presence of non-host overstory trees, and biogeographic zone, and may range from pure stands of lodgepole pine to pure stands of non-host species.

Résumé

Le présent chapitre étudie l'écologie du pin tordu latifolié (*Pinus contorta* Dougl. ex Loud. var. *latifolia* Engelm.) en rapport avec les interactions du feu et du dendroctone du pin ponderosa (*Dendroctonus ponderosae* Hopk. [Coleoptera: Scolytidae]), principalement dans l'Ouest canadien. Le pin tordu latifolié a une grande amplitude écologique. Dans l'Ouest canadien, il se rencontre dans la majorité des zones biogéographiques comprises dans son aire de répartition et joue quatre rôles dans la succession forestière, depuis le stade de transition jusqu'au stade climacique. Bien que les perturbations occasionnées par le feu ne soient pas indispensables à la régénération du pin tordu latifolié, elles jouent un rôle prédominant dans la pérennité de cette essence. La fréquence et l'ampleur moyennes des incendies sont les principaux déterminants de la répartition par âge des types de pins tordus latifoliés à l'échelle du paysage et, par conséquent, de la répartition des forêts vulnérables dans le temps et dans l'espace. Les épidémies peuvent entraîner une forte réduction des pins de grand diamètre dans les peuplements touchés, ce qui fait augmenter, par conséquent, l'élément non hôte de l'étage dominant des peuplements mixtes. La croissance des arbres survivants, tant hôtes que non hôtes, va généralement s'intensifier à la suite d'une infestation. L'établissement, après une épidémie, des types forestiers dépend de nombreux facteurs, comme les perturbations liées au feu, l'ampleur de la réduction du peuplement, une régénération préexistante, la présence d'arbres non hôtes dans l'étage dominant et la zone biogéographique. Selon le rôle joué par ces divers facteurs, la formation des nouveaux types forestiers peut aller de peuplements purs de pins tordus latifoliés à des peuplements purs d'essences non hôtes.

Introduction

The mountain pine beetle, *Dendroctonus ponderosae* Hopk. (Coleoptera: Scolytidae), is the most significant biological agent of mortality in mature pines in western North America. Adult beetles attack and cause mortality in most species of pine within the beetle's range. Early epidemics were reported primarily in ponderosa pine (*Pinus ponderosa* P.Laws. ex C.Laws). In recent years, the majority of large epidemics have occurred in lodgepole pine (*P. contorta* Dougl. ex Loud.); therefore, this chapter focuses on this host species.

Multiple-use, sustainable management of forest resources requires a sound understanding of stand dynamics resulting from mountain pine beetle outbreaks. This knowledge is crucial to managing forests in a manner that approximates natural disturbance processes and patterns while reducing future risks from mountain pine beetle attacks. Due to the importance of lodgepole pine to the ecology and economy in Canada and the USA, substantial research efforts have focused on mountain pine beetle. Considering the depth of our knowledge regarding mountain pine beetle biology and the ecology of lodgepole pine forests, very little is known about how the beetle and fire interact in lodgepole pine dominated forest stands, and how mountain pine beetle, lodgepole pine stand dynamics, and fire interact on the landscape to regulate the ecosystem as a whole.

Although a variety of silvicultural tools and management strategies can be used to minimize timber losses to mountain pine beetle (Safranyik et al. 1974; Shore and Safranyik 1992; Maclauchlan and Brooks 1994; McMullen et al.1986; Whitehead et al. 2001), effective control programs require early detection, rapid implementation, and continuous commitment. Long-term effects of these control strategies on the ecosystem are unknown (Hughes and Drever 2001), and little is known about long-term, post-epidemic development and growth of stands that have not undergone control measures. A sound understanding of the impact of mountain pine beetle outbreaks on growth and yield of surviving trees in residual stands, regeneration, woody debris dynamics, and fire potential is needed for managers to make better decisions regarding stand management in the face of mountain pine beetle infestations.

The mountain pine beetle-blue stain fungi association affects the structure and dynamics of lodgepole pine forests via interactions with individual tree characteristics, stand characteristics, and the distribution of these characteristics on the landscape (see Chapter 1).

In this chapter, we review the current knowledge of mountain pine beetle effects on lodgepole pine stand structure and dynamics. As fire plays an important role in lodgepole pine ecology (Agee 1993), we briefly review the main silvical characteristics of lodgepole pine and the effects of fire on regeneration and age distribution on the landscape. We then describe a sample of predominantly lodgepole pine stands from infestations in British Columbia as they were prior to infestation, just after infestation, and as they are currently. This information provides a foundation to the knowledge base required to manage large areas of beetle-killed forest and illuminates the gaps in knowledge that require further research.

The prevalence of lodgepole pine forests

In Canada, two subspecies of *Pinus contorta* occur: shore pine (*P. contorta* Doug. ex Loud. var. *contorta*) and lodgepole pine (*P. contorta* var. *latifolia* Engelm.). The former is confined to the coast and islands of British Columbia. Although both varieties can be attacked and killed by the mountain pine beetle, by far the most damage occurs in lodgepole pine.

Lodgepole pine is an important component of the forests of western North America. Its range extends from about 37° to about 64° latitude and from the Pacific coast to the Black Hills of South Dakota (Koch 1996). In the USA it represents about 6 million ha of commercial forest land (Koch 1996). In Canada, the total area of lodgepole pine forest type is about 20 million ha, mostly in British Columbia and Alberta. Lodgepole pine comprises 22% of the total forest in western Canada (Koch 1996). In British Columbia, pine species cover approximately 14 million ha, most of it lodgepole pine (Taylor and Carroll 2004). Prior to the current massive infestation, pine accounted for roughly 25% of the provincial timber supply in British Columbia (Taylor and Carroll, 2004). In Alberta, pine represents approximately 41% of the coniferous forests, or about 7 million ha. The majority of pine in Alberta is lodgepole pine and jack pine (*P. banksiana* Lamb.). Pine forests serve many purposes such as recreation, habitat for wildlife, cover for watersheds, lumber and fibre production.

Silvics of lodgepole pine

Lodgepole pine has large ecological amplitude. For example, in Alberta and British Columbia lodgepole pine grows in all but three of nearly 20 biogeoclimatic zones (Pojar 1985). Lodgepole pine grows from low to high elevations, from warm to cold, and from relatively dry to wet conditions, and it grows on most soil types (Schmidt 1989), but it is most prevalent within an elevation range of 800 to 1400 m. It reproduces best on bare soil. With relatively minor exception, lodgepole pine is a seral species that is highly shade intolerant but grows fast at a young age. This is an important characteristic of a pioneer species that enables it to compete successfully with other vegetation for space and light. As a consequence, most lodgepole pine stands tend to be even-aged, homogeneous in composition and, in the absence of a disturbance event such as fire, succeeded by more shade tolerant species. Commonly, the succeeding species are Douglas-fir (*Pseudotsuga menziesii* var. *glauca* [Beissn.] Franco), subalpine fir (*Abies lasiocarpa* [Hook.] Nutt.), Engelmann spruce (*Picea engelmannii* Parry ex Engelmann) and white spruce (*P. glauca* Moech [Voss]). The rate at which succession proceeds varies by site conditions, being relatively fast in low elevation mesic sites and considerably slower in northern and high-elevation forests (Schmidt 1989).

Lodgepole pine has two types of cone habits: open and serotinous. Seeds are released from open cones usually during September and October but serotinous cones require high temperatures in the range of 45° - 50° C to open and release seeds. Ambient temperatures of this magnitude can occur on or near the ground during summer in most stands, at least at lower elevations. However, in areas where lodgepole pine has a predominantly serotinous cone habit, fire events provide the most suitable conditions for a high density of seeds to be released over a short time period. This is sufficient for establishment of even-aged, new stands. The incidence of cone serotiny increases with latitude (Koch 1987) but tends to decrease with elevation. Near the northern limit of mountain pine beetle distribution (latitude 56°N), on average about 80% of mature lodgepole pine trees have serotinous cones. However, the incidence of serotiny can vary considerably among and within stands (Koch 1996). Lodgepole pines 6-10 years old start producing cones that are mainly the open cone type and cone serotiny is set between ages 17 and 60 (Koch 1987).

Four basic successional roles are described for lodgepole pine (Pfister and Daubenmire 1975):

1. *Minor seral.* Lodgepole pine is a minor component in young, even-aged, mixed species stands and is replaced by more shade-tolerant species, often within 50-100 years on more mesic sites.

2. *Dominant seral.* Even-aged lodgepole pine is the dominant cover type that is replaced by an understory of shade-tolerant species in 100-200 years.

3. *Persistent.* This is similar to the Dominant seral condition except that there is little evidence of replacement by shade-tolerant species. This situation usually occurs when there are either inadequate seed sources of shade-tolerant species or the site is poorly suited for other tree species.

4. *Climax.* These are sites where lodgepole pine is the only tree species capable of growing. Consequently, it perpetuates itself usually in uneven-aged stands. This condition is often found on sites where soils hold limited moisture.

Lodgepole pine forest and stand dynamics

The high incidence of serotinous cone habit of lodgepole pine in western Canada is an indication of the important role wildfires played in its ecology under natural conditions. The importance of fire in maintaining lodgepole pine on the landscape is well documented (Agee 1993). Although lodgepole pine produces both serotinous and non-serotinous cones, permitting successful regeneration in either the presence or absence of fire, it is considered to be a fire dependent species (Lotan et al.1985). The landscape level age-class structure of lodgepole pine can be described as a mosaic of even-aged and uneven-aged patches intermingling in space and time (Agee 1993). Whether a given patch or stand is even-aged or uneven-aged depends upon the disturbance history of the site: in the absence of fire, consecutive mountain pine beetle attacks in the stand contribute to conversion of an even-aged stand to an uneven-aged stand (Roe and Amman 1970). Non-stand-replacement fires (i.e., surface fires) also lead to creation of uneven-aged stands (Agee 1993). The type of fire regime that operates within a given stand or landscape has significant effects on stand structure. High-intensity stand-replacement fires create even-aged stands, whereas low-intensity surface regime fires contribute to development of uneven-aged stands. Falling dead trees following fire may cause mechanical injury to seedlings or residual overstory and provide entry for fungal infections, which can provide a focal point for endemic level mountain pine beetle infestations (Geiszler et al. 1984).

Lundquist and Negron (2000) developed a conceptual model of stand development in ponderosa pine that linked stand structure with underlying tree-killing disturbances. Disturbance agents could be classified into two basic ecological functions. First, new stands developed as a result of fire, wind, and epidemic populations of mountain pine beetle killing trees over large areas. Second, small-scale canopy gaps influenced stand development and structure due to a wide variety of factors killing small numbers of trees. Due to the complexity of interactions in both space and time between various disturbances, the authors indicated that direct effects of specific agents might be difficult to estimate.

Without fire control, and considering an average fire return period of 100 years and an expected negative exponential age-class distribution (Van Wagner 1978), on average only a relatively small proportion of unmanaged lodgepole pine stands would be susceptible to mountain pine beetle at any one time (Taylor and Carroll, Canadian Forest Service, Victoria, British Columbia, unpublished report). As a consequence of increased success in fire control over the past century, combined with recent (ca 40 years) commercial utilization of lodgepole pine, the area in British Columbia covered by mature lodgepole pine in 2000 was over three times that of 100 years ago (Taylor and Carroll, Canadian Forest Service, Victoria, British Columbia, unpublished report). In addition to the area occupied by lodgepole pine forests, size distribution of age-classes and their spatial arrangement on the landscape may also have important consequences for the spread of epidemics by dispersing beetles (Li et al. 2005). In a given landscape, in unmanaged natural stands, size distribution and spatial arrangement of age-classes will be dominantly affected by wildfire characteristics.

In the longer term, combinations of fire control, harvesting of commercial stands, type conversion, and use of prescribed fire in non-commercial areas will result in a reduction in the area and contiguity of susceptible stand types. These actions are not likely to reduce the frequency of mountain pine beetle outbreaks, but should certainly reduce their intensity, outbreak size and tree volumes affected. For example, consider a landscape that is dominated by lodgepole pine stand types where lodgepole pine is the preferred species for regeneration. When managed strictly on a sustained-yield basis in the long term, the area occupied by susceptible (mature) age-classes will be roughly of an area that produces a wood volume equal to yearly volume growth. Moreover, these mature stands will be interspersed with younger (less susceptible) stands.

Mountain pine beetle and lodgepole pine forests

Mountain pine beetle is the most significant forest insect affecting lodgepole pine forests in western North America. Historically, in Canada, most of the damage occurred in lodgepole pine forests of the southern interior regions of British Columbia. This insect is responsible for killing large numbers of mature pine trees in western North America each year (Ebata 2004; Gibson 2004). In the USA, the area infested by mountain pine beetle approximately doubled to 0.7 million ha in 2002 (Gibson 2004). In recent years, British Columbia has experienced an unprecedented infestation, with over 8 million hectares of lodgepole pine affected by 2005 (Ebata, T., personal communication, British Columbia Ministry of Forests, Victoria, British Columbia). This current infestation is the worst of a number of infestations that have been documented in British Columbia (Alfaro et al. 2004; Wood and Unger 1996) and has been described as the worst insect infestation ever recorded in a North American forest (British Columbia Ministry of Forests 2003).

During outbreaks, the large diameter components of stands can be heavily depleted over vast areas (Safranyik et al. 1974). Also, during and following mountain pine beetle outbreaks, populations of some secondary bark beetle species such as the pine engraver (*Ips pini* [Say]) can build up simultaneously in parts of killed trees not utilized by mountain pine beetle (Safranyik and Linton 1991). During and following the collapse of mountain pine beetle outbreaks, these secondary species often kill some trees on their own. These infestations, however, are usually short-lived and tree mortality is normally confined to smaller diameter classes (Safranyik and Linton 1991; Wood and VanSickle 1988).

In addition to socioeconomic impacts, in areas of high outbreak hazard, mountain pine beetle infestations affect the structure and dynamics of lodgepole pine stands. The magnitude of tree mortality caused by mountain pine beetle epidemics creates a situation where thousands of stands, of which lodgepole pine is a component, contain a mixture of live and dead trees. The resultant change in stand structure and characteristics has major ramifications on a number of resource issues such as timber production, forest regeneration and growth, hydrology, wildlife and biodiversity.

Effects of mountain pine beetle on lodgepole pine stand structure and dynamics

The epidemiology of mountain pine beetle is discussed in Chapter 1. The following is a brief account of the important characteristics.

Endemic populations mainly exist in unthrifty, often small diameter trees. These trees are often attacked earlier in the season by secondary bark beetle species. Many of the attacked trees are suppressed, diseased, or affected by factors such as senility, fire injury, flooding, or large fluctuations in the water table. The beginning of sustained endemic level mountain pine beetle activity tends to coincide with the attainment of maximum wood volume production per hectare (i.e., attainment of maximum current annual increment [CAI], and maximum stocking). Some trees suffering from competitive stress during and just following the period of peak wood production will be infested by secondary bark beetle species and, eventually, mountain pine beetle. An important consequence of this relationship is that, in unmanaged stands, stand hygiene plays an important role in the establishment of endemic populations.

Incipient epidemic populations of mountain pine beetle can develop in some stands when, locally, the beetles can overcome the resistance of the average large diameter trees (Safranyik 2004). This will occur either because of a decline in stand resistance due to factors such as drought, favourable conditions for beetle establishment and survival for a number of generations, immigration of beetles from another area, or a combination of these factors (Shore and Safranyik 2004). From this point on, beetles have access to the most productive trees in terms of mountain pine beetle brood, and beetle population size becomes one of the main factors in infestation growth.

Mortality

The beetle's preference for breeding in larger diameter trees results in proportionately more small-diameter trees surviving each year and following the collapse of the infestation. In general, during epidemics the percentage of trees killed is proportional to tree diameter above a minimum diameter of ca 10 cm. Above this minimum tree diameter, observed rate of increase in percentage of trees killed is 1.5% to 4% with each 1 cm increase in tree diameter (Safranyik 2004). This pattern of tree mortality indicates that the density of killed trees in a diameter at breast height (dbh) class above the minimum dbh infested will be proportional to the product of the number of trees in that dbh class and the mid-point of the dbh class. Consequently, post-infestation mean diameter and density of the residual stand will be reduced.

A commonly stated hypothesis is that mountain pine beetle acts as a thinning agent in stands, thereby reducing density and benefiting residual trees (e.g., Peterman 1978). This hypothesis may have some merit in the context of mixed species stands in that the non-host species may benefit. However, in terms of pure lodgepole pine stands, or the lodgepole pine component of mixed stands, mountain pine beetle at the incipient or epidemic level kills the biggest and apparently healthy trees and leaves smaller, possibly genetically inferior trees as residuals (Roe and Amman 1970). The effect of this preference on the genetic makeup of the seed source and subsequent replacement stand is not known.

In the Chilcotin Plateau, the highest proportion of lodgepole pine stems killed by mountain pine beetle was in diameter classes greater than 20 cm (Fig. 1). From 1987 to 2001, standing live tree volume and density was reduced for the 15 stands re-measured in 2001 by 22% and 36% respectively, although there was significant variation due to differences in stand structure (Hawkes et al. 2004a). Despite an increase in growth rates in smaller diameter residual trees, there still was a reduction in standing live volume from 1987 to 2001 due mainly to additional mountain pine beetle-caused mortality (Fig. 1).

In Kootenay National Park, live lodgepole pine density declined by 31% from 1993 to 2003 (219 stems per ha to 151 stems per ha) as a result of snag fall down and additional mountain pine beetle and other mortality (Brad Hawkes and Terry Shore, Canadian Forest Service, Victoria, British Columbia, unpublished data). Live tree density, for all tree species, declined by 16% from 1993 to 2003 (657 stems per ha to 554 stems per ha). Lodgepole pine was the dominant tree species prior to the mountain pine beetle outbreak, accounting for 47% of the live stems. In 1993, lodgepole pine accounted for 33% of the live stems. In 2003, due to additional mortality since 1993, lodgepole pine accounted for only 27% of live stems.

Reduction in pine density and resulting change in diameter distribution and mean diameter following an outbreak by mountain pine beetle depends on a number of factors such as beetle pressure (population size), diameter distribution, species composition and age of pine component in the original stand, habitat type, and climatic factors. To what extent each of these factors influences severity of stand depletion has not been investigated.

In a limited test, there was a significant correlation between the index of stand susceptibility (SI) (Shore and Safranyik 1992) and pine mortality from mountain pine beetle (Shore et al. 2000). As SI is a measure of the effects of pine age, stand density, susceptible pine basal area, and stand location (climate), these factors in combination affect mortality from mountain pine beetle. However, there was considerable variation in mortality among stands corresponding to fixed values of SI. The effect of mountain pine beetle on SI is to reduce it as susceptible pine basal area is reduced following death of the larger diameter pine component of the stand. In addition, beetle outbreaks reduce stand density. This may contribute to lower susceptibility, although dead trees still affect stand microclimate in ways favourable to beetles for several years (See chapters 7 and 8).

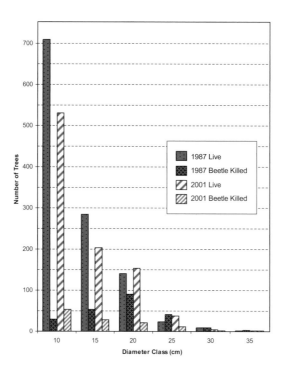

Figure 1. The number of live and beetle-killed lodgepole pines by diameter class on plots in the Chilcotin Plateau area of British Columbia at the end of the outbreak (1987) and five years later.

Mortality caused by mountain pine beetle tends to decline with elevation (Roe and Amman 1970; Amman 1973; Amman et al. 1973) mainly because of prevailing cool climate at higher elevation that negatively affects attack establishment, development rates and brood survival. Stand density affects growth rates of trees and phloem thickness as these two factors are positively correlated. Beetle production is directly related to phloem thickness (Amman 1972). Consequently, beetle production and subsequent tree mortality in dense, unmanaged stands tend to be less than in more open stands (Amman et al. 1977; Shore and Safranyik 1992). On the other hand, there is some evidence that regularly spaced (at least 4 m x 4 m spacing) mature lodgepole pine stands may sustain reduced mortality from mountain pine beetle (e.g., Whitehead et al. 2004).

Habitat types (biogeoclimatic zones in British Columbia) reflect differences in environments. Therefore, it is reasonable to assume that some differences exist among habitat types in severity and size-related mortality caused by mountain pine beetle. Indeed, Roe and Amman (1970) reported some differences in stand-level tree mortality among three habitat types. However, as there was some overlap in elevation of stands belonging to different habitat types, the elevation factor confounded the results. Comparable studies have not been done in Canada.

In British Columbia, the observed range in pine mortality in individual stands is from zero (in mostly young stands) to nearly 100% (in some mature stands growing on good sites in high climatic hazard areas). At the landscape level, however, average pine mortality by number of trees in individual stands will be in the range of 25% - 50%. This concurs with results from applying the range in rate of mortality, discussed earlier, to the usual diameter distribution of mature lodgepole pine types.

Residual stand growth and development

The residual stand following the end of an infestation will be comprised mainly of trees in the suppressed and intermediate crown classes, with some slow growing dominants and co-dominants with thin phloem (Roe and Amman 1970) and in mixed stands, non-host trees in a variety of classes. Residual pine trees may have poor growth response to release, at least on poorer sites. Heath and Alfaro (1990) examined a mixed Douglas-fir/lodgepole pine stand near Williams Lake, British Columbia, where 76% of the pine was killed by mountain pine beetle in the early 1970s. In response to this natural thinning treatment (Peterman 1978), the radial growth rate of residual Douglas-fir was enhanced for 14 years after mountain pine beetle attack with an 11.7% increase in growth rate, whereas surviving lodgepole pine experienced a 5.4% increase. Release of remnant Douglas-fir and spruce post-epidemic was also observed in Wyoming and Idaho by Cole and Amman (1980). Roe and Amman (1970) reported post-epidemic release and increased growth of both residual lodgepole pine and subalpine fir. These observations indicate that residual trees accelerate their growth when beetle-infested trees die, and suggest that stand volume lost by mortality in lodgepole pine might be, at least partially, compensated by increased growth of the residual stand by the time harvest rotation was reached.

Absence of fire in lodgepole pine stands combined with depletion of stands by mountain pine beetle favours the displacement of lodgepole pine. There is strong evidence that the growth of succeeding species is stimulated by mortality from mountain pine beetle through the release of existing reproduction and establishment of new seedlings in stand openings (Roe and Amman 1970). Hence, in the absence of fire, most stands in which lodgepole pine occupies a minor or major seral role will eventually convert to climax species, such as Douglas-fir at the lower elevations, subalpine fir and Engelmann spruce at higher elevations, and white spruce in the central interior regions of British Columbia. Roe and Amman (1970) found that repeated infestations by mountain pine beetle in the absence of fire will convert even-aged (dominant seral) lodgepole pine stands to an uneven-aged condition (and maintain a multi-age condition in climax lodgepole pine stands). However, because pine-dominant stands occur in several biogeoclimatic zones, on different soil and site types that contain differing densities of herbs and shrubs in the understory and different species mixes in the overstory, it is likely that several post-disturbance forest cover types will develop. These post-disturbance forest types may range from pure lodgepole pine to lodgepole pine-hardwood or mixed conifer-hardwood to pure stands of other conifer species (Kimmins et al. 2005).

The importance of accelerated growth as opposed to new seedling establishment following a mountain pine beetle outbreak is a major contrast to what is usually observed following high intensity fires where few trees survive (Veblen 1986, Aplet et al. 1988, Veblen et al. 1991a,b). Stand replacement fires favour regeneration of lodgepole pine and other shade intolerant species that regenerate quickly. However, ecosystem responses following a mountain pine beetle outbreak may be less rapid, because surviving trees may be old and unable to respond, and because mountain pine beetle-killed trees do not immediately drop their foliage (Waring and Pitman 1985). This would partially explain the release of saplings in the Chilcotin Plateau throughout the last thirty years.

Regeneration

Turner et al. (1999) found that lodgepole pine regeneration was more successful in severe-surface burned stands compared to stands experiencing crown fires. Stuart et al. (1989) and Mitchell and Preisler (1998) noted that the structure of lodgepole pine forests in central and southern Oregon was uneven-aged, with distinct episodic pulses pattern of regeneration strongly correlated to mountain pine beetle outbreaks and fire. The magnitude of regeneration pulse was a function of disturbance intensity. Delong and Kessler (2000) investigated the ecological characteristics of mature forest remnants left by wildfire in sub-boreal landscapes near Prince George, British Columbia, and found some remnants had an uneven-aged, episodic pattern of lodgepole pine regeneration.

On the Chilcotin Plateau, a unique multi-age and size stand structure exists as a result of lodgepole pine being able to regenerate under its own canopy, as well as past multiple mountain pine beetle outbreaks and surface fires (Hawkes et al. 2004a). Lodgepole pine understory tree density averaged 4547 and 3386 seedlings per ha in 1987 and 2001, respectively (Fig. 2).

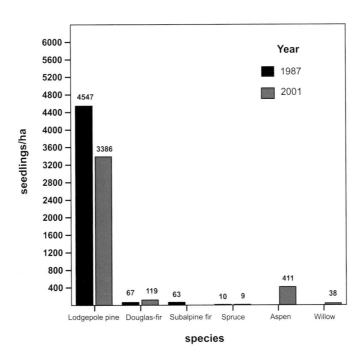

Figure 2. Understory tree density (<1.5 m height) by tree species in 15 stands in the Chilcotin Plateau area of British Columbia in 1987 and 2001.

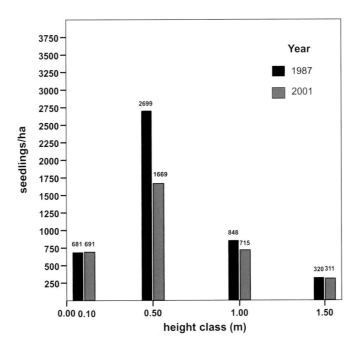

Figure 3. Lodgepole pine understory tree density (<1.5 m height) by height class in 15 stands in the Chilcotin Plateau area of British Columbia in 1987 and 2001.

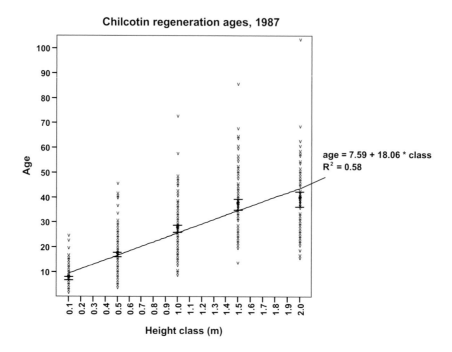

Figure 4. Lodgepole pine understory tree age (<2 m height) by height class in 30 stands in the Chilcotin Plateau area of British Columbia in 1987.

Most lodgepole pine understory trees were between 10 and 50 cm in height (Fig. 3). Lodgepole pine understory tree ages by height class ranged from a few years old at 0.1 m in height to over 100 years at 2 m in height (Fig. 4).

There was a minor amount of Douglas-fir, spruce, and sub-alpine fir in 1987. In 2001, Douglas-fir and spruce understory trees were still present in small numbers, but sub-alpine fir understory trees were no longer present and two new species, trembling aspen (*Populus tremuloides* Michx.) and willow (*Salix sp.*) appeared. Of these two new species, trembling aspen was most abundant at approximately 400 understory trees per hectare (Fig. 2). For comparison, in Kootenay National Park understory tree density averaged 1106 stems per ha. Spruce (536 stems per ha) and Douglas-fir (510 stems per ha) account for the vast majority of understory trees, with small amounts of lodgepole pine (46 stems per ha) and subalpine fir (13 stems per ha) (Brad Hawkes and Terry Shore, Canadian Forest Service, Victoria, British Columbia, unpublished data). Very little regeneration existed under 0.1 m in height. Low numbers of lodgepole pine understory trees may be due to dominance of closed cones and absence of suitable seedbed, because stand replacement fires are the most common type of fire disturbance. Absence of a suitable seedbed without recent large-scale fire disturbance may not be conducive to lodgepole pine regeneration.

Woody debris

Mitchell and Preisler (1998) found that in unthinned lodgepole pine stands in southern Oregon, mountain pine beetle-killed trees began to fall to the forest floor after 5 years, with 50% of trees falling within 9 years, and 90% fallen by 14 years post-attack. Johnson and Greene (1991) found that it is possible to make reasonable post-fire disturbance estimates of tree-fall rates by using equations of decomposition rates of trees already on the ground. Given the mass density of downed trees, rough estimates of actual time of fall could be determined. They did not examine mortality due to mountain pine beetle attack. Depending on the habitat type, beetle-killed trees begin falling within five years of the decline of an infestation (Flint 1924) and may continue 10 - 30 years thereafter. In general, because the decay process is faster under conditions of higher moisture and temperature, trees will deteriorate and fall faster under warm and humid conditions. On the other hand, under dry conditions such as in the Chilcotin Plateau, dead trees tend to dry quickly and caseharden, and a large proportion of the trees may remain standing for two decades or more.

Hawkes et al. (2004b) found that in the Chilcotin Plateau and Kamloops Forest Region standing dead lodgepole pine density in sampled stands 18 years post-attack was reduced by 52% (289 to 140 stems per ha) and 26% (370 to 273 stems per ha), respectively, due to fall down. Only about 10% of the trees had fallen 14 years after the end of an outbreak in Kootenay National Park (Hopping 1943), British Columbia. In the wetter ecosystem of the park, six mixed-species (lodgepole pine, Douglas-fir and white spruce) stands were sampled in 1993 and re-measured in 2003. Lodgepole pine accounted initially for 51% of the volume and 46.8% of the trees in the stand (Brad Hawkes and Terry Shore, Canadian Forest Service, Victoria, British Columbia, unpublished data). Mountain pine beetle-induced mortality reduced stand volume by 21.9% and live stems by 13.6% for all tree species in the stand. In 2003, 23.7% of the trees that had been standing in 1993 had fallen. Most of these trees that had fallen were killed in the 2003 mountain pine beetle epidemic (75.5%), but the balance of fallen trees had been alive at the end of the epidemic, indicating further mountain pine beetle-caused mortality between 1993 and 2003.

Hawkes et al. (2004a, 2005) found, in the early 1980s mountain pine beetle outbreak on British Columbia's Chilcotin Plateau, a link between the mortality rate of trees in lodgepole pine forests and subsequent accumulation of downed coarse woody debris over time. Coarse woody mass, averaging 20 tons per hectare, 60% of which was comprised of dead trees, fell between 1987 and 2001. In another British Columbia study area (the Kamloops Forest Region) lodgepole pine volume loss was similar to that of the Chilcotin Plateau. Coarse woody debris mass in four sampled stands was three times that found for the Chilcotin Plateau. This was because of larger sized lodgepole pine and additional windthrow of other tree species due to some stands being located in riparian leave strips in Kamloops.

Effects of mountain pine beetle on forest fire potential

It is evident that mortality imposed on lodgepole pine stands by mountain pine beetle attacks should influence fire behaviour. Mountain pine beetle kills trees, changing both the quantity and spatial distribution of fuels in the forest. During the first 2-3 years following beetle-kill, while most of the dead needles are retained on the killed trees, there is, presumably, a greater likelihood of a crown fire. This is because foliar moisture content is as low as 7% as compared to live needle moisture content of over 100%. In addition, fine branchwood in tree crowns dries, lowering its previous live fuel moisture to less than 20%, thus allowing more complete combustion during crown fires. After dead lodgepole pine needles drop to the forest floor, usually 2-3 years after trees are killed, more solar radiation reaches the surface forest litter and winds more readily penetrate the open canopy. Both factors have the potential to dry out the litter more than in a live canopy. On the other hand, once most dead needles have fallen, the remaining branchwood in dead crowns, which has lower moisture content than live branchwood, would not support development and spread of a continuous crown fire. This is because needles in crown bulk density play an important role in crown combustion. In theory, once dead trees have fallen, the increased distances among neighbouring residual trees should result in a decrease in the likelihood of a crown fire developing because of breaks in crown fuels. Fallen dead trees will increase surface woody fuel loading, increasing fire intensity and resulting flame length. However, the residual live trees may have high enough temperatures near their crown bases to result in stand-replacing crown fires.

Empirical evidence that supports the theory that there is either greater incidence of fires, greater area burned, or greater fire severity following mountain pine beetle attack is, however, very limited. Using a retrospective approach, Turner et al. (1999) found that high severity mountain pine beetle attacks (>50% of trees killed) increased crown fire probability, but intermediate or light levels of mountain pine beetle severity reduced crown fire probability during the wildfires of 1988 in Yellowstone National Park. These authors also found that once dead trees had fallen, crown fire probability increased in remaining overstory trees.

Experimental work is going on in British Columbia to examine fire behavior in mountain pine beetle affected stands, and historical fire records in mountain pine beetle affected areas. Retrospective studies of fire incidence are confounded with the effects of fire suppression; historical mountain pine beetle outbreaks in Canada occurred mainly in southern interior British Columbia where there has been a decline in area burned associated with fire suppression (Taylor and Carroll 2004).

Research needs

This synthesis points to a number of important gaps in our knowledge. Little is known about the long-term post-epidemic development and growth of stands that have not been subjected to control measures. A sound understanding of the impact of mountain pine beetle outbreaks on growth and yield of surviving trees in residual stands, regeneration, woody debris dynamics, and fire potential is needed for managers to make better decisions regarding stand management in the face of mountain pine beetle attacks. Specifically, the following knowledge gaps need to be addressed:

- Factors affecting variation in stand depletion
- Growth response of residual stands in different habitat types
- Release of advance regeneration and establishment of new regeneration in stands representing different successional stages for lodgepole pine
- Rates of deterioration and falling of beetle-killed trees in different habitat types
- More specific research on effect of mortality caused by mountain pine beetle on fire occurrence and intensity
- Ecological impacts of large outbreaks and management (control) programs on fish and wildlife.

Summary

Lodgepole pine is an important component of the forests of western North America. In Canada, the total area of lodgepole pine forest types is about 20 million ha, mostly in British Columbia and Alberta. Lodgepole pine has large ecological amplitude. In Alberta and British Columbia it occurs in all but three biogeoclimatic zones. With relatively minor exceptions, lodgepole pine is a seral species that is highly shade intolerant and reproduces best on bare soil. It has two types of cone habits: open and serotinous. Serotinous cones require high temperatures in the range of 45° - 50° C to open and release seeds. In areas where lodgepole pine has a predominantly serotinous cone habit, such as most areas in western Canada, lodgepole pine is, under natural conditions, essentially a fire-maintained species. It has four successional roles: minor seral, dominant seral, persistent, and climax. Climax sites are those on which lodgepole pine is the only tree species capable of growing.

At the landscape scale, mosaics of even-aged and uneven-aged patches of lodgepole pine are the norm and reflect disturbance history. Non-stand replacement fires and mountain pine beetle attacks contribute to conversion of even-aged stands to an uneven-aged stand. On the other hand, high intensity fires tend to create even-aged stands. Without fire control, and considering a mean fire return period of 100 years, only a relatively small portion of unmanaged lodgepole pine stands in British Columbia would be of an age susceptible to mountain pine beetle. Over the past century, increased success in fire control combined with the recent commercial utilization of lodgepole pine resulted in a ca threefold increase in the area of lodgepole pine susceptible to the mountain pine beetle.

Existing evidence does not support the popular hypothesis of a pine-beetle-fire cycle by which weakened, mature lodgepole pine give rise to mountain pine beetle epidemics and the resulting dead trees, being highly susceptible to fire, burn and give rise to new stands of lodgepole pine as a result of seeds being released from serotinous cones. Existing evidence is in strong support of outbreak development in mature forests but there is no current evidence in support of increased fire incidence in stands depleted by mountain pine beetle. However, some observations, as well as theoretical considerations, indicate that both fire severity and probability of crown fires may increase following outbreaks due to increased fuel loading and changed fuel characteristics.

In general, endemic mountain pine beetle populations get established in stands near the culmination of current annual increment (CAI), often in trees suffering from competitive stress and other forms of weakening. Incipient populations develop when beetle numbers have grown to a size sufficient to successfully attack the average large diameter trees in the stand. These trees provide the best conditions for brood survival. Under favourable conditions incipient populations develop into landscape level outbreaks in a few years. Epidemics often deplete the large diameter pine component of stands. The level of stand depletion varies with factors such as site quality, species composition, pine age, density, and climatic conditions. The residual stand is mainly composed of non-host species and lodgepole pine in the smaller diameter classes. In general, surviving trees will increase in growth in response to the increased light conditions and reduced competition. The rate of falling of dead trees depends on site conditions; generally the fall rate is greater on warm and moist sites compared with dry and cold sites.

Mortality from mountain pine beetle stimulates growth of successional species. In the absence of fire most stands in which lodgepole pine occupies a minor or dominant seral role will eventually convert to the climax species. Without fire, repeated infestations by mountain pine beetle will convert even-aged, dominant seral stands to an uneven-aged climax condition. However, pine-dominant stands occur in different biogeographic zones, on different soil and site types, with different densities of herbs and shrubs in the understory and different species mixes in the overstory. It is likely, therefore, that combinations of these variables will result in different post-disturbance forest types ranging from pure pine to various mixes of host and non-host species as well as non-host climax forests.

There are a number of important gaps in our knowledge relating to factors affecting variation in stand depletion: rates of deterioration and falling of killed trees, post-outbreak growth and development of surviving overstory trees; succession, regeneration, and effects of tree mortality on fire occurrence and intensity.

References

Agee, J.K. 1993. Fire ecology of Pacific Northwest Forests. Island Press, Washington DC. 493 p.

Alfaro, R.I.; Campbell, R.A.; Vera, P.; Hawkes, B.C.; Shore, T.L. 2004. Dendroecological reconstruction of mountain pine beetle outbreaks in the Chilcotin Plateau of British Columbia. Pages 245-256 *in* T.L. Shore, J.E. Brooks, and J.E. Stone, editors. Proceedings of the mountain Pine Beetle Symposium: Challenges and Solutions, October 30-31, 2003, Kelowna, British Columbia, Canada. Natural Resources Canada, Canadian Forest Service, Pacific Forestry Centre, Information Report BC-X-399. 298 p.

Amman, G. D. 1972. Mountain pine beetle brood production in relation to thickness of lodgepole pine phloem. Journal of Economic Entomology 65(1):138-40.

Amman, G. D. 1973. Population changes of the mountain pine beetle in relation to elevation. Environmental Entomology 2(4):541-547.

Amman, G.D.; Baker, B.H.; Stipe, L.E. 1973. Lodgepole pine losses to the mountain pine beetle related to elevation. USDA, Forest Service, Intermountain Forest and Range Experiment Station, Research Note INT-171. 8 p.

Amman, G. D.; McGregor, M. D.; Cahill, D. B.; Klein, W. H. 1977. Guidelines for reducing losses of lodgepole pine to the mountain pine beetle in unmanaged stands in the Rocky Mountains. USDA, Forest Service, Intermountain and Range Experiment Station. Ogden, UT, General Technical Report INT-36. 19 p.

Aplet, G.H.; Laven, R.D.; Smith, F.W. 1988. Patterns of community dynamics in Colorado, Engelmann spruce-subalpine fir forests. Ecology 69(2):312-319.

British Columbia Ministry of Forests. 2003. Timber supply and the mountain pine beetle infestation in British Columbia. Forest Analysis Branch, Victoria. 24 p.

Cole, W.E.; Amman, G.E. 1980. Mountain Pine Beetle Dynamics in Lodgepole Pine Forests. Part I: Course of an Infestation. USDA, Forest Service Intermountain. Range Experiment Station, General Technical Report INT-89.

Delong, C.S.; Kessler, W.B. 2000. Ecological characteristics of mature forest remnants left by wildfire. Forest Ecology and Management 131(1-3):93-106.

Ebata, T. 2004. Current status of mountain pine beetle in British Columbia. Pages 52-56 *in* T.L. Shore, J.E. Brooks, and J.E. Stone, editors. Proceedings of the mountain pine beetle symposium: challenges and solutions. Kelowna, British Columbia October 30-31, 2003, Natural Resources Canada, Canadian Forest Service, Pacific Forestry Centre, Information Report BC-X-399, 298 p.

Flint, H. R. 1924. Various aspects of the insect problem in the lodgepole pine region. United States Forest Service D-1 Applied Forestry Notes 54. 4 p.

Gara, R.I. 1988. Interactions between fires, fungi, mountain pine beetles and lodgepole pine in south-central Oregon. Northwest Environmental Journal 4(2):355-358.

Geiszler, D. R.; Gara, R. I.; Driver, C. H.; Galucci, V. F.; Martin, R. E. 1980. Fire, fungi and beetle influences on a lodgepole pine ecosystem. Oecologia 46(2):239-243.

Geiszler, D. R.; Gara, R. I.; Lidke, W. R. 1984. Bark beetle infestations of lodgepole pine following fire in south-central Oregon. Zeitschrift-Fur-Angewandte-Entomologie 98(4):389-394.

Gibson, K. 2004. Mountain pine beetle conditions and issues in the western United States, 2003. Pages 57-61 *in* T.L. Shore, J.E. Brooks, and J.E. Stone, editors. Proceedings of the Mountain Pine Beetle Symposium: Challenges and Solutions, October 30-31, 2003, Kelowna, British Columbia, Canada. Natural Resources Canada, Canadian Forest Service, Pacific Forestry Centre, Victoria, British Columbia, Information Report BC-X-399. 298 p.

Hawkes, B.; Taylor, S.; Stockdale, C.; Shore, T.; Alfaro, R.I.; Campbell, R.; Vera, P. 2004a. Impact of mountain pine beetle on stand dynamics in BC. Pages 175-195 *in* T.L. Shore, J.E. Brooks, and J.E. Stone, editors. Proceedings of the Mountain Pine Beetle Symposium: Challenges and Solutions. Kelowna, British Columbia October 30-31, 2003, Natural Resources Canada, Canadian Forest Service, Pacific Forestry Centre, Information Report BC-X-399, 298 p.

Hawkes, B.; Taylor, S.; Stockdale, C.; Shore, T.; Alfaro, R.I.; Campbell, R.; Vera, P. 2004b. Impact of mountain pine beetle on stand dynamics in British Columbia. Final report submitted to Forest Innovation Investments Ltd., Research Program, project no. FII R0-009, April 12, 2004. 34 p.

Hawkes, B.; Taylor, S.; Stockdale, C.; Shore, T.; Beukema, S.; Robinson, D. 2005. Predicting mountain pine beetle impacts on lodgepole pine stands and woody debris characteristics in a mixed severity fire regime using prognosis[BC] and the fire and fuels extension. Pages 123-135 *in* L. Lagene, J. Zelnik, S. Cadwallader, and B. Hughes, editors. Mixed severity fire regimes: ecology and management, November 17-19, 2004, Spokane, Washington. Washington State University Coop Extension Service/The Association for Fire Ecology, Pullman, Washington, Vol. AFE MISC03.

Heath, R.; Alfaro, R. 1990. Growth response in a Douglas-fir/lodgepole pine stand after thinning of lodgepole pine by the mountain pine beetle. Journal of the Entomological Society of British Columbia 87:16-21.

Hopping, G. R. 1943. Bark beetle brood development in Kootenay National Park—1942. Mimeographed Report, Department of Mines and Resources Lands, Parks and Forests Branch, Dominion Forest Service, Vernon, BC. pp. 43-75.

Hughes, J.; Drever, R. 2001. Salvaging solutions: science-based management of BC's pine beetle outbreak. David Suzuki Foundation, Vancouver BC. 39 p.

Johnson, E.A.; Greene, D.F. 1991. A method for studying dead bole dynamics in *Pinus contorta* var. *latifolia* – *Picea engelmannii* forests. Journal of Vegetation Science 2:523-530.

Kimmins, J. P.; Seely, B.; Zhong, A. 2005. Possible Forest futures: Balancing biological and social risks in mountain pine beetle epidemics. Department of Forest Sciences, Faculty of Forestry, University of British Columbia, Vancouver, BC. 53 p.

Koch, P. 1987. Gross characteristics of lodgepole pine trees in North America. USDA, Forest Service, Intermountain Research Station General Technical Report INT-227. 311p.

Koch, P. 1996. Lodgepole pine in North America. Volume 2, Chapter 11. Forest Products Society, Madison, Wisconsin. 763 p.

Li, C.; Barclay, H.; Hawkes, B.; Taylor, S. 2005. Lodgepole pine forest age class dynamics and susceptibility to mountain pine beetle attack. Ecological Complexity 2:232-239.

Lotan, J.E.; Brown, J.K.; Neuenschwander, L.F. 1985. Role of fire in lodgepole pine forests. Pages 133-152 *in* D.M. Baumgartner, R.G. Krebill, J.T. Arnott, and G.F. Weetman, editors. Symposium proceedings of lodgepole pine: the species and its management. May 8-10, 1984, Spokane Washington State University, Pullman, WA.

Lundquist, J.E.; Negron, J.F. 2000. Endemic forest disturbances and stand structure of ponderosa pine (*Pinus ponderosa*) in the upper pine creek research natural area, South Dakota, U.S.A. Natural Areas Journal 20(2):126-132.

Maclauchlan, L.E.; Brooks, J.E. 1994. Strategies and tactics for managing the mountain pine beetle *Dendroctonus ponderosae*. British Columbia Forest Service Kamloops Region, Forest Health. 60 p.

McMullen, L.H.; Safranyik, L.; Linton, D.A. 1986. Suppression of mountain pine beetle infestations in lodgepole pine forests. Agriculture Canada, Ministry of State for Forestry and Mines, Pacific Forestry Centre Information Report BC-X-276. 20 p.

Mitchell, R.G.; Preisler, H.K. 1998. Fall rate of lodgepole pine killed by the mountain pine beetle in central Oregon. Western Journal of Applied Forestry 13:23-26.

Peterman, R.M. 1978. The ecological role of mountain pine beetle in lodgepole pine forests. Pages 16-26 *in* A.A. Berryman, G.D. Amman, R.W. Stark, and D.L. Kibbee, editors. Symposium proceedings, Theory and practice of mountain pine beetle management in lodgepole pine forests. April 25-27, 1978, Pullman, WA. U.S. Forest, Wildlife and Range Experiment Station, University of Idaho, Moscow, ID.

Pfister, R.D.; Daubenmire, R. 1975. Ecology of lodgepole pine (*Pinus contorta* Douglas). Pages 27-46 *in* D.M. Baumgartner, David M., editor. Management of lodgepole pine ecosystems: symposium proceedings, October 9-11, 1973, Pullman, Washington. Washington State University Cooperative Extension Service, Pullman Washington.

Pojar, J. 1985. Ecological classification of lodgepole pine in Canada. Pages 77-88 *in* D.M. Baumgartner, R.G. Krebill, J.T. Arnott, G.F. Weetman, compilers. Lodgepole pine - the species and its management: symposium proceedings, May 8-10, 1984 Spokane, Washington, USA; repeated May 14-16, 1984 Vancouver, British Columbia, Canada. Pullman, Washington: Cooperative Extension, Washington State University.

Roe, A.L.; Amman, G.D. 1970. The mountain pine beetle in lodgepole pine forests. USDA, Forest Service, Intermountain Research Station General Technical Report INT-70. 23 p.

Safranyik, L.; Linton, D.A. 1991. Unseasonably low fall and winter temperatures affecting mountain pine beetle and pine engraver beetle populations and damage in the British Columbia Chilcotin Region. Journal of the Entomological Society of British Columbia 88:17-21.

Safranyik, L.; Shrimpton, D.M.; Whitney, H.S. 1974. Management of lodgepole pine to reduce losses from the mountain pine beetle. Canada Department of the Environment, Forest Service, Pacific Forest Research Centre. Technical Report 1. 24 p.

Safranyik, L. 2004. Mountain pine beetle epidemiology in lodgepole pine. Pages 33-40 *in*: T. L. Shore, J.E. Brooks and J.E. Stone, editors. Proceedings of the Mountain Pine Beetle Symposium: Challenges and Solutions, October 30-31, 2003, Kelowna, BC. Natural Resources Canada, Canadian Forest Service, Pacific Forestry Centre. Information Report BC-X-399. 298 p.

Schmidt, W. C. 1989. Lodgepole pine: an ecological opportunist. Pages 14-20 *in*: Amman, G.D., editor. Proceedings – Symposium on the Management of Lodgepole Pine to Minimize Losses to the Mountain Pine Beetle. USDA Forest Service, Intermountain Research Station Ogden, UT. General Technical Report INT-262, 119 p.

Shore, T.L.; Safranyik, L.; Lemieux, J.P. 2000. Susceptibility of lodgepole pine to the mountain pine beetle: testing of a rating system. Canadian Journal of Forest Research 30:44-49.

Shore, T.L.; Safranyik, L. 1992. Susceptibility and risk rating systems for the mountain pine beetle in lodgepole pine stands. Forestry Canada, Pacific and Yukon Region. Information Report BC-X-336. 12 p.

Shore, T. L.; Safranyik, L. 2004. Mountain pine beetle management and decision support. Pages 97-105 *in* T.L. Shore, J. E. Brooks and J.E. Stone, editors. Proceedings of the Mountain Pine Beetle Symposium: Challenges and Solutions, October 30-31, 2003, Kelowna, British Columbia. Natural Resources Canada, Canadian Forest Service, Pacific Forestry Centre. Information Report BC-X-399. 298 p.

Stuart, J. D.; Agee J. K.; Gara, R. I. 1989. Lodgepole pine regeneration in an old self-perpetuating forest in South-Central Oregon. Canadian Journal of Forest Research 19:1096-1104.

Taylor, S.W.; Carroll, A.L. 2004. Disturbance, forest age, and mountain pine beetle outbreak dynamics in BC: A historical perspective. Pages 41-51 *in* T.L. Shore, J.E. Brooks, and J.E. Stone, editors. Mountain Pine Beetle Symposium: Challenges and Solutions. Kelowna, British Columbia October 30-31, 2003, Natural Resources Canada, Canadian Forest Service, Pacific Forestry Centre, Information Report BC-X-399. 298 p.

Taylor, S.; Thandi, G.; Hawkes, B. 2005. Interactions between wildfire and forest insect outbreaks in British Columbia. Annual report submitted to BC Forest Science Program, Project Y05-01233, Annual Technical Report Supplement, 1 April 30, 2005.

Turner, M.G.; Romme, W.H.; Gardner, R.H. 1999. Prefire heterogeneity, fire severity, and early postfire plant reestablishment in subalpine forests of Yellowstone National Park, Wyoming. International Journal of Wildland Fire 9(1):21-36.

Van Wagner, C.E. 1978. Age-class distribution and the forest fire cycle. Canadian Journal of Forest Research 8:220-227.

Veblen, T.T. 1986. Treefalls and the coexistence of conifers in subalpine forests of the central Rockies. Ecology 67:644-649.

Veblen, T.T.; Hadley, K.S.; Reid, M.S; Rebertus, A.J. 1991a. Methods of detecting past spruce beetle outbreaks in Rocky Mountain subalpine forests. Canadian Journal of Forest Research 21:242-254.

Veblen, T.T.; Hadley, K.S.; Reid, M.S.; Rebertus, A.J. 1991b. The response of subalpine forests to spruce beetle outbreak in Colorado. Ecology 72:213-231.

Waring, R.H.; Pitman, G.B. 1985. Modifying lodgepole pine stands to change susceptibility to mountain pine beetle attack. Ecology 66(3):889-897.

Whitehead, R.J.; Martin, P.; Powelson, A. 2001. Reducing stand and landscape susceptibility to mountain pine beetle. British Columbia Ministry of Forests, Victoria, 12 pp.

Whitehead, R.J.; Safranyik, L.; Russo, G.L.; Shore, T.L; Carroll, A.L. 2004. Silviculture to reduce landscape and stand susceptibility to the mountain pine beetle. Pages 233-244 *in*: T.L. Shore, J.E. Brooks and J.E. Stone, editors. Mountain pine beetle symposium: challenges and solutions. October 30-31, 2003, Kelowna, British Columbia. Natural Resources Canada, Canadian Forest Service, Pacific Forestry Centre. Information Report BC-X-399. 298 p.

Wood, C.S.; VanSickle, A. 1987. Forest insect and disease conditions in British Columbia and the Yukon. Agriculture Canada, Ministry of State for Forestry and Mines, Pacific Forestry Centre, Victoria, BC, Information Report BC-X- 296. 40 p.

Wood, C.S.; Unger, L. 1996. Mountain pine beetle. A history of outbreaks in pine forests in British Columbia, 1910 to 1995. Natural Resources Canada, Canadian Forest Service, Pacific Forestry Centre, Victoria, BC.

Part 2

Management

Chapter 4

Principles and Concepts of Management

Terry L. Shore, Les Safranyik, and Roger J. Whitehead

Natural Resources Canada, Canadian Forest Service, Pacific Forestry Centre,
506 West Burnside Road, Victoria, British Columbia, V8Z 1M5

Abstract

In this section, an introduction to management of mountain pine beetle (*Dendroctonus ponderosae* Hopk. [Coleoptera: Scolytidae]) and its host is provided and basic principles and concepts of management are described. Preventive management is used in Western Canada to reduce tree, stand and landscape susceptibility to the mountain pine beetle. As well, direct control strategies and tactics are used to reduce mountain pine beetle populations. The two approaches are combined and form an integral part of a management plan.

Forest protection and management of forest health are vital components of land management to achieve stated objectives. Plans to manage insects, including the mountain pine beetle, are developed to support land management objectives and form an integral part of land management plans.

The principles for reducing losses of lodgepole pine (*Pinus contorta* Dougl. ex Loud. var. *latifolia* Engelm.) to the mountain pine beetle must be based on the main features of beetle population dynamics, especially the evolved insect-host interaction. Key features of this interaction are the effects of tree, stand, and site parameters on tree and stand susceptibility, the process of population change from the endemic to the epidemic state, and the role of beetle population size and spatial distribution of susceptible stands in the development and maintenance of outbreaks at the landscape level. These and other aspects of the insect host interaction are described in detail elsewhere in this volume.

Résumé

Dans la présente section, on trouve une présentation de la lutte contre le dendroctone du pin ponderosa (*Dendroctonus ponderosae* Hopk. [Coleoptera: Scolytidae]) de même que de l'hôte de ce dernier, et on décrit les principes et les concepts de base qui s'y rattachent. Dans l'Ouest canadien, on fait de la lutte préventive pour réduire la vulnérabilité des arbres, des peuplements et des paysages au ravageur. On a également recours à des stratégies de lutte directe et à des tactiques pour réduire les populations de dendroctones du pin ponderosa. Les deux approches se combinent et font partie intégrante d'un plan de lutte contre le dendroctone du pin ponderosa.

La protection et la gestion de la santé de la forêt sont des éléments essentiels de l'aménagement des terres lorsqu'on veut atteindre les objectifs qu'on s'est fixés à cet égard. Des plans de gestion des insectes, y compris du dendroctone du pin ponderosa, sont élaborés pour favoriser l'atteinte de ces objectifs, et ils font partie intégrante du plan d'aménagement des terres.

Les principes à considérer pour réduire les pertes de pins tordus latifoliés *(Pinus contorta* Dougl. ex Loud. var. *latifolia* Engelm.) causées par le dendroctone du pin ponderosa doivent tenir compte des principales caractéristiques de la dynamique des populations de dendroctones, en particulier de l'interaction insecte-hôte qui se produit. Les principaux aspects de cette interaction comprennent : les effets des paramètres qui caractérisent les arbres, les peuplements et les lieux où ils se trouvent sur la vulnérabilité des arbres et des peuplements; le processus de développement des populations de l'état endémique à celui d'épidémie et le rôle que joue la taille des populations de dendroctones ainsi que la répartition spatiale des peuplements vulnérables dans l'apparition et la continuation des infestations à l'échelle du paysage. D'autres aspects de l'interaction insecte-hôte sont également décrits dans le présent volume.

How do outbreaks begin?

At endemic levels, beetle populations persist at low numbers across the landscape and mainly breed in weakened trees, which are often widely dispersed. The transition from endemic to epidemic state occurs when local population size exceeds a minimum threshold necessary to overcome the resistance, through mass-attack of healthier, large-diameter trees that provide a high-quality habitat for large brood production. Periodically, one or both of two situations make this possible (Fig. 1). The population of mountain pine beetle may increase locally, either through immigration or because favourable weather conditions result in increased beetle survival during the winter and the flight period. Alternatively, or in addition, tree and stand resistance to attack by the beetle may be reduced during periods of drought, or if stands become too dense or too old (Fig. 1). Depending on how widespread these optimum conditions are, the population may increase quickly and spot infestations become evident in many stands. As the population gets larger, beetles can successfully attack more and more trees as large numbers of beetles eventually overcome the resin defence of even the most vigorous trees. Unless spot infestations are promptly controlled, the mountain pine beetle infestation will spread across the landscape, given abundant host material, with dispersing beetles joining resident populations to sustain an outbreak. As a result, severe losses of mature pine will occur and even some younger planted or natural pine stands can sustain heavy mortality.

Managing the beetle

Treatments aimed at reducing beetle populations are termed "direct control" and those aimed at increasing stand vigour or reducing the amount and concentration of susceptible stands are termed "indirect control" or "preventive management" (Fig. 2). The two approaches should be used in combination in a landscape-level management plan.

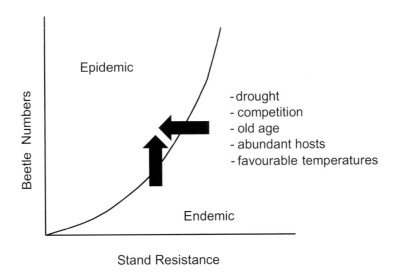

Figure 1. Factors contributing to mountain pine beetle shift from endemic to epidemic populations (after Berryman 1978). The vertical arrow represents increase in beetle population and the horizontal arrow represents a decrease in stand resistance. The curved line is the threshold between endemic and epidemic populations.

Preventive management can be considered a pro-active approach because it is primarily done before a mountain pine beetle outbreak develops. Its aim is to reduce the susceptibility of stands on the landscape using various forestry practices including prescribed fire. Direct control, on the other hand, tends to be a reactive approach aimed at reducing beetle populations by various means following observation of tree mortality. The strategic objectives of direct control mainly depend on combinations of ownership, beetle population level, access, and the resources available for implementation.

A combination of timely detection, assessment of susceptibility and risk, access development, direct control, and preventive management is required to effectively manage the mountain pine beetle. The key principles in applying direct control are the timeliness and thoroughness of detection and treatments. The key principle in applying preventive management is the continued application of well-planned forestry practices during periods when mountain pine beetle populations are at endemic levels.

The epidemiology of the mountain pine beetle has implications for management. The risk of tree mortality from the mountain pine beetle is related to the susceptibility of the trees and to the number of beetles attacking. The risk of significant economic damage from the beetle depends on the susceptibility of stands, their size and arrangement on the landscape, and the size and location of the beetle population. Thus, management of the mountain pine beetle is necessarily focused on reducing tree, stand-level, and forest-level susceptibility and on keeping the beetle population low. This requires stand-level management within a long-term strategy to reduce forest-level susceptibility to damage, yearly detection and assessment surveys, and timely and effective treatment of local infestations (Fig. 3). Decision support systems can be utilized to guide selection of treatment strategies and tactics, as described elsewhere in this volume.

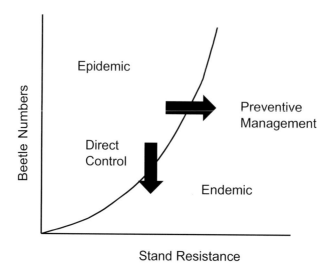

Figure 2. The role of population reduction (direct control) and preventive management in maintaining mountain pine beetle at endemic levels. The vertical arrow represents reduction in beetle population and the horizontal arrow represents an increase in stand resistance. The curved line is the threshold between endemic and epidemic populations.

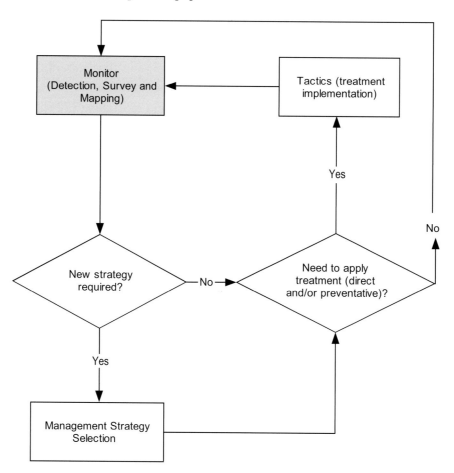

Figure 3. Flowchart of the main components of the mountain pine beetle management process.

In addition to information on the biology of the mountain pine beetle and its interaction with the host, development and implementation of a knowledge-based management system requires information on host characteristics and host distribution. Specifically, it is necessary to know the characteristics and distribution of stands on the landscape where pine is present, as well as the location and numbers of those infested with mountain pine beetle. The former is obtained through forest inventory updates and the latter is obtained through annual surveys.

Inventory information allows the manager to determine the susceptibility of the forest to mountain pine beetle. Susceptibility and risk rating systems are available to forest managers to help them set priorities for beetle control treatments and plan access development and preventive management. Other decision-support tools include stand and landscape level models in which management options can be evaluated. As management of public forests in western Canada must typically integrate objectives for several uses and values, socioeconomic considerations need to be considered.

Preventive management when the mountain pine beetle population is at an endemic level can save huge losses in the future. Similarly, timely and thorough treatment of infested trees when the beetle population is relatively low can prevent an infestation from becoming epidemic. Awareness of this fact has to be at the political level so that resources are continually available to prevent mountain pine beetle epidemics. Too often, investment in preventive management and direct control treatments are reduced during the endemic phase of the mountain pine beetle only to be followed by large, and often ineffective expenditures of resources when an epidemic arises.

The following chapters discuss mountain pine beetle management in more detail including detection and monitoring, decision support systems, preventive management and direct control, and socioeconomic concerns.

References

Berryman, A.A. 1978. A synoptic model of the lodgepole pine/mountain pine beetle interaction and its potential application in forest management. Pages 98-105 *in* Berryman, A.A.; Amman, G.D.; Stark, R.W.; Kibbee, D.L., eds. Theory and Practice of Mountain Pine Beetle Management in Lodgepole Pine Forests, Symposium Proceedings. Forest, Wildlife and Range Experiment Station, University of Idaho, Moscow, ID.

Chapter 5

Detection, Mapping, and Monitoring
of the Mountain Pine Beetle[1]

Michael A. Wulder, Caren C. Dymond, Joanne C. White, and Bob Erickson

Natural Resources Canada, Canadian Forest Service, Pacific Forestry Centre,
506 West Burnside Road, Victoria, British Columbia, V8Z 1M5

Abstract

Forest management decisions regarding the mountain pine beetle (*Dendroctonus ponderosae* Hopk. [Coleoptera: Scolytidae]) are generally driven by the location, size, and impact of the beetle population, and a variety of survey techniques are used to collect this information. The methodology used and the scale (level of detail) of the survey are determined by the management objectives. The survey may be done on a tree-by-tree basis on the ground, from an airborne platform, or with satellite-based sensors. As a result, the extent of the survey may range from a few hectares to millions of hectares. This chapter reviews the tools and approaches available to forest managers for the detection, mapping, and monitoring of mountain pine beetle. The information content and limitations associated with each survey method are provided to facilitate informed choices between available survey methods and information sources. Also presented in this chapter is the concept of an information hierarchy, whereby multiple sets of survey data may be nested for any given area of interest. For example, a lower-cost overview survey may be used to guide the selection of locations requiring more intensive (and more expensive) surveys. Survey recommendations, based upon the information hierarchy, are also provided.

Résumé

La prise de décisions concernant la gestion des forêts touchées par le dendroctone du pin ponderosa (*Dendroctonus ponderosae* Hopk. [Coleoptera: Scolytidae]) est généralement guidée par les éléments que sont l'emplacement des secteurs affectés, la taille de la population de dendroctones et les conséquences de son passage. Divers types de relevés peuvent être utilisés pour recueillir ces données. La méthode utilisée et la portée (niveau de précision recherché) du relevé dépendent des objectifs de gestion. Le relevé peut être effectué sur le terrain, arbre par arbre, ou à partir d'un aéronef, ou encore à l'aide de capteurs satellitaires. La superficie couverte par un relevé peut donc varier de quelques hectares à plusieurs millions d'hectares. Dans le présent chapitre, on examine les outils

---

[1] This chapter is an update of material previously published as:
   Wulder, M.A.; Dymond, C.C.; Erickson, B. 2004. Detection and monitoring of the mountain pine beetle. Natural Resources Canada, Canadian Forest Service, Pacific Forestry Centre. Information Report BC-X-398. 28p.

et les méthodes dont disposent les gestionnaires des forêts en matière de dètection, de cartographie et de surveillance du dendroctone du pin ponderosa. On y expose la teneur et les limitations des données associées à chaque type de relevé afin d'aider les gestionnaires à faire un choix éclairé parmi les méthodes de relevés et les sources de données disponibles. On y présente également le concept de hiérarchie de l'information, selon lequel de multiples jeux de données de relevés peuvent être imbriqués pour s'appliquer à n'importe quel champ d'intérêt. Il peut être utile, par exemple, d'effectuer un premier relevé général, moins coûteux, pour délimiter les endroits nécessitant des relevés plus détaillés (et plus coûteux). Enfin, on y retrouve des recommandations fondées sur le concept de hiérarchie de l'information pour effectuer des relevés.

Introduction

Forest management decisions regarding the mountain pine beetle (*Dendroctonus ponderosae* Hopk. [Coleoptera: Scolytidae]) (Belton and Eidt 1999) are generally driven by the location, size, and impact of the beetle population. For example, small groups of timber infested with mountain pine beetle may not be considered for mitigation in an endemic population condition. However, if monitoring of the beetle across the landscape indicates a population increase, action may be taken to address these patches of infestation to prevent or reduce future losses. Without control action, infestations within susceptible forests can expand until large numbers of trees are killed (Safranyik et al. 1974). Generally, the most severe infestations occur in mature stands of lodgepole pine (*Pinus contorta* Dougl. ex Loud. var. *latifolia* Engelm.), but other pine species, such as ponderosa pine (*P. ponderosa* Lawson) and white pine (*P. monticola* Douglas), may also be attacked.

Information regarding the location, size, and impact of mountain pine beetle populations is collected using a variety of survey techniques. The survey method is selected based on the information required for a particular aspect of forest management. The survey may be done on a tree-by-tree basis on the ground, from an airborne platform, or using satellite-based sensors. As a result, the extent of the survey may range from a few hectares to millions of hectares. Each survey method has limitations, with the collected data being applicable to different management situations.

The methodology and scale of a survey is defined by the management question being addressed. Questions regarding tree- or stand-level characterization of beetle impacts require different support data than required at the landscape level. Mountain pine beetle infestations are detected with systematic surveys conducted at regular time intervals. Surveys must locate the infestations as quickly as possible in order to contain and reduce beetle populations (Safranyik et al. 1974). In this chapter, detection is defined as the identification and documentation of locations of previously affected trees and probable locations of currently attacked trees. Detection information may be used to position field crews for infestation assessments or to facilitate mitigation options (Safranyik et al. 1974). Mapping is defined as spatially explicit estimates of the number of trees affected, or of the volume affected, for a particular management unit (e.g., at the forest stand level). Monitoring is defined as repeatable, comparable estimation of beetle populations and impacts over time in order to detect trends in population dynamics and spatial pattern. Under all population conditions, monitoring enables forest managers to anticipate possible risks associated with the infestation.

Federal, provincial, and state governments are primarily interested in the broad-scale detection of red attack trees across their political jurisdictions. Aerial overview survey operations are used to satisfy this information need (Wiart 2003). The information is used to monitor and report on overall forest health (e.g., USDA Forest Service 2003). Government agencies concerned with forestry or environmental protection also use the red attack detection information for strategic planning (e.g., British Columbia Ministry of Forests 2001), which includes identifying areas for more intensive information gathering, mitigation resources, timber sales, and targeted protection. In addition, locations of red attack trees are used to identify probable locations for green attack trees, thereby facilitating more aggressive mitigation activities.

Forestry companies and government agencies work together during timber supply reviews and in planning for land and resource management. Sub-provincial- or county-level monitoring, typically from aerial sketch mapping, is used to alter volumes and areas, which in turn are used to adjust the annual allowable cut and refine timber supply forecasts (British Columbia Ministry of Forests 2003). Maps of forest damage also may be used to adjust land use plans and provide information of ecological interest. Forest licensees and private landholders require detection of red attack trees at a larger scale, with more detailed information about attack locations and intensities across their land bases (Wiart 2003). These general locations are then used to direct additional, more detailed detection and mapping efforts. Results from local area mapping of red attack are used to guide surveys for associated green attack trees, and to aid in the design of logging and sanitation plans.

Information needs may require different survey techniques in order to provide the appropriate level of detail. Survey techniques also vary with timing of the survey relative to expression of attack in tree-crown foliage. In general, green attack is not operationally detectable without direct physical contact with the trees in question. Red attack is operationally detectable with a broad range of survey techniques (field, airborne, and satellite). While currently less reliable than red attack survey, grey attack may also be detected with a range of survey techniques. The red attack stage is the focus of the detection methods presented in this chapter.

Anecdotal accounts of mountain pine beetle-induced mortality in lodgepole pine stands have been recorded by early explorers of British Columbia. Today, the provincial government conducts annual systematic surveys of forest damage and mortality. The native range of mountain pine beetle includes southern and central British Columbia where pine species grow (Amman 1978). Populations of mountain pine beetle are also historically present in southwestern Alberta. Insect-induced mortality of mature pine in British Columbia is largely a result of attack by mountain pine beetle. For example, surveys conducted by the Canadian Forest Service, Forest Insect and Disease Survey (FIDS) estimated average annual

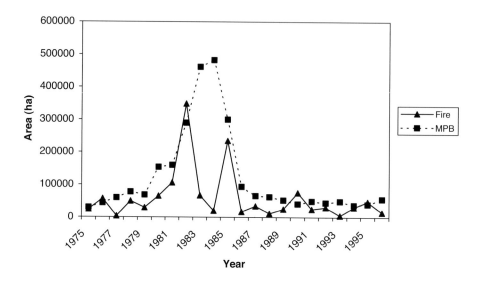

Figure 1. Comparison of annual area burned by forest fires to annual area killed by mountain pine beetle (Canadian Council of Forest Ministers 2003).

loss to mountain pine beetle infestations to be 7.8 million mature pine trees (over a 34-year time period ending in 1995), with losses peaking in 1983 at 80.4 million mature pine trees (Wood and Unger 1996). The spatial extent of the current infestation in British Columbia is increasing annually, with areas reported to be approximately 2 million ha in 2002 (Westfall 2003), and estimated at more than 4 million ha in 2003 (British Columbia Ministry of Forests 2003). In Figure 1, the total area impacted by mountain pine beetle in each year between 1975 and 1996 is compared to the total area burned by forest fires each year during the same period.

The impact of mountain pine beetle is evident throughout its biological range, beetle being the second greatest contributor to tree mortality within the national forests of Colorado, South Dakota, and Wyoming. Over 300 000 trees were killed during 1997, 1998, and 1999 within the Rocky Mountain region of the United States (Harris et al. 2001). The number of trees killed increased each year from 1996 to 2001, with more than 800 000 trees killed over a 142 410-ha area (converted from a reported 300 000 acres) (Johnson 2002).

Insect disturbances are systematically monitored on an annual basis to assess extent and impact on forest resources. Mountain pine beetle impacts are observed and recorded as a component of insect-monitoring surveys. Detection and mapping of mountain pine beetle provide a record of tree mortality and, thus, a record of the beetle's impact. These records are carried out using a range of techniques, each with its own advantages and disadvantages. Ground-based surveys are the most reliable source of information about the agent responsible for forest damage. Field surveys are undertaken judiciously due to their high per-hectare cost. Aerial surveys have the advantages of lower cost per hectare and reliable recognition of the damage agent. However, the points and polygons noted by aerial surveyors tend to be problematic in terms of positional accuracy and estimation of attack magnitude. Both ground and aerial surveys produce data that must be digitized to facilitate further analysis or for integration with forest inventory data or decision support systems. Alternatively, digital remote sensing produces data that may be quickly integrated with forest inventory databases and models. Some digital remote sensing instruments can also offer high positional accuracy (Dial et al. 2003; Tao et al. 2004). However, depending on the sensor and type of processing used, costs per hectare can be low or high. The choice of detection method must, therefore, be considered in the context of the value of the information to the forest manager.

When considering different approaches to detection – whether analogue or digital – it must be noted that the fading of foliage in response to mountain pine beetle attack is not uniform among all attacked trees. The foliage of a host tree changes gradually. Twelve months after being attacked, more than 90% of killed trees have red needles (red attack). Three years after being attacked, most trees have lost all needles (grey attack) (British Columbia Ministry of Forests 1995). Generally, foliage fades from green to yellow to red during the first spring and summer after attack (Amman 1982; Henigman et al. 1999); leaves gradually desiccate, and pigment molecules break down. Initially, green chlorophyll pigments are lost, then yellow carotenes and red anthocyanins (Hill et al. 1967). Needles drop gradually until the tree is defoliated. In Figure 2, we present the rate at which sampled trees faded in response to attack by mountain pine beetle. During the base year, all trees were at green attack stage. When the same trees were inspected during the summer following the initial attack, some still appeared to be in the green attack stage, while others had faded to red attack. Similarly, red attack and grey attack co-occurred during the second and third summers following attack.

The general trend in fade rates is captured in Figure 3, where the fading of 15 lodgepole pine trees is indicated with the overlap between the expressions of attack stages in crown foliage. Fade trends that should be noted include no trees appearing as green stage after 12 months, all trees reaching red stage by 12 months, and grey stage initially evident after 13 months. Overlap of red and grey stages subsequent to a successful mountain pine beetle attack is also evident. Although this is a limited sample, additional samples support the same trends (refer to Figure 2 error bars for an indication of the range of variability by attack stage). The variability in the rate of change is greater across larger areas as more variability in tree characteristics and environments occurs. In general, red attack surveys should occur from mid-July to mid-September in most of British Columbia. Exact dates depend on local conditions; appropriate dates for other jurisdictions may differ. The implication of variable fade rates is that any non-field-based survey technique, even if it is highly accurate, may not detect all attacked trees, as the attack may not yet be evident in foliage.

In this chapter, we present a summary of the different survey approaches for characterizing mountain pine beetle across a range of scales. The scale, or detail, of a survey is linked to the type of forest management that the data are intended to support (after Shore 1985; British Columbia Ministry of Forests 1995; British Columbia Ministry of Forests 2000). Current operational survey methods include both aerial and ground surveys. Aerial surveys capture the infestation extent and intensity. Ground surveys are conducted on a sample basis to confirm insect species, to evaluate timber killed, to locate and identify trees currently under

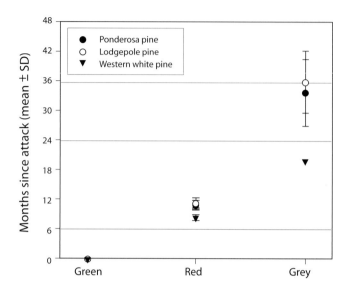

Figure 2. Foliage changes following mass attack at 12 sites in the Kamloops Forest District between 1962 and 1967. The foliage conditions of 134 individuals from three different tree species were monitored. Illustrated are the number of months for a sample of mass-attacked trees to reach 100% of a given attack stage; variability is demonstrated between stands (1 standard deviation error bars) and between species.

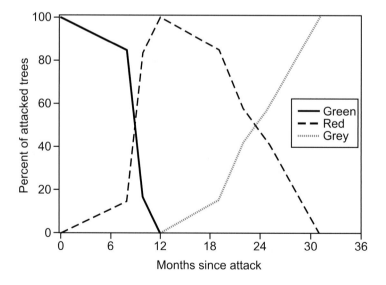

Figure 3. The variability in foliage-fade rate within a sample lodgepole pine stand, post-mass attack (Fountain Valley Site 2, Kamloops Forest District, between 1962 and 1967). This example stand was composed of 15 attacked trees.

attack (green attack), and to collect mensurational data. Survey methods that use digital remote sensing technology (airborne and satellite-based sensors) are emerging. Although not yet in widespread use, some of these data sources are operationally viable and should be considered within the hierarchy of mountain pine beetle-survey methods.

This chapter reviews tools and approaches available to forest managers for the detection, mapping, and monitoring of mountain pine beetle. Survey recommendations, based upon the above survey hierarchy, are also included. The methods presented here are generalizations of techniques currently in use. The types of surveys, or the specific methods used to implement the surveys, may vary by jurisdiction (Churcher and Carlson, 1984).

Aerial survey

Aerial surveys allow observers in fixed- or rotary-wing aircraft to detect red attack trees. Aerial survey methods considered in this chapter include:

• aerial overview sketch mapping;
• helicopter-based global positioning systems surveys; and
• aerial photography (analogue).

Viewing conditions and target pests must be considered when planning aerial surveys. Of primary importance are good visibility and a minimum cloud ceiling of approximately 1000 metres. Clear and sunny days are preferred, but a consistent high, overcast sky that provides even illumination is acceptable. Broken-cloud conditions or low sun angles are not recommended, as clusters of infested trees can be missed in the resulting shadows. Timing of surveys generally coincides with the insects' specific survey bio-window. The bio-window is the optimum time for visual expression of major forest pests and related damage (British Columbia Ministry of Forests 2000). For instance, the bio-window for the survey of mountain pine beetle impacts is between mid-July and mid-September for most of British Columbia.

Topographic maps used during aerial surveys may be enhanced by aerial photographs or other remotely sensed imagery, especially in areas of extensive pest damage on even terrain that has few geographic features. Up-to-date aerial photos can indicate logging, burns and other details that observers can delineate from infested timber. If available, custom-drawn GIS maps that highlight cut blocks, roads, water bodies and other landmarks greatly improve observers' ability to orient themselves quickly, thus enhance the accuracy of pest-polygon placement. Notes made by observers during an aerial survey vary depending on agency; however, all surveys note location and identity of the pest, and estimate intensity of attack. Maps by multiple observers are combined, and infestations are digitized. Correct identification of tree species, insect pest, and attack category is difficult from the air; this survey method is effective only when combined with current information gathered from area ground surveys conducted before and after the sketch mapping. Observer knowledge of the local forest and local pests is also important for accurate mapping.

Aerial survey maps must be supplemented with ground-survey assessments to estimate extent of the beetle population and impact of the infestation. The exact number of affected trees or precise area cannot be efficiently assessed using aerial surveys alone (Harris and Dawson 1979). This limitation results in survey maps on which estimates of intensity are noted as classes, rather than as exact values. Furthermore, location errors due to off-nadir (not directly beneath the satellite) viewing may render some surveys unreliable for dispatching ground crews (Aldrich et al. 1958). For a given area, assessment of aerial-survey accuracy and presence of bias is best determined using a multi-stage sampling procedure where aerial sketch mapping, global positioning system (GPS) point data, aerial photography, and ground plot data are collected and compared, thereby enabling cross-validation.

Aerial overview sketch mapping

The most general approach to detection of an infestation is to sketch map red trees that are visible from a fixed-wing aircraft. Notations are made on topographic maps at scales from 1:100 000 to 1:250 000 over millions of hectares, although provincial agencies in British Columbia occasionally use 1:50 000-scale base maps. While potentially providing greater spatial precision, map scales that are too large result in logistical problems in the aircraft, as too many maps are required to characterize the large territories typically mapped.

Sketch maps provide timely information for strategic planning during epidemics (Heller et al. 1955; Aldrich et al. 1958; Waters et al. 1958). Consistency between observers can be verified with a small number of check flights that repeat sampling of an area. If mapping has been consistent, cumulative mortality in specific stands can be estimated by overlaying successive years of damage (with interpretation, including consideration of photo-acquisition dates and variability in fade rates). Care must be taken to ensure that the above-mentioned scales are considered when undertaking additional analyses, especially if the analyses are spatial in nature. Sketch-map data are collected to represent large areas, often at the regional or provincial level. As a result, disturbance characteristics over the large area are well characterized, but issues related to the accuracy of polygon boundaries may emerge when attempting to integrate the information with spatial datasets representing smaller areas.

Sketch mapping of forest disturbances has a long history in North America. Archival data exists for much of British Columbia and the Pacific Northwest to aid in understanding disturbance activity over time. For instance, there are more than 2100 different maps depicting mountain pine beetle infestations from 1959 to 1995. Other sketch maps of infestations, scanned from archival reports dating back to 1928, have been added to the historical collection on the beetle. Due to the nature of the data collection and digital conversion, positional accuracy is variable and must be considered by users. An additional issue to consider regarding archival data is spatial extents of surveys. For instance, absence of infestation noted at a particular location or time may be due to lack of a spatially exhaustive survey. Flight-line information to accompany sketch-map survey results would ameliorate this issue.

A cost-effective approach to improve spatial accuracy and attack-magnitude estimates of sketch-mapped polygons is the use of Landsat imagery as an underlay for sketch mapping. The sketch base map contains the same information currently portrayed on the 1:100 000-scale map sheets (e.g., roads, urban areas, lakes, etc.), with the added benefit of a continuous view of the landscape from the image data as a backdrop. Polygon placement is aided by additional context information conferred by the imagery. Magnitude labelling can also be reassessed after the aerial survey, as the actual disturbance that is outlined may be evident in the imagery (depending on the date of image acquisition).

Forest management agencies in the Canadian provinces of Alberta, Manitoba, and Quebec have adopted the use of tablet PC-based, GPS-guided GIS mapping tools to directly digitize sketch-mapping information. The United States Department of Agriculture's Forest Service has investigated the potential of a similar digital system to replace or augment current sketch-mapping methods (Schraeder-Patton 2003). A digital sketch-mapping system provides accurate navigation for sketch mappers, as GPS identifies precise locations on the map at all times. One advantage of this approach is that information contained on the sketch maps is captured in digital format, so there is no time-consuming post-flight digitization. This enhances turnaround time of deliverables, reducing it from several months to several weeks (Schraeder-Patton 2003). Furthermore, use of real-time GPS navigation and orthophotos or other customized base maps can enhance positional accuracy of sketch mapping. Disadvantages associated with digital aerial sketch mapping are related primarily to hardware and software; however, the technology is evolving rapidly, and current limitations may be overcome in the near future (Schraeder-Patton, 2003). In addition, data gathered through digital aerial sketch mapping must still be subjected to quality-assurance procedures.

Helicopter-based global positioning system surveys

Once sketch maps have been obtained, infested areas are subjected to more detailed aerial surveys. These may be conducted using air photos acquired at a scale of 1:30 000, or by using a GPS unit mounted in a helicopter. For helicopter surveys, red trees are detected visually, their locations are recorded with a GPS and noted on topographic maps of 1:20 000 to 1:50 000 scale. The helicopter pilot hovers above the centre of a group of attacked trees, while a second person operates the GPS unit and captures the GPS waypoint for the site. An estimate of the number of infested trees at that location and the type of insect are also noted. The purpose of the GPS survey is to accurately locate beetle impacts to aid in local or regional strategic decision-making.

The likelihood of observers logging a non-existent red attack location (an error of commission) is extremely low. However, not detecting red attack areas on the landscape (errors of omission) depends on the survey effort covering a specific area. Beetle population size is also requisite support information for helicopter GPS surveys. The density of affected trees at a given point is also an issue. For a given survey point, trees identified as red attack may be dispersed or clustered, yet this is not captured in the survey (Fig. 4). Users must be aware of errors associated with GPS technologies (Kaplan 1996). Furthermore, the viewing

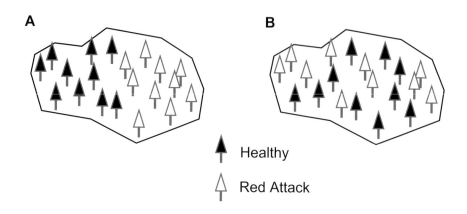

Figure 4. An illustration of (a) concentrated attack, and (b) dispersed attack (adapted from British Columbia Ministry of Forests 2003).

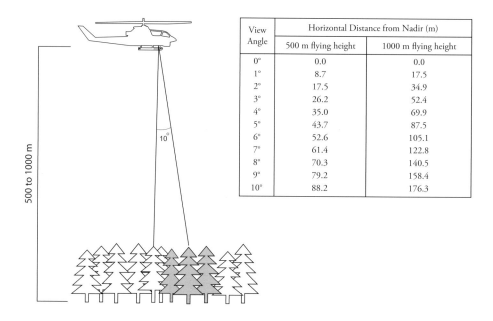

View Angle	Horizontal Distance from Nadir (m)	
	500 m flying height	1000 m flying height
0°	0.0	0.0
1°	8.7	17.5
2°	17.5	34.9
3°	26.2	52.4
4°	35.0	69.9
5°	43.7	87.5
6°	52.6	105.1
7°	61.4	122.8
8°	70.3	140.5
9°	79.2	158.4
10°	88.2	176.3

Figure 5. An illustration of how flying height and view angle can affect positional accuracy of aerially surveyed GPS points.

platform (helicopter) itself is a source of error; slight angles between viewing location and the perceived centre of infestation can affect positional accuracy (Fig. 5). The advantages of helicopter GPS survey over aerial photography are a wider window of survey opportunity, the short turnaround time for mapping survey results, and a wider weather window (more flexible opportunities) than afforded by traditional photography. Another advantage of helicopter GPS surveys is that they allow better identification of the pest agent than photos do, because helicopter surveying permits observers to see the entire tree crown at oblique viewpoints.

Aerial photography

Aerial photography is the most common imagery used in forest inventories for the purposes of characterizing forest attributes and meeting management objectives. Surveys that use aerial photography can be grouped into classes based upon the type of information collected (after Wear et al. 1966):

- damage detection;
- damage location;
- damage amount; and
- estimation of relative size of insect population and its capacity for future damage.

Aerial photography is not as suitable for initial damage detection as visual aerial survey methods are, such as overview sketch mapping. Information regarding the current status of insect populations and potential of the insects to cause future damage is best collected through field surveys. However, aerial photography can be used to generate mortality estimates and precisely locate infested areas. Either normal-colour or colour-infrared photos can be visually interpreted for signs of mountain pine beetle red attack (Murtha 1972). Photos are collected at scales ranging from 1:1 000 to 1:65 000. At a scale of 1:8 000, individual trees can be identified; whereas, at a scale of 1:19 000, only the proportion of forest damage can be estimated (Gimbarzevsky et al. 1992). However, the total area covered by a 1:8 000 photo is much less. Furthermore, results may be affected by the experience of interpreters (Klein 1973). Ground surveys can be used to define confidence limits around mortality estimates generated from aerial photos (Aldrich and Drooz 1967; Harris et al. 1982). For instance, Sharpnack and Wong (1982) present an approach where photos are used to calibrate damage estimates made from attack areas depicted on sketch maps. Photos may also be used independently to sample an area to estimate mortality rates (Hamilton 1981).

In 2004, British Columbia implemented the use of 1:30 000 aerial photography for more detailed detection and mapping of red attack. Photos were acquired in areas that had been identified for suppression in the province's strategic beetle management plan (British Columbia Ministry of Forests 2001). The air photos were collected between July and mid-September, and were then digitized (scanned). Red attack damage was visually interpreted from the photos using digital photogrammetric software (softcopy), and an output "measle map" of red attack areas was generated (Fig. 6). The photos provide a permanent record of the survey and may be used for other applications, such as updating topographic base maps.

Air photos may be used to generate estimates of damage (or mortality) and to locate infested trees for salvage or to aid in mitigation activities. Air photos may be combined with field data samples to reduce field costs, while still generating robust estimates of infestation location and magnitude (Sharpnack and Wong 1982). A procedure for combining the two data types is double sampling with regression (Wear et al. 1966). The method is based upon the premise that field measurements of damage or mortality are related to what can be interpreted from photos. Where field data is sampled and extrapolated with a regression-based approach using photo measurements, cost savings can be realized when appropriate conditions are met. If the photo plots are not completed at a substantially lower cost than the collection of field data, such an approach may not be warranted. The general approach, when using double sampling with regression to characterize damage or mortality, is to sample field conditions within a predefined population area. Procedures for combining field- and photo-based estimates are provided in Wear et al. (1966). To compute the area damaged using this regression-based approach, measurements must be made both on the ground and from photographs. The nature of the field sample (i.e., number and distribution of plots) and definition of the population area (i.e., size and shape) must also be correctly specified for robust estimates of damage to be generated. Meeting all statistical and operational requirements of this regression-based approach enables the final calculation of an estimate for total amount of mountain pine beetle damage. Integration of field and photo data in a sampling and regression framework to facilitate estimates of damage over large areas is analogous to the use of field data to calibrate damage estimates made from remotely sensed data.

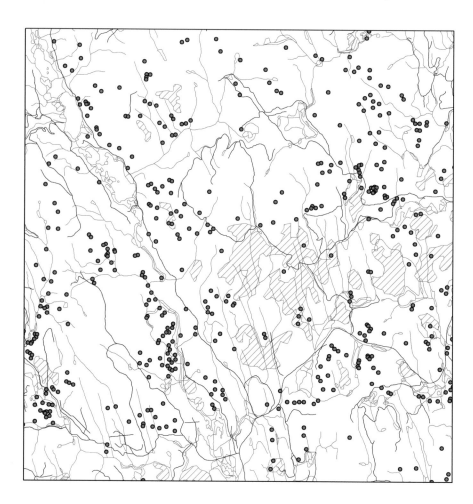

Figure 6. A sample of a red attack "measle map" generated from the manual interpretation of 1:30 000 colour aerial photography. Individual red points indicate clusters of individual red attack trees. Large polygons indicate areas of more spatially extensive red attack damage. This mapsheet is located near Merritt, British Columbia (092H087), and was provided courtesy of Tim Ebata, British Columbia Ministry of Forests, Victoria, British Columbia.

Ground survey

The objective of ground surveys depends on the management strategy designated for an area. Where precise information on location and number of trees requiring treatment is needed to direct single-tree treatments, ground surveys are designed to pinpoint green attacked trees. This method of ground survey exploits current knowledge of mountain pine beetle behaviour at sub-outbreak levels; this knowledge indicates that mountain pine beetle is most likely to re-attack in close proximity to the red attacked trees. The level of precision that is necessary to determine the status of individual trees requires the most accurate information possible and is usually employed where beetle attacks are at their lowest density. Where the objective is to determine the infestation rate at stand level, systematic surveys – grid lines or cruise plots – are used to obtain an average level of attack per hectare. This information is used in "holding and salvage beetle management units" where harvesting priorities are determined based on the level of new and old attack. Inventory and planning require estimates of average attack (green, red, and grey attack) at the stand and forest levels; therefore, the required precision of ground-survey data is lower.

Ground surveys assess population size, or degree of forest infestation, within a local area. Sample plots are generally less than one hectare in size. Population estimates indicate whether a local beetle population is increasing, static, or decreasing. These estimates provide a coarse index of population trend based on beetle probe surveys conducted across the landscape. Infestation estimates, or damage estimates, indicate the impact of a particular beetle population. Both types of estimates (population and damage) are used to drive selection of the most appropriate management response.

Population assessments may be based upon field surveys or aerial surveys. Field surveys enable brood assessments to be undertaken. Brood assessments are carried out in the late summer to fall, and in the spring. Beginning in mid-July, population surveys with sketch mapping may be undertaken. These aerial surveys influence placement of subsequent ground surveys. Aerial survey data collected during consecutive years may also be compared to indicate population trends.

Brood assessment ground surveys may be done in September to October based upon a timber cruising technique. The timber cruising operation records information such as tree species, diameter at breast height, and pest status (healthy, currently attacked, or partially attacked, pitch outs, and foliage colour) (Shore 1985; British Columbia Ministry of Forests 1995). In the spring following attack, assessment surveys account for overwintering brood mortality and losses to natural enemies such as parasites and predators – particularly woodpeckers (British Columbia Ministry of Forests 1995). A fixed-size bark area (typically 900 cm^2) is removed and examined to form a statistically valid sample of trees to determine the stand average trend ratio (Equation 1) and the percent overwintering mortality (Equation 2) (Shore 1985).

The average trend ratio (r) for each stand is determined as follows:

$$r = \frac{\sum\limits_{t}(y+o)/g)}{t}$$ [1]

Where,

y = number eggs and larvae
o = number pupae and adults
g = number of galleries
t = number of sampled trees

Percent of overwintering mortality may subsequently be computed for each stand as:

$$r = \frac{(r\_fall - r\_spring) \times 100}{r\_fall}$$ [2]

The results are used to indicate population trend. For instance, average population trend ratios can be interpreted as follows: if the result of r is less than 2.6, the population is decreasing; if the value of r ranges from 2.6 to 4.0, the population is static, and; if r is greater than 4.0, the population is increasing. These values are heuristic in nature and should be used to support interpretation, not to act as the sole source of information on trends of a given population. Population trends may also be inferred from aerial photographs, with the area, or count, of red attacked trees compared over successive years. This relationship is useful as an indicator of general population trend; however, this relationship should not supplant brood assessments.

Brood assessments are carried out in the months following fading of foliage to red, which indicates trees attacked in the previous year (the survey should begin approximately mid-July). The survey locates green attacked trees containing mountain pine beetle broods that will be the source of future infestations. Any survey system similar to prism or strip cruising will usually work. Surveys start near red trees, and progress outward in a grid or other systematic pattern to locate currently attacked trees. Crews must be well trained before they begin, and their work must be checked periodically; the extra time needed to properly train and check crews cannot be neglected, as correct identification of both pest and attack category (Table 1) is critical to the success of the ground survey effort.

Infestation-assessment techniques range from simple identification of trees under attack to a complete mensuration of the infestation. Walk-throughs are used largely as initial ground-reconnaissance surveys to determine characteristics of attacked stands and to contribute towards identifying information needs for more intensive surveys. Probes are systematic strip surveys that collect more detailed information than do walk-through surveys.

Table 1. Definition of mountain pine beetle attack categories

Attack Category	Definition
Endemic	Mountain pine beetles attack and kill stressed trees, often in concert with secondary bark beetle species.
Incipient	Mountain pine beetle population within a stand is sufficiently large that healthy trees are killed. The killed trees usually occur in patches of various sizes and are generally confined to limited areas (e.g., stands).
Outbreak or Epidemic	Mountain pine beetle population and tree mortality occur at the landscape level.

Probe information is compiled on a polygon basis and includes attributes such as: location on map; size of beetles under bark; relative brood success; percentage of attack category; rate of spread; and stems per hectare (British Columbia Ministry of Forests 1995). Although useful, these survey techniques do not provide sufficient information for assessment of volume or area infested. Prism cruises, on the other hand, are used for detection and impact assessment, in which volume affected can be estimated on a stand-level basis. Line transects are also used for detection and impact assessment, and are more efficient than prism cruising (Safranyik and Linton 2002). With these data, affected volume and area can be estimated from the survey, and may be statistically extrapolated to represent larger areas. An additional means to characterize the population trend of a mountain pine beetle infestation is by calculating a green-to-red ratio. A green-to-red ratio is the estimated number of currently attacked trees compared to the number of red attacked trees. This ratio provides a rough indication of population growth.

Digital remote sensing

Digital remote sensing involves the use of sensors (mounted on either airborne or satellite platforms) that collect digital imagery of various spatial and spectral resolutions. Extensive research has been conducted into the use of digital remote sensing for detection and mapping of various stages of mountain pine beetle infestation. This chapter presents both airborne-based and satellite-based sensors, and then summarizes mapping methods for green, red, and grey attack. One advantage of using digital images in mapping red attack stage trees is that the images represent continuous data across a landscape. In this way, all areas in the image are examined for possible red attack, independent of accessibility or position in a watershed. Another advantage of mapping from remotely sensed digital imagery is the reduction or elimination of interpreter bias afforded by automated classification algorithms. By avoiding visual interpretation, products have greater consistency and reliability between different areas or dates. Increased reliability also results from the high positional accuracy of image data compared to aerial survey data. The standard geometric pre-processing of satellite images results in data that can be confidently integrated with forest inventory polygons and other spatial data sets (e.g., elevation data, road access). Results of analyses of remotely sensed data are typically subjected to accuracy-assessment protocols, and this is an element unique to remote sensing analyses compared to the more heuristic assessments of aerial survey products. Accuracy of an attribute, such as red attack, may be characterized in relation to an independent validation dataset. Use of an independent validation dataset allows for characterization of accuracy, in terms of correct identification and distribution of error. Infested areas that are missed and, conversely, locations that are falsely indicated, may also be characterized (for theory, see Congalton 1991; for an example, see Franklin, S.E. et al. 2003).

Issues to be considered when planning to map mountain pine beetle red attack using digital imagery include the spatial, temporal, spectral, and radiometric resolution of the imagery. Spatial resolution, or pixel size, ranges from less than one metre to more than one kilometre for different sensors. Similar to the collection of aerial photography, there is a trade-off between improving spatial resolution and both reducing image extent and increasing costs (Franklin et al. 2002). An understanding of the link between sensor acquisition characteristics and subsequent image-information content is critical to the success of a mapping exercise (Lefsky and Cohen 2003). For instance, the ability to discern differing objects on a landscape is linked to spatial resolution (Franklin, J. et al. 2003). If a single pixel is composed of more than one element (e.g., part tree crown, part shadow, part ground vegetation), the pixel represents the collective spectral characteristics of those elements. Spectral signatures that are developed in such instances have suppressed variances that diminish the power of predictive algorithms. However, when a single pixel represents only one element (e.g., a portion of a tree crown), the spectral signature is unique to that pixel (e.g., Wulder and Dymond 2004). The sensitivity to spectral differences between red attack and healthy trees (spectral resolution) also varies between different sensors. However, sensitivity to the condition of vegetation is a high priority for developers of satellite sensors, resulting in many detection options for the end user.

Temporal resolution, or image-acquisition frequency, affects the sensor's ability to collect information regarding a particular attack stage. Airborne digital sensors can capture image data on cloud-free days that correspond to the bio-window for red attack detection, when feasible or possible. Typically, satellite sensors have fixed revisit rates, such as 16 days between acquisitions of Landsat scenes over an area. The revisit cycle is based upon factors such as sensor elevation, orbit characteristics, and scene footprint. New high spatial resolution space-borne satellites, such as IKONOS and QuickBird, have directable sensor heads, which enable capture of images for areas other than those located directly below the sensors. Imagery collected off-nadir (not directly beneath the satellite) should be inspected and used with caution as the altered view angle affects how the forest is characterized.

The key to employing digital data for mapping mountain pine beetle impacts is to match the information needs of forest managers with image information content and resolution characteristics. For example, under endemic conditions, information needs are for detection of single and small clusters of red attack trees. To produce this information, the imagery must have sufficiently high spatial and spectral resolution. In contrast, under epidemic conditions, information needs are for quantifying the impact of large groups of red attack trees over large areas. Therefore, less expensive imagery with medium spatial resolution and moderate spectral resolution would be sufficient.

One advantage of digital imagery is that it may be geocorrected (two dimensions) or orthorectified (three dimensions); these corrections facilitate integration of the remotely sensed imagery with other spatial datasets, such as forest inventory polygons or GPS point data. These corrections also make it possible to compare images collected over multiple years, thereby providing an important monitoring tool. Additional strengths supporting the use of digital data are that objective, repeatable analyses of the data are carried out with equal effort across the landscape, and that digital techniques are applied in a systematic, consistent, and transparent manner. These features help reduce inconsistencies that may result from visual interpretation. Main impediments to widespread use of digital data are sophisticated processing needs, costs per hectare, and a mismatch between user needs and results generated. The use of aircraft results in similar considerations for airborne imagery collection as for aerial surveys. Days that are best for data collection have even-light conditions, without clouds or with high, overcast cloud. Timing of flights would occur when trees are in the red attack stage.

Airborne platforms

Digital images may be collected from airborne platforms above areas identified as infested during aerial surveys. The key differences between digital airborne imagery or aerial photography and aerial overview sketch mapping or ground surveys are that the spectral characteristics of the entire forest are permanently captured in the imagery for that particular location and time, and the data can later be re-examined if uncertainties occur. Digital airborne imagery includes traditional air photos scanned into digital format (Nelson et al. 2001), digital camera images, videography, multispectral scanners, and imaging spectrometers. Airborne images may be used to map the location of small clusters or scattered red trees. The results are used to direct ground surveys or to dispatch ground crews for sanitation treatment. The airborne digital imagery may be subjected to enhancements that highlight locations of red attacked trees (Fig. 7). Digital camera technology is sufficiently sophisticated for direct image capture. Most high-quality digital cameras are based on modified 35-mm or medium-format cameras. The spatial and spectral resolutions of these cameras match the quality of medium-speed film (Graham and Koh 2002). The digital format eliminates the developing and scanning necessary for film-based photographs to be analyzed in softcopy format.

Airborne scanners and imaging spectrometers collect digital images directly, similar to digital cameras. The spatial resolution (from less than 1 m to greater than 10 m) and the sensitivity to different wavelengths of energy can be adjusted to address particular information needs. Red attack trees can be successfully detected, and the digital nature of the data provides for rapid integration with other digital datasets (Kneppeck and Ahern 1989; Ahern et al. 1986).

Figure 7. Red attack trees depicted on a high spatial resolution digital colour aerial photograph (collected with a 30-cm pixel). This photo was acquired by Terrasaurus Ltd. on September 24th, 2004 at a site near Merritt, British Columbia. Photo provided courtesy of Jamie Heath, Terrasaurus Ltd., Vancouver, British Columbia.

Airborne scanners have not found wide operational implementation for mapping mountain pine beetle red attack, due largely to high per-hectare costs.

Aerial videography provides some operational advantages over air photos: lower cost; no delay for photographic development; the option to include audio commentary; and high light sensitivity (Ciesla 2000). Additionally, camera settings can be adjusted as the imagery is acquired during data collection. Similar to most airborne sensors, the disadvantages are primarily associated with image extent and resolution characteristics. Otherwise, planning and processing options that are available are similar to those of the digital camera systems described above.

Satellite platforms

Satellite images may be collected to map infested areas over a range of scales. Satellite imagery is similar to airborne imagery in that the data is continuous across the extent of the sampled area. In general, the comparatively high orbits of satellite systems result in a more favourable viewing geometry when compared to the low altitudes of airborne systems. Airborne systems often generate data requiring sophisticated processing to compensate for aircraft motion, view angles, and variable illumination conditions throughout the acquisition period. Satellite images are available across a range of spatial, spectral, and temporal scales. Therefore, they can be used to address a variety of strategic and tactical planning decisions. The large image extents of satellite imagery enable economies of scale (based on cost per hectare).

Mapping of red attack trees under epidemic conditions has been documented using satellite imagery. Due to the large cluster sizes and landscape-scale extent associated with epidemic conditions, low-cost imagery from Landsat Thematic Mapper (TM) (single date) has been used to successfully map mountain pine beetle infestations (Franklin, S.E. et al. 2003). However, higher accuracy of red attack mapping resulted when multi-temporal Landsat TM and Enhanced Thematic Mapper (ETM+) datasets were used (Skakun et al. 2003). Although the Landsat mapping efforts have generated products representative of landscape-level characteristics, the higher spatial resolution satellites capture characteristics at the stand or tree level, and have potential for surveying under incipient population conditions. Wulder et al. (2005a) demonstrated that the ability to detect red attack with multi-temporal Landsat data decreases with increasing time since attack. By using one Landsat image collected in 1996 and another in 2001, a multi-temporal classification of the image was completed, as per methods described in Franklin, S.E. et al. (2003). Helicopter GPS data collected annually from 1995 to 2001 were used to validate the classification. The results (Table 2) indicate that recent red attack was more successfully detected than older red attack, suggesting that monitoring surveys that examine long-term impacts and forest change resulting from an infestation of mountain pine beetle have a limited temporal window for completion. The strong spectral signal of the red attack stage of mountain pine beetle infestation diminishes over time as foliage of infested trees gradually fades from red to grey.

Commercially delivered, high spatial resolution satellite data are a potential source for cost-effective collection of accurate, consistent, and timely data regarding mountain pine beetle red attack. IKONOS provides global coverage, a consistent acquisition schedule, and near-nadir viewing angles. The resolution of the sensor is suitable for high-accuracy photogrammetric processing and mapping applications (Tao et al. 2004). In addition, the IKONOS 4-metre multispectral channels have similar spectral properties in the visible and near-infrared wavelengths as the Landsat ETM+ channels (Goward et al. 2003). The IKONOS sensor has four 4-metre multispectral bands centred at 480.3 nm, 550.7 nm, 664.8 nm, and 805.0 nm, respectively. Average bandwidth of these multispectral bands is 80 nm. In contrast, the single IKONOS 1-metre panchromatic band is centred at 727.1 nm, and has a bandwidth of 403 nm. The large bandwidth of the panchromatic channel results in lower spectral sensitivity. The implications of this are that, despite its high spatial resolution, this band cannot be used to detect mountain pine beetle red attack. Other high spatial resolution sensors, which offer both panchromatic and multispectral bands, have similar limitations.

White et al. (2004) investigated the merits of using IKONOS 4-metre multispectral data at a study site near Prince George, British Columbia (Fig. 8). The project examined use of an unsupervised clustering of image spectral values to detect mountain pine beetle red attack at susceptible sites (i.e., with known risk factors for infestation) that were considered to be lightly infested (1% to 5% of trees red attacked) or moderately infested (greater than 5% and less than 20% trees red attacked). A 4-metre buffer (analogous to a single IKONOS pixel) was applied to the red attack pixel identified on the IKONOS imagery in order to account for positional error. When compared to an independent set of validation data, it was found that 70.1% (lightly infested sites) and 92.5% (moderately infested sites) of the red attack trees existing on the ground were identified correctly through classification of remotely sensed IKONOS imagery. Analysis of red attack trees missed in the classification of the IKONOS imagery indicated detection of red attack was most effective for larger tree crowns (diameter >1.5 metres) that were less than 11 metres from other red attack trees.

Other high spatial resolution satellite data, such as QuickBird, may offer potential for red attack mapping. New commercial high spatial resolution satellites are scheduled for deployment over the next 5 to 10 years – further increasing options for the detection and mapping of red attack (Glackin and Peltzer 1999).

Table 2. The characterization of red attack detection accuracy using multi-temporal Landsat TM (1996) and ETM+ (2001) imagery. Validation data was collected each year from 1995 to 2001. Generally, measures of producers' and users' accuracies decrease with increasing time since the initial attack.

Time since trees turned red	Year of validation points	Number of red attack validation points	Number of correctly classified points	Producers accuracy (%) [1] (90% confidence intervals)	Users accuracy (%) [2] (90% confidence intervals)
1– 2 months	2001	204	162	79 (73 84)	76 (70 81)
1 year	2000	213	172	81 (75 86)	77 (71 82)
2 years	1999	215	165	77 (71 82)	76 (70 81)
3 years	1998	193	140	73 (66 79)	73 (66 79)
4 years	1997	290	215	74 (70 78)	81 (77 85)
5 years	1996	221	146	66 (59 72)	74 (67 80)
6 years	1995	164	112	68 (61 74)	68 (61 74)
Totals		1500	1112	74 (73 76)	75 (74 77)

[1] A measure of the accuracy of a particular classification scheme, this shows what percentage of a particular ground class was correctly classified. Accuracy is calculated by dividing the number of correct pixels for a class by the actual number of ground truth pixels for that class.

[2] A measure of the reliability of an output map generated from a classification scheme. This statistic can tell the user of the map what percentage of a class corresponds to the ground-truthed class. Users accuracy is calculated by dividing the number of correct pixels for a class by the total pixels assigned to that class.

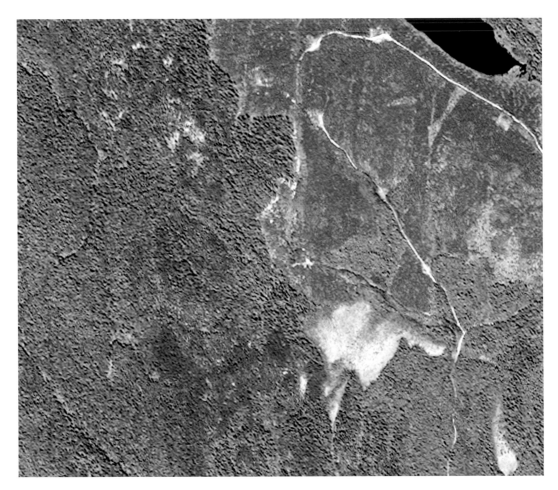

Figure 8. A portion of an IKONOS image acquired near Prince George, British Columbia (approximately 64 km^2). Mountain pine beetle red attack is visible in the image. ©2002 Space Imaging Inc. All rights reserved.

Mapping methods

Green attack stage

Detecting green attack trees is a sought-after, yet elusive goal for remote sensing researchers. Water stress in mass-attacked trees has been detected at the leaf and branch scales (Murtha 1985; Ahern 1988; Rock et al. 1988). However, some studies have found detection difficult when other image elements were integrated into the analysis (foliage, branches, and other background objects) (Puritch 1981). The key issue in mapping green attack is the subtle change in the spectral signal of the foliage. In order to detect this change, the number of objects within a pixel must be minimized and the relative differences maximized; this requires a sensor with both high-spatial and high-spectral resolution. To objectively classify such data, calibration data collected in the field must be precisely located and be representative of the green attack stage. The spatial resolution of the sensor must be sufficiently high that individual pixels represent only sunlit foliage in a tree crown. In turn, the spectral resolution of the sensor must also be sufficiently fine, with sufficiently sensitive optics, to enable a unique spectral signature to emerge that represents the green attack stage.

Regardless of the technical limitations of successfully detecting green attack, there are substantial logistical limitations to the operational feasibility of undertaking a survey intended to capture the green attack stage of a mountain pine beetle infestation. Current methods of identifying green attack use known locations of existing red attack as a starting point to search for probable locations of green attack. Therefore, for a green attack survey method to be significantly better than the current method, large areas of healthy forest would have to be surveyed annually to identify green attack trees. These surveys would require the use of data that has both high-spatial and high-spectral resolution, and the data would have to be collected at the appropriate time of year. Selecting an appropriate time to conduct a survey is difficult, because the rate at which foliage of a tree crown shows symptoms of a mountain pine beetle attack is variable (this applies across all stages of attack, not to only the green stage). The fading of foliage in the crown of a tree infested with mountain pine beetle is not a consistent, linear process (Fig. 2). Additional insights on variability in fade rates and associated detection possibilities can be found in Roberts et al. (2003).

The earlier the detection of attack is attempted, the higher the omission rate of actual green attack trees will likely be. This variability in timing requirements for green attack surveys necessitates continuous monitoring of an area for a set period of time each year, if the survey is to be effective. Environmental aspects such as cloud cover, drought stress or snow accumulations may further impair detection capabilities. In addition to these data-collection constraints, field calibration, data processing, product development (maps of known areas of green attack), and product delivery must all occur within a time period that enables the forest manager to act upon the information generated. Furthermore, accuracy of green attack detection must be high if it is to be useful in a management context. The costs of remotely sensed green attack surveys must also be lower than the costs of existing field survey methods. Given the current high cost of high-spatial and high-spectral resolution data, and the large areas and periods of time involved, it is unlikely that such a survey method would be cost effective in an operational context.

Red attack stage

Detecting and mapping red attack trees has been successful at various scales and with a variety of digital sensors. However, research has been largely targeted towards a specific set of conditions, and accuracy-assessment protocols have been inconsistent. Therefore, the ability to map red attack with different tools, under different conditions and attack intensities, requires additional research before being considered operational.

A key issue in mapping red attack trees is the size of clusters of red trees. The spectral difference between red attack and healthy trees is detectable under some conditions with some spectral mixing of pixels (Franklin, S.E. et al. 2003). If the cluster of red attacked trees is large, with attacked trees concentrated, ability to map the attack accurately is improved. The larger the cluster, the lower the spatial and spectral resolution required of the sensor. This relationship translates into low per-hectare costs for mapping epidemic conditions.

The highest accuracy in digitally mapping red attack has resulted when multi-temporal data were used. For the most accurate results, multi-temporal sets of images should be taken from the same sensor view angle and under similar illumination conditions. Otherwise, differences between two images may be an artifact of the data collection process, and may obscure subtle changes in the landscape. For the same reason, similar radiometric and other corrections must be applied to each image (Peddle et al. 2003). It is common practice to geometrically correct a master image, then register all subsequent images to it, with an error of less than one pixel (also known as rubber-sheeting). This approach optimizes the likelihood that detected changes reliably indicate the situation on the ground.

Assigning agents to areas of detected change within a landscape can be the most difficult aspect of the remote sensing project. Foliage fading (appearing red or yellow) can occur for many reasons, including mountain pine beetle, other pests and diseases, drought, or senescence. Additional data can help at this point; a digital elevation model and an inventory of forest species can eliminate forests not susceptible to mountain pine beetle (Shore and Safranyik 1992). Furthermore, ground-validation or forest inventory data can help eliminate other agents.

Spatial processing of the image or ancillary data can help improve the accuracy of mapping of red attack. One approach is to stratify the area into susceptible and non-susceptible stands or trees, based on entomological pest-host models (Shore and Safranyik 1992). This enhances spectral differences between non-attacked and red attack areas. Franklin, S.E. et al. (2003) found that damage caused by mountain pine beetle was not confounded by uncontrolled natural stand variability or the relatively small spectral influence of a few damaged crowns within a small area. Another key element of satellite-image processing is to incorporate the temporal aspect of the change. This means using multi-date or multi-temporal imagery where detection of change is based on differences in the forest from year to year. An example of this analysis approach for mapping red attack incorporates multi-temporal data with a transformation of spectral data in calculating the Enhanced Wetness Difference Index (EWDI) (Skakun et al. 2003).

Grey attack stage

Detection and mapping of grey attack trees has been as accurate as mapping of red attack when it is included in the study design (Klein 1973; Harris et al. 1982; Gimbarzevsky et al. 1992). However, these studies tested only air-photo interpretation. Extensive research indicates that techniques developed for assessing forest impacts similar to grey attack (but caused by defoliators) may be used for assessing the magnitude of impact of a mountain pine beetle infestation (as indicated by the presence of grey attack trees). The primary issue for mapping grey attack is the time between attack and when data are collected. If grey attack trees are not harvested, impediments to their detection may include blow-down, development of neighbouring crowns of healthy trees, development of understory species, and vigorous growth of ground cover. Intuitively, use of data from a single date may be adequate for grey attack mapping because the difference between healthy and defoliated trees is relatively large; however, in practice, the range of spectral variability representing grey attack stage is large, and often impedes robust algorithm development. Multi-temporal imagery may be required to consistently map grey attack stage. Care must be taken to differentiate changes due to mountain pine beetle from other changes occurring on the landscape in the intervening time. The mapping of red attack and the later inference of grey attack may be a more robust approach because of the unique spectral signature of red attack (single date) and the greater multi-date spectral differences. When mapping or accounting for areas that have been impacted by mountain pine beetle, access to salvage harvest records will also be required. Grey attack is not captured by the annual aerial overview surveys, so other methods to detect grey attack may be important for studies looking at the long-term consequences of the current epidemic.

Data integration

Forest inventory datasets are developed over a timeframe that allows for photo commissioning, collection, interpretation, and digitization (Gillis and Leckie 1996). Data capture for a forest inventory often happens on a 10-year cycle. Forest disturbance, such as that caused by mountain pine beetle, can occur within an inventory cycle. A forest inventory database requires maintenance over time or the data can quickly become outdated. Polygon decomposition was developed as a tool to integrate different data layers, such as aerial survey data or satellite image classifications, with existing GIS data to provide timely and accurate estimates of forest change (Wulder and Franklin 2001). Remotely sensed estimates of red attack are easily integrated with the forest inventory data (Fig. 9). Integration facilitates the polygon-specific accounting of areas or proportions of individual forest stands (Wulder et al. 2005b;). Other products generated from remotely sensed data that may be useful for beetle management include inventory updates, change detection, and performance monitoring of harvesting (i.e., how much of the infestation was cut per year by the licensee).

Detection and mapping of mountain pine beetle impacts can also be integrated into decision support systems. Various models exist to aid managers in the planning and treatment of forests with mountain pine beetle populations. One type of model assesses the infestation risk of different forest stands (Shore and Safranyik 1992; Chojnacky et al. 2000). Spatially explicit models, such as that developed by Fall et al. (2002), may also capitalize on input of remotely sensed estimates of infestation locations, to aid in providing baseline data for course projections of future outbreaks. These models require information on the current locations of attacked trees to predict possible future risk. The attack maps generated through remote sensing can be used as input to these models. For example, the forest inventory and digital elevation data provide a rating of susceptibility for each stand (Shore and Safranyik 1992). Overlaying the point data from a detailed aerial survey provides intuitive information, but additional utility is found by integrating this detailed data into the model to generate a relative risk index (Fig. 10).

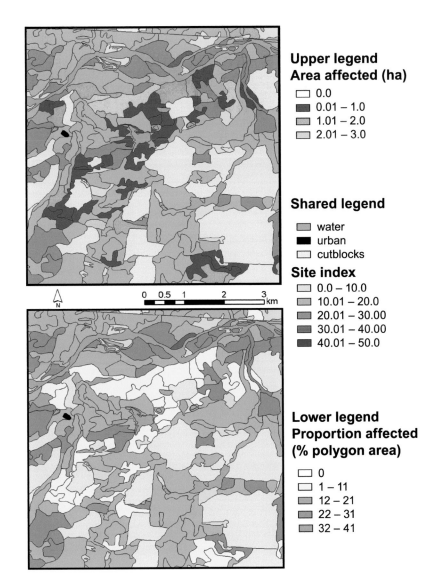

Figure 9. An illustration of the integration of mountain pine beetle maps into forest management information systems. Undisturbed forest management stands are shaded by site index. Stands disturbed by mountain pine beetle are shaded by the area of red attack in the stand (number of hectares), shown in the upper tile; or proportion of red attack in the stand (percent polygon area), depicted in the lower tile. As indicated in the legend shared by both tiles, harvested stands are shaded grey.

Management options and recommendations

Field-based methods for detection of mountain pine beetle are well established and routinely undertaken by forest managers. Mitigation and harvest-planning decisions are based upon these field surveys. Intensive field surveys benefit from more spatially extensive survey techniques, operating in an information hierarchy, that enable stratification of the landscape which can be used to focus field surveys in areas most likely to be impacted by mountain pine beetle.

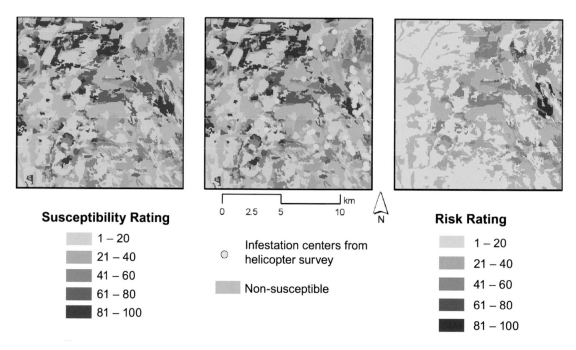

Susceptibility Rating

- 1 – 20
- 21 – 40
- 41 – 60
- 61 – 80
- 81 – 100

○ Infestation centers from helicopter survey

Non-susceptible

0   2.5   5   10   km

N

Risk Rating

- 1 – 20
- 21 – 40
- 41 – 60
- 61 – 80
- 81 – 100

Figure 10. An illustration of the integration of global positioning data with the Shore and Safranyik (1992) mountain pine beetle risk rating system.

Provincial and state governments are interested primarily in detection of red attack trees within their political boundaries (Wiart 2003). This information is used for reporting and strategic planning. At this scale, aerial sketch mapping is the recommended approach. To provide additional information regarding attack intensity and location of red attack, mapping approaches based upon medium-resolution satellite imagery may be used. Additionally, to determine attack date in order to aid shelf-life studies, a change-detection framework may be used that incorporates time-series analyses of multiple images. Also of interest at provincial or state levels is the use of samples of high-spatial resolution satellite data or aerial photography to provide accurate and independent estimations of red attack over large population areas. These samples of red attack locations may be used to validate disturbance magnitude and estimates of affected area on a management-unit level (following an approach akin to the double sampling procedure previously described for air photos).

Forest licensees and government agencies require detection and mapping of infestations (red attack and grey attack trees) across their land bases. Aerial sketch maps do not capture areas of grey attack, and at the landscape scale, sketch maps may not offer sufficient detail regarding red attack. Medium- to high-spatial resolution satellite or airborne imagery is recommended for red attack mapping at the landscape level. Medium spatial resolution imagery is recommended under epidemic conditions, whereas high spatial resolution imagery is more appropriate for non-epidemic conditions. Aerial photographs, which are often collected to meet other management needs, are also an appropriate source of information for red attack mapping. Integration of red attack locations into the forest inventory is useful as new attributes, such as the area or proportion of a polygon expected to be at red attack stage, enable synergistic applications with forest inventory data and models.

For instance, other attributes in the forest inventory database may be used to validate results of red attack mapping. Layout, access, and operability are examples of elements that may be combined with red attack information to aid forest managers. Integration of red attack mapping data with forest inventory data is a low-cost approach to updating or auditing the forest inventory data within forest inventory measurement cycles.

At the individual forest stand scale, forest licensees require detailed maps of red attack to determine locations where field crews should be deployed to conduct detailed ground surveys. At this scale, high-spatial resolution imagery – either satellite or airborne – is required to map areas affected by red attack with sufficient degree of detail. Field crews conduct ground surveys in identified red attack areas in order to confirm estimates of red attack and to identify trees that are currently infested (green attack). Established field techniques are appropriate for in situ determination of mountain pine beetle attack; it is the only method that provides reliable estimates of green attack.

Conclusions

For any survey methodology intended to meet forest management needs induced by mountain pine beetle activity, it is critical to link information needs to the type of survey undertaken. Survey data are inherently tied to scales of information, with attendant expectations of both attribute and spatial accuracies. Higher-order information needs (e.g., detailed counts of trees attacked per stand for volume-impact estimation) may require an information hierarchy in which multiple sets of survey data, collected with increasing levels of detail, are nested together. For example, using lower-cost, coarse-level overview survey information to guide more-intensive survey sites enables cost efficiencies. Understanding the information content of a range of data sources, as presented in this chapter, increases the ability to judiciously select the most appropriate data source to populate the information hierarchy. Ultimately, this information hierarchy is used to meet the mandates of mountain pine beetle mitigation and management.

Many new survey options are available, including an array of sensors mounted on both airborne and satellite platforms. These options for detecting and mapping impacts of mountain pine beetle infestation must be considered in relation to the information needs and business drivers of forest managers. These new technologies are populating the information hierarchy at levels between the data provided by coarse aerial overview surveys and the data collected through detailed field surveys. Limitations of the technologies must be acknowledged and considered within an operational framework; in particular, forest managers must be aware of the technical and logistical limitations associated with using remotely sensed data for green attack detection. Finally, integration of survey data, regardless of its origin, within existing forest inventory data in a GIS environment generates value-added information for forest managers. The forest inventory also provides a context and a source of validation data for information extracted from remotely sensed data.

Acknowledgements

We are grateful to Les Safranyik, of the Canadian Forest Service, for provision of the data used to develop Figures 2 and 3, and to Tim Ebata, of the British Columbia Ministry of Forests, for providing the data used to generate Figure 6. Figure 7 was provided courtesy of Jamie Heath, of Terrasaurus Ltd.

References

Ahern, F.J. 1988. The effects of bark beetle stress on the foliar spectral reflectance of lodgepole pine. International Journal of Remote Sensing 9:1451–1468.

Ahern, F.J.; Bennett, W.J.; Kettela, E.G. 1986. An initial evaluation of two digital airborne images for surveying spruce budworm defoliation. Photogrammetric Engineering and Remote Sensing 52:1647–1654.

Aldrich, R.C.; Drooz, A.T. 1967. Estimated Fraser fir mortality and balsam woolly aphid infestation trend using aerial colour photography. Forest Science 13:300–313.

Aldrich, R.C.; Heller, R.C.; Bailey, W.F. 1958. Observation limits for aerial sketch-mapping southern pine beetle in the southern Appalachians. Journal of Forestry 56:200–202.

Amman, G.D. 1978. Biology, ecology and causes of outbreaks of the mountain pine beetle in lodgepole pine forests. Pages 39–53 *in* A.A. Berryman, G.D. Amman and R.W. Stark, eds. Theory and practice of mountain pine beetle management in lodgepole pine forests, Symposium proceedings, April 25-27, 1978, Pullman, WA. University of Idaho, Moscow, WA.

Amman, G.D. 1982. The mountain pine beetle – identification, biology, causes of outbreaks, and entomological research needs. Pages 7-12 *in* D.M. Shrimpton, ed. Proceedings of the Mountain Pine Beetle Problem Review, November 3-4, 1981, Fairmont Hot Springs, BC. Canadian Forest Service, Victoria, BC, Information Report BC-X-230.

Belton, E.M.; Eidt, D.C., eds. 1999. Common names of insects in Canada. The Entomological Society of Canada, Ottawa, ON. Also available online at http://esc-sec.org/menu.htm.

British Columbia Ministry of Forests. 1995. Bark beetle management guidebook (Forest Practices Code). Forest Practices Branch, Victoria, BC, 45 p.

British Columbia Ministry of Forests. 2000. Forest health aerial overview survey standards for British Columbia, Version 2.0. Forest Practices Branch and Canadian Forest Service, Victoria, BC, 48 p.

British Columbia Ministry of Forests. 2001. West-Central BC mountain pine beetle action plan 2001. Forest Practices Branch, Victoria, BC, 15 p.

British Columbia Ministry of Forests. 2003. Timber supply and the mountain pine beetle infestation in British Columbia. Forest Analysis Branch, Victoria, BC. 27 p.

Canadian Council of Forest Ministers. 2003. Compendium of Canadian forestry statistics. National Forestry Database: http://nfdp.ccfm.org/.

Chojnacky, D.C.; Bentz, B.J.; Logan, J.A. 2000. Mountain pine beetle attack in ponderosa pine: Comparing methods for rating susceptibility. USDA Forest Service, Rocky Mountain Research Station, Fort Collins, CO. RMRS-RP-26. 10 p.

Ciesla, W.M. 2000. Remote sensing in forest health protection. USDA Forest Service, Rocky Mountain Research Station, Fort Collins, CO. FHTET Report No. 00-03. 266 p.

Congalton, R. 1991. A review of assessing the accuracy of classifications of remotely sensed data. Remote Sensing of Environment 37:35–46.

Churcher, J.J.; Carlson, J.A. 1984. A study of methods currently in use in Canada to harvest or salvage or treat lodgepole pine stands affected by the mountain pine beetle. Progressive Forest Management Systems Ltd., Vancouver, BC, 87 p.

Dial, G.; Bowen, H.; Gerlach, F.; Grodecki, J; Oleszczuk, R. 2003. IKONOS satellite, imagery and products. Remote Sensing of Environment 88(1–2):23–36.

Fall, A.; Sachs, D.; Shore, T.; Safranyik, L.; Riel, B. 2002. Application of the MPB/SELES landscape-scale mountain pine beetle model in the Lakes Timber Supply Area Final Report. British Columbia Ministry of Forests, Forest Practices Branch, Victoria, BC, 29 p.

Franklin, J.; Phinn, S.R.; Woodcock, C.E.; Rogan, J. 2003. Rationale and conceptual framework for classification approaches to assess forest resources and properties. Pages 279–300 *in* M.A. Wulder and S.E. Franklin, eds. Remote sensing of forest environments: Concepts and case studies. Kluwer Academic Publishers, Boston, MA.

Franklin, S.E.; Wulder, M.A.; Skakun, R.S.; Carroll, A.L. 2003. Mountain pine beetle red attack damage classification using stratified Landsat TM data in British Columbia, Canada. Photogrammetric Engineering and Remote Sensing 69:283–288.

Franklin, S.E.; Lavigne, M.; Wulder, M.; Stenhouse, G. 2002. Forest change detection and landscape structure mapping in Canada's model forests: The role of satellite remote sensing. Forestry Chronicle 78(5):618–625.

Gillis, M.; Leckie, D. 1996. Forest inventory update in Canada. Forestry Chronicle 72(2):138–156.

Gimbarzevsky, P.; Dawson, A.F.; Van Sickle, G.A. 1992. Assessment of aerial photographs and multi-spectral scanner imagery for measuring mountain pine beetle damage. Forestry Canada, Pacific Forest Research Centre, Victoria, BC, Information Report BC-X-333. 31 p.

Glackin, D.L.; Peltzer, G.R. 1999. Civil, commercial, and international remote sensing systems and geoprocessing. The Aerospace Press, El Segundo, CA.

Goward, S.N.; Davis, P.E.; Fleming, D.; Miller, L.; Townshend, J.R. 2003. Empirical comparison of Landsat 7 and IKONOS multispectral measurements for selected Earth Observation System (EOS) validation sites. Remote Sensing of Environment 88:80–99.

Graham, R.; Koh, A. 2002. Digital aerial survey: Theory and practice. CRC Press LLC, Boca Raton, FL.

Hamilton, D. 1981. Large-scale color aerial photography as a tool in sampling for mortality rates. USDA Forest Service, Intermountain Forest and Range Experiment Station, Missoula, MT. Research Paper INT-269. 8 p.

Harris, J.W.E.; Dawson, A.F. 1979. Evaluation of aerial forest pest damage survey techniques in British Columbia. Environment Canada, Canadian Forest Service, Pacific Forest Research Centre, Victoria, BC, Information Report BC-X-198. 22 p.

Harris, J.W.E.; Dawson, A.F.; Brown, R.G. 1982. Evaluation of mountain pine beetle damage using aerial photography, Flathead River, BC. 1980. Environment Canada, Canadian Forest Service, Pacific Forest Research Centre, Victoria, BC, Information Report, BC-X-228. 10 p.

Harris, J.L.; Frank, M.; Johnson, S. eds. 2001. Forest insect and disease conditions in the Rocky Mountain Region 1997-1999. USDA Forest Service, Rocky Mountain Region, Renewable Resources and Forest Health Management, Lakewood, CO. 39 p.

Heller, R.C.; Coyne, J.F.; Bean, J.L. 1955. Airplanes increase effectiveness of southern pine beetle surveys. Journal of Forestry (July):483–487.

Henigman, J.; Ebata, T.; Allen, E.; Holt, J.; Pollard, A., eds. 1999. Field guide to forest damage in British Columbia. British Columbia Ministry of Forests, Victoria, BC. 348 p.

Hill, J.B.; Popp, H.W.; Grove, A.R. Jr. 1967. Botany: A textbook for colleges. 4th ed. McGraw-Hill Book Co., Toronto, ON.

Johnson, E. 2002. 2001 Aerial detection survey of the Rocky Mountain Region. USDA Forest Service, Rocky Mountain Region, Renewable Resources and Forest Health Management, Lakewood, CO. R2-02-09. 20 p.

Kaplan, E.D., ed. 1996. Understanding GPS: Principles and applications. Artech House Inc., Boston, MA.

Klein, W.H. 1973. Beetle-killed pine estimates. Photogrammetric Engineering 39:385–388.

Kneppeck, I.D.; Ahern, F.J. 1989. A comparison of images from a pushbroom scanner with normal color aerial photographs for detecting scattered recent conifer mortality. Photogrammetric Engineering and Remote Sensing 55:333–337.

Lefsky, M.A.; Cohen, W.B. 2003. Selection of remotely sensed data. Pages 13–46 in M.A. Wulder and S.E. Franklin, eds. Remote sensing of forest environments: Concepts and case studies. Kluwer Academic Publishers, Boston, MA.

Murtha, P.A. 1972. A guide to air photo interpretation of forest damage in Canada. Canadian Forest Service, Ottawa, ON. Publication No. 1292. 62 p.

Murtha, P.A. 1985. Interpretation of large-scale color-IR photographs for bark beetle incipient attack detection. Pages 209–219 in PECORA 10 Symposium Proceedings, August 20–22, 1985, Fort Collins, CO. American Society for Photogrammetry and Remote Sensing, Falls Church, VA.

Nelson, T.; Wulder, M.; Niemann, K.O. 2001. Spatial resolution implications of digitising aerial photography for environmental applications. Journal of Imaging Science 49:223–232.

Peddle, D.R.; Teillet, P.M.; Wulder, M.A. 2003. Radiometric image processing. Pages 181–208 in M.A. Wulder and S.E. Franklin, eds. Remote sensing of forest environments: Concepts and case studies. Kluwer Academic Publishers, Boston.

Puritch, G.S. 1981. Nonvisual remote sensing of trees affected by stress: A review. Environment Canada, Canadian Forest Service, Pacific Forest Research Centre, Victoria, BC. Forestry Technical Report 30. 38 p.

Roberts, A.; Dragicevic, S.; Northrup, J.; Wolf, S.; Li, Y.; Coburn, C. 2003. Mountain pine beetle detection and monitoring: remote sensing evaluations. (Forestry Innovation Investment) Operational Report with Reference to Recipient Agreement R2003-0205, April 10, 2003. 45 p.

Rock, B.N.; Hoshizaki, T.; Miller, J.R. 1988. Comparison of in situ and airborne spectral measurements of blue shift associated with forest decline. Remote Sensing of Environment 24:109–127.

Safranyik, L.; Shrimpton, D.; Whitney, H.S. 1974. Management of lodgepole pine to reduce losses from the mountain pine beetle. Canadian Forest Service, Pacific Forest Research Centre, Victoria, BC. Forestry Technical Report 1. 24 p.

Safranyik, L.; Linton, D.A. 2002. Line transect sampling to estimate the density of lodgepole pine currently attacked by mountain pine beetle. Natural Resources Canada, Canadian Forest Service, Pacific Forestry Centre, Victoria, BC. Information Report BC-X-392. 10 p.

Schraeder-Patton, C. 2003. Digital aerial sketchmapping: Interim project report. USDA Forest Service, Remote Sensing Applications Centre, Fort Collins, CO. Report No. RSAC-1202-RPT2. 14 p.

Sharpnack, N.; Wong, J. 1982. Sampling designs and allocations yielding minimum cost estimators for mountain pine beetle loss assessment surveys. USDA Forest Service, Forest Pest Management, Fort Collins, CO. Report Number 83-3. 11 p.

Shore, T. 1985. Forest Insect and Disease Survey, Pacific Region: General Instruction Manual. Canadian Forest Service, Pacific Forest Research Centre, Victoria, BC, 125 p.

Shore, T.; Safranyik, L. 1992. Susceptibility and risk rating systems for the mountain pine beetle in lodgepole pine stands. Canadian Forest Service, Pacific Forest Research Centre, Victoria, BC, Information Report BC-X-336. 12 p.

Skakun, R.S.; Wulder, M.A.; Franklin, S.E. 2003. Sensitivity of the Thematic Mapper Enhanced Wetness Difference Index (EWDI) to detect mountain pine needle red attack damage. Remote Sensing of Environment 86:433–443.

Tao, C.V.; Hu, Y.; Jiang, W. 2004. Photogrammetric exploitation of IKONOS imagery for mapping applications. International Journal of Remote Sensing 25(14):2833–2853.

USDA Forest Service. 2003. America's forests: 2003 health update. USDA, Washington, DC. Agriculture Information Bulletin 776. 19 p. http://www.fs.fed.us/publications/documents/forest-health-update2003.pdf

Waters, W.E.; Heller, R.C.; Bean, J. L. 1958. Aerial appraisal of damage by the spruce budworm. Journal of Forestry (April):269–276.

Wear, J.; Pope, R.; Orr, P. 1966. Aerial photographic techniques for estimating damage by insects in western forests. USDA Forest Service, Pacific Northwest Research Station, Portland, OR. 79 p.

Westfall, J. 2003. 2002 Summary of forest health conditions in British Columbia. British Columbia Ministry of Forests, Forest Practices Branch, Victoria, BC, 29 p.

White, J.C.; Wulder, M.A.; Brooks, D.; Reich, R.; Wheate, R.D. 2004. Mapping the impacts of mountain pine beetle infestation with high spatial resolution satellite imagery. Forestry Chronicle 80:743–745.

Wiart, R.J. 2003. Detecting and mapping mountain pine beetle infestations: Defining the role of remote sensing and establishing research priorities. Workshop Summary Report, June 26-27, 2003, Vancouver, British Columbia, 27 p.

Wood, C.; Unger, L. 1996. Mountain pine beetle: A history of outbreaks in pine forests in British Columbia, 1910 to 1995. Natural Resources Canada, Canadian Forest Service, Pacific Forest Research Centre, Victoria, BC. 61 p.

Wulder, M.A.; Dymond, C.C. 2004. Remote sensing technologies for mountain pine beetle surveys. Pages 146–153 *in* T.L. Shore, J.E. Brooks and J.E. Stone, eds. Proceedings of the mountain pine beetle symposium: Challenges and solutions, Oct. 30–31, 2003, Kelowna, BC. Natural Resources Canada, Canadian Forest Service, Pacific Forest Research Centre, Victoria, BC. Information Report BC-X-399. 298 p.

Wulder, M.A.; Franklin, S.E. 2001. Polygon decomposition with remotely sensed data: Rationale, methods, and applications. Geomatica 55:11–21.

Wulder, M.A.; Skakun, R.S.; Dymond, C.C.; Kurz, W.A. 2005a. Characterization of the diminishing accuracy in detecting forest insect damage over time. Canadian Journal of Remote Sensing 31:421-431.

Wulder, M.A.; Skakun, R.S.; Franklin, S.E; White, J.C. 2005b. Enhancing forest inventories with mountain pine beetle infestation information. Forestry Chronicle 81(1):149–159.

Chapter 6

Direct Control: Theory and Practice

Allan L. Carroll, Terry L. Shore, and Les Safranyik

Natural Resources Canada, Canadian Forest Service, Pacific Forestry Centre,
506 West Burnside Road, Victoria, British Columbia, V8Z 1M5

Abstract

Direct control programs intended to minimize the impacts of epidemic mountain pine beetle (*Dendroctonus ponderosae* Hopk. [Coleoptera: Scolytidae]) populations began 100 years ago. Since then, many tactics have been developed that are capable of introducing significant mortality into a beetle population. These tactics include cultural and mechanical treatments, chemical insecticides and semiochemical manipulation of populations. This chapter reviews the suite of operational tactics that have been, and are currently, used to control mountain pine beetle populations. Based upon simple population processes, a framework for successful control is also presented. This framework is considered within the larger context of control programs over large landscapes where multiple objectives may be desired. Finally, previous attempts at mitigating mountain pine beetle impacts are assessed in relation to the direct control framework. A successful direct control program requires prompt and thorough application of the most appropriate treatments at a magnitude dictated by the population size and rate of increase.

Résumé

Les programmes de lutte directe destinés à atténuer les effets des épidémies de dendroctones du pin ponderosa (*Dendroctonus ponderosae* Hopk. [Coleoptera: Scolytidae]) ont débuté il y a cent ans. Depuis, on a mis au point de nombreuses tactiques permettant de décimer les populations de ce ravageur. Ces moyens comprennent des traitements mécaniques et culturaux, l'application d'insecticides chimiques et la manipulation des populations à l'aide de substances sémiochimiques. Le présent chapitre examine la série de tactiques opérationnelles qui ont été utilisées et celles auxquelles on a recours à l'heure actuelle pour lutter contre le dendroctone du pin ponderosa. On y présente également un cadre de lutte efficace fondé sur des processus démographiques simples. Puis ce cadre est pris en considération dans le contexte plus vaste des programmes de lutte à l'échelle des grands paysages pouvant comporter plusieurs objectifs. Enfin, on y évalue les interventions passées destinées à réduire l'impact du ravageur en relation avec le cadre de lutte directe. Le succès d'un programme de lutte directe repose sur l'application rapide et rigoureuse des traitements les plus appropriés dans une proportion qui dépend de la taille et de la rapidité de croissance de la population de ravageurs.

Introduction

Mountain pine beetle (*Dendroctonus ponderosae* Hopk. [Coleoptera: Scolytidae]) outbreaks are periodic landscape-level disturbance events that occur in pine forests of western North America. Typically, they last from 3 to 20 years and invariably result in the destruction of large-diameter trees within affected stands (Safranyik et al. 1974). The potential for outbreaks to negatively affect timber supplies was recognized nearly 100 years ago (Mason 1915). As a consequence, during the past century many large-scale and costly programs aimed at mitigating the impacts of mountain pine beetle epidemics were undertaken in the USA and Canada (reviewed by Klein 1978).

A mountain pine beetle outbreak requires both a supply of susceptible host trees and a large population of beetles. Therefore, mitigating the impacts of an epidemic may be achieved theoretically through treatments aimed at limiting the amount of susceptible trees or reducing the number of beetles. The former is termed "indirect control" or "preventive management", whereas the latter is considered "direct control", the central topic of this chapter.

Between outbreaks, mountain pine beetle populations normally exist at very low endemic levels, constrained by biotic and abiotic mortality factors. Relaxation of the effects of these mortality factors allows populations to erupt into epidemics. The objective of a direct control program is to limit beetle epidemics to levels that do not cause economically important damage (McMullen et al. 1986). Biologically, this means that successful direct control tactics are those that can introduce sufficient mortality into an increasing population to limit its rate of increase, or ideally, return it to the endemic phase.

The first documented direct control program against the mountain pine beetle occurred between 1902 and 1903 in South Dakota, USA (Hopkins 1905). Since then, some level of control has been attempted against most significant infestations throughout the beetle's range. During the last several decades, exploitation of lodgepole pine (*Pinus contorta* var. *latifolia* Engelm.) for forest products has increased tremendously (e.g., Taylor and Carroll 2004), and the necessity for more effective mountain pine beetle control programs in that forest type has increased accordingly.

The objectives of this chapter are as follows. First, a brief review of the direct control tactics that have been, and continue to be, employed against the mountain pine beetle in lodgepole pine forests will be presented. This review will mainly focus on tactics that have been used operationally; however, where necessary for a complete overview, some tactics still within the realm of research will be considered. Second, a theoretical framework for suppression of the mountain pine beetle using direct control tactics, derived from simple population processes, will be presented. Third, the framework will be considered within the larger context of control programs over large landscapes where multiple objectives may be desired. Finally, the theoretical framework will be used to critically assess previous efforts at direct control (insofar as the literature will permit).

Direct control past and present

The tactics associated with operational direct control programs can be grouped into three broad categories based upon their mode of action: cultural and mechanical treatments that entail killing beetles by destroying the bark of infested trees; chemical tactics that are based upon the application of insecticides either directly or as systemics; and semiochemicals involving the use of signal-bearing volatile compounds to manipulate beetle populations, most often in concert with other direct control efforts. To date, there are no biological control alternatives for the treatment of mountain pine beetle infestations (see Safranyik et al. 2002). Depending upon the logistics of their application, tactics may be applied to individual infested trees, or more broadly to whole stands or groups of stands.

Cultural and mechanical tactics

There are a variety of techniques available for the cultural and mechanical treatment of mountain pine beetle infested lodgepole pine trees; some more effective than others. Due to the time and effort associated with felling trees, many tactics have been developed for application to standing infested trees, whereas others were designed to be applied after trees have been felled.

Fire has been a common tool in the direct control of mountain pine beetle infestations, although its efficacy in many circumstances can be unsatisfactory. Early attempts to burn standing infested trees resulted in fires that were seldom hot enough to kill a significant proportion of the brood, even if the trees were sprayed first with fuel oil (Evenden 1927, 1929). Later, pressurized flame throwers were employed (Klein 1978; McMullen et al. 1986). Even though higher burn intensities and greater brood mortality were possible, this technique was limited by high fire hazard conditions and difficult access in dense stands and steep terrain (McMullen et al. 1986).

Fire has also been applied as prescribed or broadcast burns to control larger mountain pine beetle infestations. In these treatments, controlled fires are ignited in an infested stand or group of stands. Although a potentially valuable tactic in remote locations or areas where other treatment options are not permitted or feasible, appreciable mortality can only be attained with very high fire intensity (Stock and Gorley 1989; Safranyik et al. 2001). Given the difficulty of controlling high-intensity fires (e.g., Hirsch et al. 1998), prescribed fire to suppress beetle populations is unsuitable in most situations.

Perhaps the most effective means of ensuring significant mortality of broods is to remove the bark of infested trees before beetles complete their development. The first efforts at debarking standing trees involved the use of long-handled spuds to peel bark from the lower 3-4 m of the bole (Evenden 1927). Later, in an effort to establish a less labour-intensive treatment, several attempts were made to debark trees using explosive detonating cord wrapped around the stem (Adams 1926; Whitney et al. 1978). Notwithstanding the obvious risks associated with handling explosives, it was found that unless all of the bark was blown off the main stem, many beetles survived intact beneath the bark. More recently, a self-climbing mechanical tree pruning device known as a "tree monkey" was modified to peel the bark from standing infested trees (Whitney et al. 1978). Unfortunately, the variable morphology among the stems of trees rendered the device too unreliable.

In spite of the convenience of treating standing trees, felling infested trees prior to treatment remains the most dependable technique to ensure significant brood mortality. Under natural conditions during hot, dry weather, beetle broods may suffer extensive mortality due to drying. Patterson (1930) attempted to exploit this phenomenon by felling trees, removing their limbs and exposing them to direct sunlight. However, he found that bark temperatures above 43°C were required for several hours, and that the logs had to be rolled daily for several days to achieve significant mortality. Consequently, the tactic was considered too labour intensive and suitable only for the hottest periods of the summer in very warm regions.

Regardless of the many and varied attempts at developing alternative effective control techniques, felling and destroying or harvesting and processing trees remains the most common tactic for the control of mountain pine beetle populations (Klein 1978). This tactic can take the form of single tree treatments, which are used to deal with small isolated groups of infested trees, or stand level applications which are used for larger scale infestations.

The treatment of single trees can take one of several forms. Where it is economically feasible, individual infested trees may be harvested and transported to mills where beetle broods will be killed during processing. If individual or small groups of infested trees are uneconomic to harvest and process, they may be felled, cut into manageable pieces, piled up over the stump and burned. As outlined above, however, achieving a thorough, high-intensity burn is essential to kill the beetles due to the insulating properties of bark. Often, fuel oil is used to increase the intensity of the fire, particularly when the bark is moist (McMullen et al. 1986). When it is impractical to remove or burn infested trees, they may be debarked after felling. However, this treatment is much more laborious than the preceding alternatives, and therefore, less desirable.

Where infestations encompass whole stands or groups of stands, block harvesting may be used to control populations in a tactic known as "sanitation logging". This is the most commonly utilized tactic for dealing with larger groups of infested trees. It can be effective in reducing beetle populations, but is limited by the availability of road access to stand(s), land tenure considerations, non-timber forest values (e.g., riparian/wildlife habitats) and timber markets (McMullen et al. 1986). In spite of these limitations, sanitation logging is more cost-effective than individual tree treatments and is often the only method suitable for treating large infestations (McMullen et al. 1986).

Sanitation logging in itself will not kill a significant proportion of mountain pine beetles. Since beetle broods can complete their development in trees that have been felled and decked in a mill yard, infested logs must be milled before new adults emerge and disperse. The restricted window during which harvesting and processing (thereby debarking) can be effective against developing beetles may, in some circumstances, limit the value of this direct control tactic. However, treatments have been developed that are capable of removing this constraint. McMullen and Betts (1982) found that by sprinkling log decks with water, the survival of beetle broods was reduced to 5% compared to 93% in controls. Similarly, Safranyik and Linton (1982) found that submersion of infested logs in water for 6 weeks will cause 100% mortality of developing bark beetles.

Chemical tactics

Given that the mountain pine beetle spends all but a very brief part of its life cycle beneath the bark of its host trees, it is not amenable to the application of broadcast insecticides in the way that many other forest insect pests, such as defoliators, have been. Nonetheless, pesticides became popular for the direct control of beetle populations during the middle of the last century, and considerable research efforts were devoted to identifying the most effective chemical, carrier and application method (reviewed by Klein 1978). Based upon their method of application, two broad categories of insecticides have been developed; chemicals designed to be applied to the bark over the bole of the tree, and those injected into trees as systemics.

Insecticides applied to the bole have been used both to kill mountain pine beetle broods within infested trees by penetrating the bark, and to prevent attacks of susceptible trees by killing the beetles as they attack. The earliest penetrating chemical formulation comprised naphthalene in an oil carrier (Salman 1938; Gibson 1943). Although this mixture proved to be effective at killing beetle broods, it was difficult to use due to the relative insolubility of the naphthalene (Gibson 1943). Orthodichlorobenzene (Gibson 1941, 1943), or ethylene dibromide (Massey et al. 1953; Kinghorn 1955), in diesel oil were also found to be effective penetrating insecticide formulations, and the former became one of the most common direct control tactics applied during the 1940s and 1950s in the USA (Klein 1978). Since oil solutions are expensive, unpleasant to use, and associated with skin irritation, research was conducted to develop water-based formulations of bark penetrants. Ethylene dibromide in water was found to be very effective in killing mountain pine beetle broods (Stevens 1957, 1959), and therefore, became the standard chemical tactic for controlling infestations during the 1960s and 1970s (Klein 1978).

Interest in protecting trees from attack, rather than treating them after infestation, stimulated the development of preventive insecticides. Formulations of lindane or carbaryl in fuel oil were found to give excellent levels of protection from mountain pine beetle attacks (Smith 1970; Gibson 1977; Smith et al. 1977). However, the oil-based carriers were often found to kill the very trees they were intended to protect (Rogers 1976). Lindane or carbaryl formulated with water as a carrier also worked well at preventing attacks under a variety of conditions (Gibson 1977; Smith et al. 1977) and were both widely used in the USA and Canada.

Due to their ease of application, preventive or penetrating insecticides sprayed on the bole of trees were favoured by forest managers. However, the subcortical habits of the mountain pine beetle suggest that systemic insecticides should be more effective at killing brood beetles. Nevertheless, the number of systemic pesticides used as operational direct control tactics against the mountain pine beetle has been relatively small. Copper sulfate applied to a shallow axe frill cut into the sapwood of newly infested trees was found to be effective (Bedard 1938). Much later, monosodium methanearsonate (MSMA), also applied to an axe frill, was determined to be successful in killing beetle broods (Maclauchlan et al. 1988). MSMA is an arsenical herbicide with insecticidal properties that has been widely used to control a variety of bark beetle species (e.g., O'Callaghan and Fairhurst 1983; Holsten 1985).

Systemic formulations have advantages over other insecticides in that impacts to non-target species can be minimized. Unfortunately, the attack dynamics of the mountain pine beetle renders successful application of systemics somewhat problematic. Tunneling by the beetles and their offspring in the phloem tissue beneath the bark, combined with the colonization of the sapwood by the blue stain fungi that beetles introduce, severely impairs the ability of trees to translocate. Therefore, application of systemic insecticides too long after beetles colonize trees will be largely ineffectual since the formulation will not move up the stem and come into contact with the beetles. Indeed, for this reason it is recommended that systemics such as MSMA are applied within three weeks of initial attacks (McMullen et al. 1986; Maclauchlan et al. 1988).

In spite of the efficacy of chemical tactics for direct control, their toxicity to the environment and workers has led to the discontinuation of their use in virtually all operational direct control programs (although in some jurisdictions, several insecticides may be available for use on private lands). Currently, MSMA is the only registered pesticide that is widely used against the mountain pine beetle in Canada, and its continued use is in jeopardy due to limitations of supply and environmental challenges.

Semiochemical tactics

Semiochemicals are signal-bearing chemicals involved in interactions among organisms. There are several different types depending upon the "message" contained in the semiochemical and/or the behaviour it evokes in the recipient (e.g., Nordlund 1981). For example, pheromones are substances emitted by an organism that cause a specific reaction in a receiving organism of the same species, whereas kairomones are substances that evoke in the receiver a reaction that favours the receiver but not the emitter. The mountain pine beetle employs a complex suite of pheromones and kairomones to mediate its attack behaviour (e.g., Borden et al. 1987).

As the semiochemical system employed by the mountain pine beetle has been elucidated, two broad strategies have emerged to exploit it in direct control programs. The first is based upon the beetle's aggregation behaviour during mass attacks, the second is derived from its use of antiaggregation pheromones to terminate mass attacks and minimize intraspecific competition (Borden 1989). The primary semiochemical constituents of the aggregation response of mountain pine beetles in lodgepole pine forests are the pheromones *trans*-verbenol and *exo*-brevicomin, and the host-tree produced kairomone myrcene (Conn et al. 1983; Borden et al. 1983a, 1987). The antiaggregation response is largely a function of the pheromone verbenone (Ryker and Yandell 1983; Borden et al. 1987). These compounds have been developed into commercial devices intended to either focus or concentrate (i.e., aggregate) beetle populations in stands, or deter or redirect (i.e., antiaggregate) them from stands (Borden 1995).

Since the application of semiochemicals does not directly cause the mortality of beetles, they are normally used in conjunction with the cultural/mechanical or chemical tactics described above. For example, in treating isolated small infestations where falling and burning/ peeling is impractical, infested trees may be treated with an insecticide [e.g., sprayed with carbaryl or injected with MSMA (Borden and Lindgren 1989; Borden 1995)] to kill brood beetles. Trees around the infestation would then be baited with the synthetic aggregation semiochemicals to induce any beetles that survived the initial treatment to attack nearby trees (i.e., not disperse), after which those trees would be treated with insecticides.

Aggregation semiochemicals are often used in conjunction with sanitation logging of larger infestations in a treatment known as "post-logging mop-up" (Borden et al. 1983b). Since it is difficult to remove every infested stem in a sanitation logging treatment when infestations become reasonably large, aggregation semiochemicals are often applied to residual susceptible trees in the vicinity to ensure that remaining beetles do not disperse and can be easily located for follow-up treatments. This tactic can be quite successful when applied over several years, and is common in western Canada (Borden 1995).

The mountain pine beetle's aggregation response has also been exploited to extend the utility of direct control efforts during widespread increases of infestations over the landscape. During these periods, the number of infestations often exceeds the capacity of forest managers to treat them before the beetles emerge and disperse, causing existing infestations to grow and new ones to establish, frequently at significant distances from the original infestation. In a tactic known as "containment and concentration", infested stands are inundated with synthetic aggregation semiochemicals, allowing infestations to intensify without expanding, thereby facilitating sanitation logging during the subsequent season (Borden et al. 1983c). This has proven to be an effective means of slowing the spread of mountain pine beetle infestations (Gray and Borden 1989), and has been employed operationally in western Canada since the early 1980s (Borden and Lacey 1985).

Exploitation of the antiaggregation pheromones of the mountain pine beetle still lies in the realm of research. However, several trials (e.g., Amman et al. 1989; Lindgren et al. 1989) have shown that when verbenone release devices are placed in an infested stand, the number of attacked trees can be reduced relative to control stands. Borden (1995) has proposed that the most operationally feasible use of antiaggregation pheromones would be to deploy them in one stand while using aggregation pheromones in another to push beetles from high-value areas and draw them into adjacent trees slated for treatment.

A Population-based Framework for Successful Control

Knowledge of the basic population processes associated with the mountain pine beetle is essential to effective control efforts. In populations where conditions have changed such that reproduction outweighs mortality, unless a sufficient amount of additional mortality is introduced, the infestation will expand. From the above review of direct control tactics, it is clear that an array of alternatives is available for the treatment of mountain pine beetle infestations. The relative success of these tactics, however, is dependent upon the state of the beetle population.

Since, on average, female mountain pine beetles produce 60 eggs and two-thirds of offspring (i.e., 40) are female (Reid 1962), then given that only one female offspring needs to survive to achieve replacement, approximately 97.5% generation mortality (i.e., 39/40) is required to keep populations static. Interestingly, only a small rise in survival is required for populations to increase dramatically. For example, if generation mortality declines from 97.5% to 95.0%, then populations have the potential to double in size.

Initially, mountain pine beetle populations appear to grow relatively slowly. As an illustration, consider a stand with one infested tree and a population where the generation mortality has declined slightly to allow it to double each year (i.e., a rate of increase, $R = 2$). After 10 years, only 512 trees would be killed (Fig. 1). This represents less than 2% of the trees within a 20 ha stand, and therefore the population may escape detection or concern for a number of years (e.g., Shore and Safranyik 2004). If the infestation was detected and, in an effort to control it, 37.5% of the infested trees were treated during the fourth year, 194 fewer trees would be killed by year 10, but the population would continue to expand (Fig. 1). From this example, the question arises: What level of mortality must be added and how often, to slow or stop an increasing population?

The general concept is straightforward. Assuming that the number of infested trees is a good index of beetle population size (a reasonable assumption for increasing populations [e.g., Safranyik 1988]), then, to maintain a static population, a proportion of infested trees (P) must be treated in each year equivalent to:

$$P = 1-1/R \qquad\qquad [1]$$

where R is the yearly rate of increase in the population. In other words, if the population is expected to triple yearly ($R = 3$), then two-thirds of all infested trees would have to be treated before the flight period each year. Obviously, if population reduction is the goal, then treatment rates must exceed two-thirds. The concept is presented graphically in Figure 2. For any measured rate of increase, unless sufficient mortality is introduced into a population that equals or exceeds the yearly growth in a population, it will continue to increase.

With the above framework in mind, control efforts must be considered in light of the size of the beetle population. When populations are very small (i.e., endemic), their rates of increase are usually constrained to unity. This is the point at which management efforts can have their greatest impact. Beetles are usually restricted to a few weakened or damaged trees within a stand, so relative to the potential rate of increase and the number of trees involved, removal of any of the infested stems would suppress the population, and perhaps even cause local extinction (Fig. 2). Thus, provided they can be detected, endemic populations are highly amenable to direct control.

Larger incipient-epidemic, or "spot" infestations, by virtue of their size and more obvious impacts, are much easier to detect. Because they have gained access, through mass attack, to healthy, large-diameter trees, their rates of increase are often between two- and fourfold yearly. Typically, when these populations are first detected, the number of trees involved is still relatively small (<500), and the area they occupy is well defined and often much less than a whole stand. To limit the potential for increase if $R = 4$, then $\geq$75% of the infested trees must be treated every year (Fig. 2). If 500 trees were found, then at least 375 stems must be treated that season, and a similar proportion in subsequent seasons provided R remains constant. If there is ready access to the infestation, it is highly amenable to many of the available direct control tactics.

An incipient-epidemic population may take only 2 to 3 years to develop into a full outbreak if left untreated and rates of increase remain high. During an outbreak, the number of trees killed annually is often in the millions and may encompass hundreds of thousands of hectares. The rate of increase may not be more than that of an incipient population, but its size renders most management tactics useless. As an example, if an outbreak is spread across 300 000 ha and $R = 2$ (a conservative rate during peak outbreak years), then 150 000 ha of infested trees must be harvested in each year just to keep the infestation static. Logistically, detection and removal of such a vast number of infested trees is impossible.

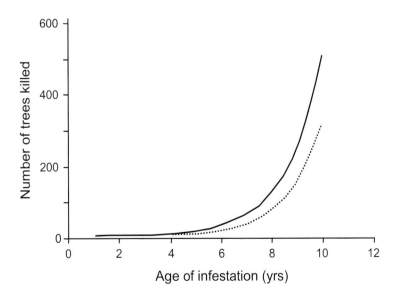

Figure 1. Number of trees killed by mountain pine beetle versus age of infestation for a population doubling in size yearly [i.e., the yearly rate of increase R = 2 (solid line)]. The broken line represents the same population with the removal of 37.5% of the population (i.e., 3 of 8 infested trees) during year 4.

Interestingly, even if a proportion of a mountain pine beetle infestation in excess of the threshold derived by equation 1 (Fig. 2) can be treated with direct control tactics, it may not be sufficient in an operational context to suppress a population if its initial size and/or rate of increase is large. During a direct control program, the number of trees infested (N) in any given year will be a function of the number of trees initially infested (N_o), the yearly rate of increase (R), the proportion of trees treated each year (P) and the number of years (t), such that:

$$N = N_o[R(1-P)]^t \qquad\qquad [2]$$

If the objective of the control effort is suppression (i.e., where $N = 1$), then the number of years (t) of continuous direct control can be determined given knowledge of R and P, provided $P > 1-1/R$ (see Fig. 2). This concept is illustrated in Figure 3. If direct control tactics were employed against a mountain pine beetle infestation involving 10,000 infested trees, doubling yearly, such that 80% of infested trees were treated each year, then it would take 10 years to reduce the infestation to a single infested tree (Fig. 3a). If that population was tripling or quadrupling yearly, then it would take 18 or 41 years, respectively, of continuous 80% treatment to suppress it. Obviously, if a greater proportion of trees could be detected and treated, then suppression would be possible in a shorter time. For example, if it was possible to detect and treat 90% of infested trees each year, then it would require either 6, 8 or 10 years of continuous effort to suppress a population initially infesting 10,000 trees and increasing at a rate of two, three or four times yearly, respectively (Fig. 3a). If an infestation was allowed to increase by an order of magnitude to 100,000 infested trees

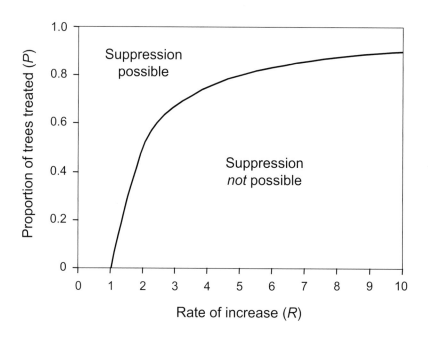

Figure 2. Graphical representation of the proportion of a mountain pine beetle population (P) that must be removed in relation to the yearly rate of increase (R) to suppress population growth ($P = 1-1/R$). The area below the curve represents treatment levels where suppression is not possible, treatment levels above the curve (applied yearly) will suppress populations. See text for details.

without intervention, then the time to suppression increases, even if the same proportion of trees are detected and treated. In the case of 80% treatment, where $R = 2$, 3 or 4, continuous control efforts would be required for 13, 23 or 52 years to achieve suppression (Fig. 3b). If 90% detection and treatment were possible in this circumstance, then 7, 10 or 13 years would be needed.

In each of the theoretical scenarios just described, the proportion of trees treated was within the "suppression possible" zone indicated in Figure 2. However, suppression would be operationally intractable in virtually all of the scenarios due either to the number of years of continuous treatment necessitated, or the level of detection and treatment required. In most cases, a consistent direct control program lasting 10 years against a single infestation would be difficult to maintain, let alone one requiring 40 to 50 years (assuming there is sufficient mature pine to sustain an infestation for that duration). Moreover, whereas the detection and treatment of 80% of infested trees may, in some cases, be possible, given the challenges associated with detecting mountain pine beetle infestations, identification and treatment of a greater proportion of a population in a single season is unlikely.

From the preceding discussion, there emerges three points that cannot be overemphasized if direct control is to be effective in the management of mountain pine beetle populations. First, growing infestations must be detected as early as possible. Second, aggressive direct control tactics must be applied promptly and thoroughly. Third, control programs must be continuous until the desired population level is achieved. If small incipient-epidemic populations are allowed to grow, either through lack of detection or as a consequence of intermittent control interventions, the probability of successful suppression will decline dramatically, often within only a few years.

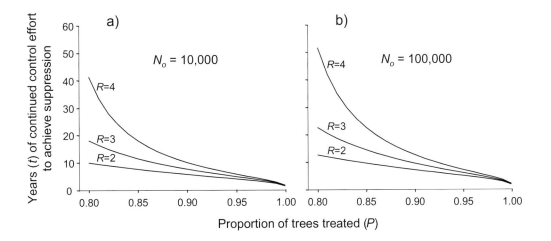

Figure 3. Graphical representation of the number of years (t) of continued control effort to achieve suppression (number of infested trees, $N = 1$) given a proportion of trees (P) treated yearly and a yearly rate of increase (R) based upon (a) 10,000 or (b) 100,000 trees infested initially (N_o). $N = N_o[R(1-P)]^t$ where $P > 1-1/R$.

Direct control over landscapes

The preceding discussion of direct control has centred upon the application of tactics for the suppression of individual infestations. However, when mountain pine beetle populations increase to epidemics, they often do so synchronously over very large areas (Taylor and Carroll 2004). Widespread, synchronous increases in population levels may exceed the capacity of forest managers to implement suppression activities over a large area. Furthermore, the strategy of suppression may not meet the objectives of all jurisdictions associated with forest management, such as parks and protected areas where natural disturbance events are important components of forest ecosystems. Therefore, alternative strategies for the application of direct control tactics may be required for the management of mountain pine beetle impacts across large and varied landscapes.

Perhaps the most comprehensive example of the application of alternative strategies for the direct control of mountain pine beetle populations over large areas is found in British Columbia, Canada, where two outbreak events during the previous three decades, involving millions of hectares of forests, have challenged the sustainability of forestry in lodgepole pine-dominated landscapes. A series of strategies, based upon the application of relevant direct control tactics, were developed to encompass a complex mix of land uses, tenures, ecosystems and economic circumstances (Hall 2004). The four main strategies are: (i) suppression/prevention, where aggressive direct control tactics are applied to reduce populations to endemic levels within a few years; (ii) holding, where control efforts are aimed at maintaining population levels at no more than current levels, often until more resources become available or until the underlying cause of the infestation subsides; (iii) salvage, where aggressive options are deemed unlikely to succeed and, therefore, efforts are diverted to recovering dead timber while it still retains value; and (iv) monitor, where the preceding strategies are inappropriate, such as in inaccessible or inoperable regions, parks and protected areas (Hall 2004). Obviously, the strategies of "suppression/prevention" and "holding" require the application of some or all of the direct control tactics previously described. Provided these strategies are implemented within the population-based framework for successful control, the probability of realizing their objectives remains high.

Evaluation of a selected strategy for a portion of a larger landscape (e.g., management unit) must consider the resource objectives, the number of infested trees, the risk to surrounding resources, the financial and physical resources available to apply to the strategy, and the potential for success. Each year these factors need to be re-evaluated to determine if a shift in strategy is required. Decision support tools (Shore and Safranyik 1992) are available to facilitate the process of strategy selection and application.

Trials and errors: lessons from the past

Lodgepole pine forests occur over approximately 160 million ha of western North America. The mountain pine beetle is a ubiquitous component of mature stands over much of this area. Despite the vastness of the region in which mountain pine beetle populations exist, epidemics normally initiate and spread from well defined epicenters (Aukema et al., 2006). Therefore, direct control tactics aimed at controlling developing epicenters in the incipient-epidemic phase are theoretically amenable to a suppression strategy.

Despite many significant efforts at direct control of mountain pine beetle populations during the previous century, suppression was seldom, if ever, achieved and, at best, the rate of tree mortality was reduced only marginally (Craighead et al.1931; Amman and Baker 1972; Klein 1978; Amman and Logan 1998). A brief examination of historical control activities in light of the framework proposed above reveals three major shortcomings. First, most efforts targeted treatment of infested trees as either a fixed percentage of the total or of the area involved (e.g., Klein 1978, and references therein). Without assessments of the yearly rate of population increase, the treatment levels were most often insufficient. Second, even when a sufficient proportion of a population was removed in one year, the efforts frequently did not persist in subsequent years (e.g., Craighead et al. 1931). Since building populations often have very high rates of increase, and conditions amenable for increase typically persist for more than a single year, a single aggressive intervention may slow the development of an epidemic, but not prevent it (see Fig. 1). Finally, early control programs suffered from the inability to accurately detect and delimit increasing populations. As a consequence, they were often abandoned when populations erupted in adjacent unsurveyed jurisdictions (e.g., Evenden 1944). In recent years, detailed systematic aerial survey techniques have been applied, and remote sensing techniques are being developed to provide accurate, real-time quantification of the abundance, distribution and rates of increase of the mountain pine beetle over the landscape.

Interestingly, there is one documented example of successful suppression of a mountain pine beetle population. During the early 1940s, an incipient epidemic was detected near Banff, Alberta, Canada. Every tree in the vicinity of the infestation was checked over two years, and any tree with evidence of mountain pine beetle attack was felled and burned. During the third year, no beetles could be found (Hopping and Mathers 1945; Hopping 1946). Although rates of increase were not considered, it is not surprising that such an aggressive and consistent intervention was successful.

More general issues may also be at the root of failures to manage mountain pine beetle populations using direct control tactics. For example, where drought has caused the reduction of host resistance over relatively large areas, the increase in beetle populations may be more widespread than initially recognized. Combined with the difficulties of early detection of scattered infested trees, the sudden eruption of infestations over the landscape can quickly outstrip the resources available for treatment. Moreover, improperly applied treatments such as low-intensity fires that were not hot enough to kill the developing brood under the bark, incomplete peeling of the bark, or poorly timed application of systemic insecticides, can mislead the forest manager into thinking an area has been successfully treated when it has not. Therefore, the meagre historical record of direct control in reducing beetle epidemics may be more a result of poor execution than poor theory.

Conclusions

There exists a large suite of tactics for direct control of mountain pine beetle populations. Many of the tactics are highly complementary and can be applied in an integrated management program. However, it cannot be overemphasized that for direct control to work, there must be prompt and thorough application of the most appropriate treatments at a magnitude dictated by the population size and rate of increase. Furthermore, direct control tactics must include a persistent follow-up; possibly the most important, yet most neglected aspect of mountain pine beetle management (Whitney et al. 1978).

Efforts to mitigate the impacts of mountain pine beetle outbreaks have been ongoing for nearly 100 years. During that time, options for direct control have come and gone, but the potential efficacy of the current toolbox is unparalleled. Interestingly, many of the basic requirements for successful direct control were recognized many years ago. Indeed, some of the recommendations, listed below, of Hopping and Mathers (1945) are particularly noteworthy given the preceding discussion:

- Control work must be started when the first signs of abnormal bark beetle increase become apparent.
- Control work must be continued as long as the underlying causes of the infestation are operative.
- The objective must be to treat every infested tree, over the entire area.
- As long as the character of the stand remains the same, future outbreaks may be expected whenever tree vigour is seriously reduced.
- The only permanent solution to the problem in high-hazard areas is to change the composition of the stands on the landscape.

It is important to realize that any successful direct control program is by its very nature only temporary. Any stand of lodgepole pine within the range of mountain pine beetle that reaches maturity will very likely contain a large proportion of trees that are susceptible to beetle attacks. Therefore, retention of lodgepole pine on the landscape for future harvesting will require future direct control of mountain pine beetle populations.

References

Adams, A.C. 1926. Memorandum for the files: Beaverhead-Bitterroot project-season of 1926. USDA Forest Insect Laboratory. Bureau of Entomology and Plant Quarantine, Couer d'Alene, ID. 4 p.

Amman, G.D.; Baker, B.H. 1972. Mountain pine beetle influence on lodgepole pine stand structure. Journal of Forestry 70:204-209.

Amman, G.D.; Logan, J.A. 1998. Silvicultural control of mountain pine beetle: Prescriptions and the influence of microclimate. American Entomologist (44)3:166-177.

Amman, G.D.; Their, R.W.; McGregor, M.D.; Schmitz, R.F. 1989. Efficacy of verbenone in reducing lodgepole pine infestations by mountain pine beetles in Idaho. Canadian Journal of Forest Research 19:60-64.

Aukema, B.H.; Carroll, A.L.; Zhu, J.; Raffa, K.F.; Sickley, T.; Taylor, S.W. Landscape level population dynamics of mountain pine beetle in British Columbia, Canada: spatiotemporal development, spatial synchrony, and land tenure within the present outbreak. Ecography, in press.

Bedard, W.D. 1938. Control of the mountain pine beetle by means of chemicals. Journal of Forestry 36:35-40.

Borden, J.H. 1989. Semiochemicals and bark beetle populations: exploitation of natural phenomena by pest management strategists. Holarctic Ecology 12:501-510.

Borden, J.H. 1995. Development and use of semiochemicals against bark and timber beetles. Pages 431-449 *in* J.A. Armstrong; W.G.H. Ives, eds. Forest Insect Pests in Canada. Natural Resources Canada, Canadian Forest Service, Science and Sustainable Development Directorate. 732 p.

Borden, J.H.; Lacey, T.E. 1985. Semiochemical-based manipulation of the mountain pine beetle, *Dendroctonus ponderosae* Hopkins: a component of lodgepole pine silviculture in the Merritt Timber Supply Area of British Columbia. Zeitschrift Fur Angewandte Entomologie 99:139-145.

Borden, J.H.; Lindgren, B.S. 1989. The role of semiochemicals in IPM of the mountain pine beetle. Pages 247-255 *in* T.L. Payne and H. Saarenmaa, eds. Integrated Control of Scolytid Bark Beetles. Virginia Polytechnic Institute and State University, Blacksburg, VA.

Borden, J.H.; Conn, J.E.; Friskie, L.M; Scott, B.E.; Chong, L.J.; Pierce, H.D., Jr.; Oehlschlager, A.C. 1983a. Semiochemicals for the mountain pine beetle, *Dendroctonus ponderosae* (Coleoptera: Scolytidae), in British Columbia: baited tree studies. Canadian Journal of Forest Research 13:325-333.

Borden, J.H.; Chong, L.J.; Fuchs, M.C. 1983b. Application of semiochemicals in post-logging manipulation of the mountain pine beetle, *Dendroctonus ponderosae* (Coleoptera: Scolytidae). Journal of Economic Entomology 76:1428-1432.

Borden, J.H.; Chong, L.J.; Pratt, K.E.G.; Gray, D.R. 1983c. The application of behaviour-modifying chemicals to contain infestations of the mountain pine beetle, *Dendroctonus ponderosae*. Forestry Chronicle 59:235-239.

Borden, J.H.; Ryker, L.C. Chong, L.J.; Pierce, H.D., Jr.; Johnston, B.D.; Oeschlager, A.C. 1987. Response of the mountain pine beetle, *Dendroctonus ponderosae* Hopkins (Coleoptera: Scolytidae), to five semiochemicals in British Columbia lodgepole pine forests. Canadian Journal of Forest Research 17:118-128.

Craighead, F.C.; Miller, J.M.; Evenden, J.A.; Keen, F.P. 1931. Control work against bark beetles in western forests and an appraisal of results. Journal of Forestry 29:1001-1018.

Conn, J.E.; Borden, J.H.; Scott, B.E.; Friske, L.M.; Pierce, H.D.; Oehlschlager, A.C. 1983. Semiochemicals for the mountain pine beetle in British Columbia: field trapping studies. Canadian Journal of Forest Research 13:320-324.

Evenden, J.C. 1927. Big Hole Basin insect control project, Beaverhead National Forest. Progress report for the season of 1927. USDA Forest Insect Laboratory, Bureau of Entomology and Plant Quarantine. Couer d'Alene, ID. 22 p.

Evenden, J.C. 1929. Plan of operation for control of the mountain pine beetle in lodgepole pine by burning standing trees. USDA Forest Insect Laboratory, Bureau of Entomology and Plant Quarantine. Couer d'Alene, ID. 23 p.

Evenden, J.C. 1944. Montana's thirty-year mountain pine beetle infestation. USDA Forest Insect Laboratory, Bureau of Entomology and Plant Quarantine, Coeur d'Alene, ID. 23 p.

Gibson, A.L. 1941. Status of the mountain pine beetle infestation in lodgepole pine on the Grand Teton National Park, 1940. USDA Forest Insect Laboratory, Bureau of Entomology and Plant Quarantine. Couer d'Alene, ID. 4 p.

Gibson, A.L. 1943. Penetrating sprays to control the mountain pine beetle. Journal of Economic Entomology 36:396-398.

Gibson, K.E. 1977. Results of a pilot study to test the efficacy of three insecticides in preventing attacks by the mountain pine beetle in lodgepole pine. USDA Forest Service, Intermountain Region, Ogden, UT. 7 p.

Gray, D.R.; Borden, J.H. 1989. Containment and concentration of mountain pine beetle (Coleoptera: Scolytidae) infestations with semiochemicals: validation by sampling of baited and surrounding zones. Journal of Economic Entomology 82:1399-1405.

Hall, P.M. 2004. Provincial bark beetle strategy: technical implementation guidelines. Pages 67-75 *in* T.L. Shore; J.E. Brooks, J.E. Stone, eds. Proceedings of the mountain pine beetle symposium: Challenges and solutions, October 30-31, 2003, Kelowna, British Columbia, Canada. Natural Resources Canada, Canadian Forest Service, Pacific Forestry Centre, Victoria, British Columbia. Information Report BC-X-399. 298 p.

Hirsch, K.G.; Corey, P.N.; Martell, D.N. 1998. Using expert judgement to model initial attack fire crew effectiveness. Forest Science 44:539-549.

Holsten, E. 1985. Evaluation of monosodium methanearsonate (MSMA) for lethal trap trees in Alaska. USDA Forest Service Technical Report R10-7.

Hopkins, A.D. 1905. The Black Hills beetle. USDA Bureau of Entomology, Washington, DC, Bulletin 56. 24 p.

Hopping, G.R. 1946. Control of the more injurious bark beetles of the Canadian Rocky Mountain region. Dominion of Canada, Department of Agriculture, Science Service, Division of Entomology, Processed Publication No. 49. 8 p.

Hopping, G.R.; Mathers, W.G. 1945. Observations on outbreaks and control of the mountain pine beetle in the lodgepole pine stands of western Canada. The Forestry Chronicle, June 1945:1-11.

Kinghorn, J.M. 1955. Chemical control of the mountain pine beetle and Douglas-fir beetle. Journal of Economic Entomology 48:501-504.

Klein, W.H. 1978. Strategies and tactics for reducing losses in lodgepole pine to the mountain pine beetle by chemical and mechanical means. Pages 54-63 *in* D.L. Kibbee, A.A. Berryman, G.D. Amman, R.W. Stark, eds. Theory and practice of mountain pine beetle management in lodgepole pine forests. Symposium Proceedings, University of Idaho, Moscow, ID. 224 p.

Lindgren, B.S.; Borden, J.H.; Cushon, G.H.; Chong, L.J.; Higgins, C.J. 1989. Reduction of mountain pine beetle (Coleoptera: Scolytidae) attacks by verbenone in lodgepole pine stands in British Columbia. Canadian Journal of Forest Research 19:65-68.

Machlauchlan, L.E.; Borden, J.H.; D'Auria, J.M.; Wheeler, L.A. 1988. Distribution of arsenic in MSMA-treated lodgepole pine trees infested by the mountain pine beetle, *Dendroctonus ponderosae* (Coleoptera: Scolytidae), and its relation to beetle mortality. Journal of Economic Entomology 81:274-280.

Mason, D.T. 1915. Utilization and management of lodgepole pine in the Rocky Mountains. USDA Forest Service Bulletin No. 234. Washington, DC. 54 p.

Massey, C.L.; Chisholm, R.D.; Wygant, N.D. 1953. Ethylene dibromide for control of Black Hills beetle. Journal of Economic Entomology 46:601-604.

McMullen, L.H.; Betts R.E. 1982. Water sprinkling of log decks to reduce emergence of mountain pine beetle in lodgepole pine. The Forestry Chronicle 58:205-206.

McMullen, L.H.; Safranyik, L.; Linton, D.A. 1986. Suppression of mountain pine beetle infestations in lodgepole pine forests. Agriculture Canada, Ministry of State for Forestry and Mines, Pacific Forestry Centre, Victoria, British Columbia. Information Report BC-X-276, 20 p.

Nordlund, D.A. 1981. Semiochemicals: a review of the terminology. Pages 13-28 *in* Nordlund, D.A.; Jones, R.L.; Lewis, W.J., eds. Semiochemicals: their role in pest control. Wiley, NY.

O'Callaghan, D.P.; Fairhurst, C.P. 1983. Evaluation of the trap tree technique for control of Dutch elm disease in northwest England. Forestry Commission Bulletin 60:23-28.

Patterson, J.E. 1930. Control of the mountain pine beetle by solar heat. USDA Forest Service Technical Bulletin 195. Washington DC. 19 p.

Reid, R.W. 1962. Biology of the mountain pine beetle, *Dendroctonus monticolae* Hopkins, in the east Kootenay region of British Columbia. II. Behaviour in the host, fecundity, and internal changes in the female. The Canadian Entomologist 94:605-613.

Rogers, S.W. 1976. An analysis of the phytotoxic reaction of lodgepole pine following treatment with fuel oil-formulated insecticides. USDA Forest Service, Intermountain Region, Ogden UT. 7 p.

Ryker, L.C.; Yandell, K.L. 1983. Effect of verbenone on aggregation of *Dendroctonus ponderosae* Hopkins (Coleoptera: Scolytidae) to synthetic attractant. Zeitschrift Fur Angewandte Entomologie 96:452-459.

Safranyik, L. 1988. Estimating attack and brood totals and densities of the mountain pine beetle in individual lodgepole pine trees. The Canadian Entomologist 120:323-331.

Safranyik, L.; Linton, D.A. 1982. Mortality of spruce beetle broods in bolts submerged in water. Journal of the Entomological Society of British Columbia 79:8-11.

Safranyik, L.; Shrimpton, D.M.; Whitney, H.S. 1974. Management of lodgepole pine to reduce losses from the mountain pine beetle. Canadian Forest Service, Technical Report 1. 24 p.

Safranyik, L.; Linton, D.A.; Shore, T.L.; Hawkes, BC. 2001. The effects of prescribed burning on mountain pine beetle in lodgepole pine. Natural Resources Canada, Canadian Forest Service, Pacific Forestry Centre, Victoria, British Columbia. Information Report BC-X-391. 9 p.

Safranyik, L.; Shore, T.L.; Moeck, H.A.; Whitney, H.S. 2002. *Dentroctonus ponderosae* Hopkins, mountain pine beetle (Coleoptera: Scolytidae). Pages 104-109 *in* P.G. Mason, J.T. Huber, eds. Biological Control Programmes in Canada, 1981-2000. CABI Publishing, NY, 583 p.

Salman, K.A. 1938. Recent experiments with penetrating oil spray for the control of bark beetles. Journal of Economic Entomology 31:119-123.

Shore, T.L.; Safranyik, L. 1992. Susceptibility and risk rating systems for the mountain pine beetle in lodgepole pine stands. Natural Resources Canada, Canadian Forest Service, Information Report BC-X-336. 12 p.

Shore, T.L.; Safranyik, L. 2004. Mountain pine beetle management and decision support. Pages 97-105 *in* T.L. Shore, J.E. Brooks, J.E. Stone, eds. Challenges and solutions: Proceedings of the mountain pine beetle symposium, October 30-31, 2003, Kelowna, British Columbia, Canada. Natural Resources Canada, Canadian Forest Service, Pacific Forestry Centre, Information Report BC-X-399. 298 p.

Smith, R.H. 1970. Length of effectiveness of lindane against attacks by *Dendroctonus brevicomis* and *D. ponderosae* in California. Journal of Economic Entomology 63:1180-1184.

Smith, R.H.; Trostle, G.C.; McCambridge, W.F. 1977. Protective spray tests on three species of bark beetles in the western United States. Journal of Economic Entomology 70:119-125.

Stevens, R.E. 1957. Ethylene dibromide emulsion spray for the control of the mountain pine beetle in lodgepole pine. USDA Forest Service Research Note 122. Pacific Southwest Forest and Range Experiment Station, Berkeley, CA. 4 p.

Stevens, R.E. 1959. Ethylene dibromide sprays for controlling bark beetles in California. USDA Forest Service Research Note 147. Pacific Southwest Forest and Range Experiment Station, Berkeley, CA. 6 p.

Stock, A.J.; Gorley, R.A. 1989. Observations on a trial of broadcast burning to control an infestation of the mountain pine beetle, *Dendroctonus ponderosae*. The Canadian Entomologist 121:521-523.

Taylor, S.W.; Carroll, A.L. 2004. Disturbance, forest age, and mountain pine beetle outbreak dynamics in BC: a historical perspective. Pages 41-51 *in* T.L. Shore, J.E. Brooks, J.E. Stone, eds. Challenges and solutions: Proceedings of the mountain pine beetle symposium, October 30-31, 2003, Kelowna, British Columbia, Canada. Natural Resources Canada, Canadian Forest Service, Pacific Forestry Centre, Information Report BC-X-399. 298 p.

Whitney, H.S.; Safranyik, L.; Muraro, J.S.; Dyer, E.D.A. 1978. In defense of the concept of direct control of mountain pine beetle populations in lodgepole pine: some modern approaches. Pages 54-63 *in* D.L. Kibbee, A.A. Berryman, G.D. Amman, R.W. Stark, eds. Theory and practice of mountain pine beetle management in lodgepole pine forests. Symposium Proceedings, April 25-27, 1978, Pullman, WA. University of Idaho, Moscow, ID. 224 p.

Chapter 7

Preventive Management

Roger J. Whitehead, Les Safranyik, and Terry L. Shore

Natural Resources Canada, Canadian Forest Service, Pacific Forestry Centre,
506 West Burnside Road, Victoria, British Columbia, V8Z 1M5

Abstract

Except for wildfire suppression, management and utilization of lodgepole pine, *Pinus contorta* Dougl. ex Loud. var. *latifolia* Engelm., was essentially ignored in western Canada until quite recently. Consequently, the landscape now includes many older stands that matured without any silviculture to modify characteristics that make them susceptible to mountain pine beetle (*Dendroctonus ponderosae* Hopk. [Coleoptera: Scolytidae]) outbreaks. Susceptibility of this forest to extensive mountain pine beetle damage is an outcome of well-understood ecological relationships between the insect and its host acting on the current condition and distribution of the lodgepole pine forest. Whatever the management objective for a landscape unit, the key to reducing future damage is the same: consistent application of well-planned management to prevent infestations at the stand level and to relieve forest-level conditions that allow rapid expansion of local infestations to landscape-level outbreaks. This chapter describes the basic principles of preventive management based on key interactions between lodgepole pine and mountain pine beetle.

Résumé

Jusqu'à tout récemment, pratiquement aucune attention n'était portée à l'aménagement et à l'utilisation du pin de tordu latifolié, *Pinus contorta* Dougl. ex Loud. var. *latifolia* Engelm., dans l'Ouest du Canada, sauf pour l'extinction des feux de forêt. Par conséquent, le paysage de cette région comprend maintenant de nombreux peuplements plus âgés qui ont vieilli sans qu'aucun traitement sylvicole n'y soit pratiqué pour modifier les caractéristiques qui les rendent sensibles à des infestations du dendroctone du pin ponderosa (*Dendroctonus ponderosae* Hopk. [Coleoptera: Scolytidae]). La vulnérabilité de cette forêt à des dégâts à grande échelle causés par le dendroctone est l'aboutissement d'une interaction écologique bien connue entre l'insecte et son hôte qui agit sur l'état actuel et la répartition de la forêt de pins de tordu latifolié. Quel que soit l'objectif d'aménagement d'une unité de paysage, la clé du succès pour réduire les dégâts futurs reste la même : l'application systématique de mesures d'aménagement bien planifiées visant à prévenir les infestations au niveau du peuplement et à remédier aux conditions forestières qui favoriseraient une propagation rapide des infestations locales et même une flambée à l'échelle du paysage. Le présent chapitre décrit les principes de base d'un aménagement préventif qui sont fondés sur les interactions entre le pin de tordu latifolié et le dendroctone du pin ponderosa.

Introduction

Recent epidemic outbreaks of mountain pine beetle (*Dendroctonus ponderosae* Hopk. [Coleoptera: Scolytidae]) in western Canada are a result of well-understood ecological relationships between pine trees and the insect acting on the current forest conditions. Age, composition, and structure of lodgepole pine (*Pinus contorta* Dougl. ex Loud. var. *latifolia* Engelm.) stands and their distribution on the landscape are the key elements of forest condition and they may be changed with management over time. A good understanding of the insect – host relationship and of lodgepole pine stand dynamics enables forest managers to direct these changes to reduce the probability and severity of future outbreaks.

Lodgepole pine

Lodgepole pine is an aggressive pioneer species that thrives in a wide variety of habitats and that establishes readily on burned-over areas (Smithers 1961; Brown 1975; Lotan and Critchfield 1990; Koch 1996). Extensive pure and mixed lodgepole pine-dominated stands have occupied continental plateaus and mid-elevation habitats in mountainous regions of western Canada since soon after the last ice age (Schmidt 1989; Koch 1996). For thousands of years prior to European settlement, the age, composition, and structure of these forests was quite diverse in space and time because of frequent stand-replacing wildfires (Brown 1975). In striking contrast, many large fires during the early years of settlement, followed by increasingly intensive fire suppression without substitution of another stand-replacing disturbance, produced the very extensive tracts of older homogeneous lodgepole pine present today (Brown 1975; Lotan et al. 1985; Gara et al. 1985; Wong et al. 2003). In British Columbia, the area of lodgepole pine greater than 80 years of age increased from about 2.5 million ha in 1910 to more than 8 million ha in 1990 (Taylor and Carroll 2004). Lodgepole pine now contributes more volume to annual timber harvests in western Canada than any other softwood species, but extensive industrial harvesting of lodgepole pine is a relatively recent phenomenon (Smithers 1961; Kennedy 1985; Koch 1996).

Although aboriginal peoples used lodgepole pine for tipi, travois, and corral poles and burned some older forest to enhance forage, impacts of these activities were small at the forest level (van Hooser and Keegan 1985). Early European settlers also harvested lodgepole pine locally for building materials, mine timbers, railway ties, or fencing, and sometimes deliberately or accidentally set fires that burned large areas, which later regenerated to lodgepole pine. Wildfire suppression to protect communities and resource values intensified with development through the 20th century, but until about 1970, the developing timber industry in western Canada ignored vast expanses of lodgepole pine forest. Domestic and export markets favoured other readily available timber species. As a consequence, most lodgepole pine forest in Alberta and British Columbia is now found in extensive tracts of homogeneous stands of 80 to140 years of age. Most have developed without any silviculture to control species composition, form, patch-size, density or growth rate. As these stands naturally developed characteristics of interest to the timber industry (large piece size in moderately dense stands), they also became increasingly susceptible to outbreaks of mountain pine beetle (Safranyik et al. 1974,1975). Since then, competition between mountain pine beetle and humans to harvest mature pine trees has been intense (Gibson 1989).

Natural history of mountain pine beetle

Mountain pine beetle is native to western North America and, like fire, has long been a natural part of lodgepole pine ecosystems (Roe and Amman 1970; Wellner 1978; Stark 1978; Carter 1978; Kohler 1981). This insect causes little damage to forests at low population levels, but when populations build to an epidemic outbreak, timber losses occur at the landscape level and are normally severe. Where extensive tracts of susceptible lodgepole pine dominate, outbreaks may last 10 or more years and kill most large-diameter pine trees on hundreds of square kilometres. When that happens, management of all forest resources is disrupted and effects on forest-dependent values and communities persist for decades.

Large mountain pine beetle outbreaks have occurred periodically in western Canada throughout recorded history. Hewitt first noted significant outbreaks in British Columbia in 1910 (cited in Powell 1961) and since then reports of mountain pine beetle activity have been made more or less annually (Powell 1961; Graham and Miller 1989; van Sickle 1989; Ebata 2004). Historically, outbreaks have been restricted by climate to a portion of the pine forest (Safranyik et al. 1974; Amman et al. 1977). However, suitable range for mountain pine beetle has expanded during a recent warming trend and future outbreaks are now likely at higher elevations or more northerly latitudes than in the past (Carroll et al. 2004). Increasing mountain pine beetle activity is already becoming apparent beyond the northern limit of its historical range in British Columbia and on the eastern slopes of the Rocky Mountains in Alberta (Carroll et al. 2004). The potential for future expansion into jack pine, *P. banksiana* Lamb., forests across Canada has been discussed (Ono 2004). Lessons learned in areas historically subject to outbreaks may be applied in all of these forests.

History of research and management

Amman and Logan (1998) reviewed the evolution of mountain pine beetle control in western North America and its relationship with research and experience. As interest in the timber value of lodgepole pine grew, mountain pine beetle research progressed from an initial focus on taxonomy and distribution (Hopkins 1902; Swaine 1918) to ecology of insect-host interactions (e.g., Hopping and Beall 1948; Reid 1963) and methods to destroy beetles through direct control (e.g., Hopkins 1905; Hopping and Mathers 1945). With improved understanding of ecosystem dynamics and a broadening of forest management objectives, the emphasis increasingly shifted away from managing the pest to managing the forest to reduce damage (e.g., Roe and Amman 1970; Safranyik et al. 1974).

Silvicultural treatments specifically directed at mountain pine beetle began in 1938 with a crop-tree thinning experiment in ponderosa pine (Eaton 1941). In lodgepole pine, Hopping (1951) recognized that "...treating infested trees is only a palliative..." and suggested that a more permanent solution lay in increased utilization and type conversion. Initially, types of silvicultural treatments suggested and researched for lodgepole pine were targeted to existing mature stands based on observed relationships between outbreak hazard, stand age, stand composition, diameter distribution, and stand density (e.g., Hopping 1951). As utilization of lodgepole pine increased, these observations also gave rise to suggestions to create age and species mosaics (Amman and Safranyik 1985; Amman and Schmitz 1988) and to manage lodgepole pine on short rotation in high hazard areas (e.g., Smithers 1961).

Diameter-limit cuts (e.g., Cole and Cahill 1976; McGregor et al. 1987), thinning based on basal area reduction (e.g., Amman et al. 1977; Cahill 1978; Bennett and McGregor 1980), and selective removal of trees with thick phloem were tried in existing mature stands with mixed results (e.g., Roe and Amman 1970). Attention to the role of microclimate and tree spacing in addition to tree vigour in outbreak development increased. Shepherd (1966) discussed orientation and rates of beetle activity relative to heat and light intensity. Geiszler and Gara (1978) discussed the role of tree spacing in switching of attacks from a tree under attack to a nearby tree. Amman et al. (1988) suggested that change in microclimate was the principal factor responsible for reduced attack after thinning, and Bartos and Amman (1989) further discussed the role of stand microclimate in mountain pine beetle infestation. Based on this research and experience, current strategies for reducing susceptibility of existing mature stands are focused on achieving optimum microclimate, vigour, and inter-tree distance by thinning from below to regular spacing (Safranyik et al. 2004). Whitehead et al. (2004) documented the success of this approach for preventing outbreaks at the stand-level under several levels of beetle pressure from surrounding stands.

Most basic principles needed to manage forests to reduce beetle-caused loss were known by the mid-1970s (Safranyik et al. 1974). Since then, research has increasingly focused on developing decision aids, such as hazard- and risk-rating systems (Amman et al. 1977; Amman and Anhold 1989; Shore et al. 1989; Shore and Safranyik 1992; Shore and Safranyik 2004). Attention has gradually shifted from reactive (direct control) to proactive (preventive) mountain pine beetle management. There has also been increasing recognition of the need to integrate mountain pine beetle management with management of timber and non-timber resources (e.g., Bollenbacher and Gibson 1986). In Canadian National Parks in the Rocky Mountains, prescribed fire programs to increase forest diversity for wildlife habitat and reduce fire hazard have been adapted to consider mountain pine beetle susceptibility. Over the past decade, considerable research effort has focused on development of landscape-level models (Riel et al. 2004) to predict patterns of mountain pine beetle outbreak development, compare potential outcomes of control strategies, and project impacts on forest management objectives (Fall et al. 2004).

The purpose of this chapter is to present general principles for preventive management that are applicable to any landscape with a high proportion of lodgepole pine forest. The key elements of preventive management are a focus on long-term planning and consistent management to alleviate conditions that lead to outbreaks at the landscape level (Safranyik et al. 1974). We present an overview of this concept, in two parts:

1) landscape planning to prevent expansion to epidemic outbreaks; and

2) stand management to prevent incipient infestations.

Landscape planning

In this section we briefly discuss options for developing landscapes with low susceptibility to landscape-level damage. Planning to reduce landscape susceptibility must be based on basic biology and epidemiology of the mountain pine beetle and its relationships with the stand dynamics of lodgepole pine (Roe and Amman 1970; Safranyik et al. 1975; Peterman 1978; Safranyik 2004) and its distribution on the landscape. Whether emphasis is on managing pine for wildlife habitat, recreation, commercial timber or domestic water supply, the principles behind management to reduce damage from mountain pine beetle are the same; only the methods of implementing the required changes differ.

Three conditions must be satisfied for a landscape level outbreak to occur. First, several years of suitable weather (mild winters and warm, dry summers) are required to allow endemic populations to surpass a threshold where large trees can be successfully attacked. At that point, small patch "incipient infestations" begin developing where lodgepole pine and mountain pine beetle occur together. Second, at least some of these infestations must develop, unchecked by weather or management action, until they begin to export very high numbers of mountain pine beetles. Lastly, there must be an abundance of susceptible stands on the landscape to sustain high beetle populations. Periods of favourable weather occur from time to time throughout the range of mountain pine beetle, and the weather is not subject to management intervention. Timely and aggressive suppression of incipient infestations can slow or prevent transition to an outbreak at the landscape level, but in the current landscape of western Canada, direct control will remain difficult and costly until the underlying problem (a concentrated abundance of susceptible stands) is addressed and better access to remote stands is developed.

When planning preventive management, forested landscapes must be considered as a collection of stands where specific characteristics of individual stands and arrangement of stands relative to each other in space and time are both important in determining susceptibility. If climate is not limiting (Safranyik 1978), specific stand characteristics usually associated with outbreaks in natural stands include: stand age (more than 80 years at breast height); average tree diameter (greater than 20 cm); and stand density (750 to 1500 trees/ha) (Hopping and Beall 1948; Safranyik et al. 1974; Cole and Cahill 1976; Shore and Safranyik 1992; Shore et al. 2000). With age, trees become less resistant to the blue stain fungus carried by attacking beetles (Safranyik et al. 1975). Diameter is associated with food and space requirements needed to support brood development for expanding populations (Cole and Amman 1969; Amman 1972). Stand density affects tree vigour and within-stand microclimate, which in turn influence success of bark beetle dispersal, host selection, attack or brood development (Bartos and Amman 1989; Amman and Logan 1998). Growth modelling for pure lodgepole pine (Farnden 1996) suggests that unmanaged natural-origin stands, which start at any density between 900 and 9000 trees/ha at breast height age on land with typical site indices[1], will follow stand growth trajectories to a susceptible density and average diameter within 80 to 100 years (Fig. 1).

Susceptibility of any landscape unit to an epidemic outbreak depends on the amount of area in susceptible stands, how the stands are spatially arranged, and how easy they are to access for direct control of incipient infestations. The current landscape in western Canada is very susceptible. Examining age-class distribution of pine-leading stands in an area is a simple way of assessing the proportion of area carrying susceptible stands. Two-thirds of the lodgepole pine-leading forest of British Columbia is now in this age range (Fig. 2). It is the concentration of these contiguous susceptible stands across large areas that makes expansion of unchecked incipient infestations to landscape-level outbreaks highly likely through a combination of local population growth and long-range dispersal. This underscores the need to bring the current landscape under active management to prevent future epidemic outbreaks.

Planning long-term preventive management requires a ranking of pine stands based on relative susceptibility, while prioritization of short-term direct control options requires a ranking of stands for risk of significant loss over a shorter term (Shore and Safranyik 1992).

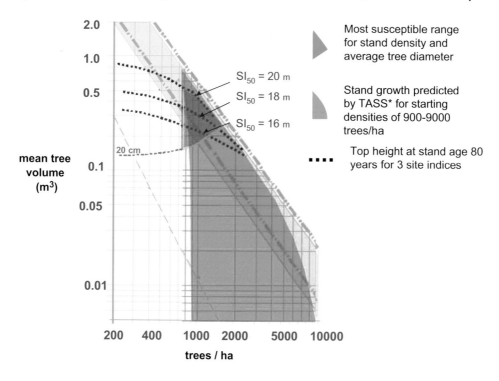

* British Columbia Ministry of Forests - Tree and Stand Simulator

Figure 1. Stand Density Management Diagram for natural origin lodgepole pine, illustrating how all stands starting at breast height age from densities between 900 to 9000 trees/ha become susceptible to mountain pine beetle outbreaks within 80 to 100 years.

[1] Site Index (SI_{50}) is a measure of site productivity for a tree species, expressed as top height in metres at 50 years breast height age.

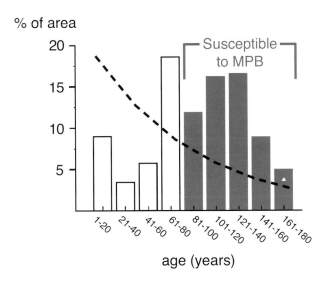

Figure 2. Age-class distribution of pine-leading stands in the SBS, SBPS, and MS biogeoclimatic zones of British Columbia. Dashed line indicates expected frequency distribution with a 100-year fire-return interval. (MPB = mountain pine beetle)

Hence, both detailed stand inventory information and consistent monitoring of bark beetle activity is required for rating stand susceptibility and risk. Over the past decade, introduction of Geographic Information Systems to forest operations, and increases in computing power, have made it possible to process data and plan efficiently for both short-term direct control and long-term stand replacement. Development of road access to mature pine stands for timely direct control of infestations, harvest of stands at highest risk, and proactive management of stand susceptibility are key elements in the planning process.

Stand replacement

The primary action required to lower current landscape susceptibility is reduction of the amount and concentration of susceptible lodgepole pine through planned stand replacement (Cole 1978; Cole and Amman 1980; Coulson and Stark 1982; Amman and Safranyik 1985; Cole and McGregor 1985; Amman and Schmitz 1988; Gibson 1989; Cole 1989). Logging and fire (whether prescribed or wild) are the main tools available. Targets for desired future age-class distribution and landscape pattern will depend on land use emphasis and landscape management objectives. As a general principle, a planner should strive to create a landscape mosaic with less old pine in smaller and more widely separated parcels, and a diversity of pine age classes and species mixes that will not favour the development of large-scale outbreaks (Amman and Safranyik 1985; Amman and Schmitz 1988).

Two of many possible low-susceptibility options for the lodgepole component of a landscape unit are illustrated in Figure 3. One scenario approximates average age-class distribution expected in unmanaged landscapes with a natural wildfire return interval of 100 years. Such might be a desired condition for lands managed as parkland or "wilderness." The other illustrates a sustained timber yield for commercial timberlands with most stands cycled on an 80-year rotation. Consistent management input is required to create and maintain either scenario over the long term.

If there were no mountain pine beetle, adjusting age-class distribution and redistributing it across the landscape in smaller patches would be relatively simple over time. Several decades of scheduled stand replacement based on a spatially explicit inventory (through timber harvest or prescribed burning), and subsequent stand management to adjust density, growth rate, or species composition, would create the desired landscape condition. In the presence of mountain pine beetle the process is more complex (Fig. 4). Access development and scheduling of stand replacement must be flexible enough to incorporate prompt direct control actions required to keep beetle populations low while adjustments to the forest mosaic are made.

Assessing risk and susceptibility of existing stands is a critical step in long-term planning for stand replacement. Consistent and thorough monitoring of the status and location of mountain pine beetle populations is necessary for risk rating and for directing control activities during incipient infestations. High-risk stands should be removed at the earliest opportunity. Access must be developed and maintained into areas of susceptible pine at lower current risk so that they can be broken into smaller patches in a mosaic with diverse age and species composition as opportunity allows. It is important to remember that the extensive mountain pine beetle damage seen over the last few decades developed because of the sheer size of the lodgepole forest and the high proportion of overmature stands where road access was poorly developed (making timely control difficult). Bringing forested lands under active management should relieve these conditions. Access development facilitates both monitoring and control of incipient infestations, while recycling stands on rotations shorter than 100 years limits potential damage by reducing the amount of susceptible pine at any one time.

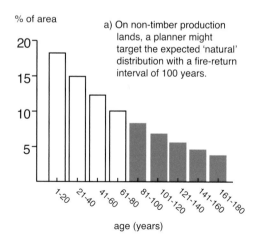
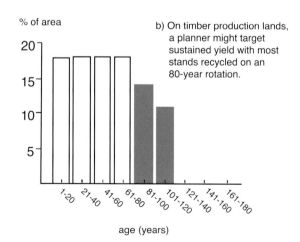

Figure 3. Two of many possible targets for the age-class distribution of pine stands in a landscape planning unit which would reduce the proportion of susceptible pine to less than 30% of the total.

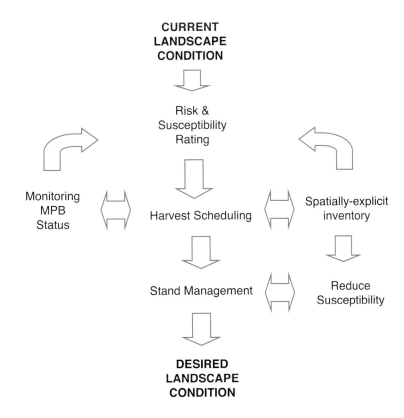

Figure 4. A simplified model for landscape management in pine-dominated operating areas. (MPB = mountain pine beetle)

Stand management

Here we briefly discuss stand-level management options for currently susceptible stands, and for planning and managing new stands to avoid the site and stand conditions that favour outbreaks. If applied as part of a landscape-level plan that reduces the amount and concentration of old lodgepole pine and promptly controls incipient infestations, stand-level management plays a key role in reducing damage.

Maintaining stand hygiene and vigour

Endemic mountain pine beetle populations generally require weakened or decadent trees for successful completion of their life cycle (Coulson 1979; Coulson and Stark 1982). Silvicultural practices which promote timber production, such as density management to limit inter-tree competition for moisture and nutrients, will produce more vigorous trees– ones less likely to succumb to attack when beetle populations are low. Similarly, silvicultural practices that promote stand hygiene can be effective in managing endemic mountain pine beetle populations to prevent their increase beyond endemic levels. Removing damaged or diseased trees during stand tending should limit endemic populations in stands managed for timber and reduce probability of incipient outbreaks when weather favours population growth (Cole 1989; Cole and McGregor 1985). Removal of larger-diameter trees infested with dwarf mistletoe, or damaged during stand tending, or weakened by wind or snow damage is especially important. During periods of weather favourable to beetle survival, such trees are very vulnerable and provide opportunities for expansion of mountain pine beetle populations to levels where even healthy trees may succumb to mass attack.

Managing species composition

Mountain pine beetle attack tends to hasten succession of lodgepole stands to climax forest types, and many existing lodgepole pine stands will succeed to more shade-tolerant species in the absence of a stand-replacing disturbance. In such cases, species conversion through selective removal of pine from mature mixed-species stands will contribute to the landscape plan to reduce the amount of susceptible forest while maintaining mature forest cover for other values. Discrimination against lodgepole pine in mixed stands during intermediate cuttings provides another way of varying the forest mosaic, and it may allow for longer rotations than is safe with pure stands (Cole 1989). Where appropriate and where needed in the landscape plan, species conversion can be achieved through preserving seed trees and advanced regeneration of nonpine species during stand replacement, or by planting alternative species after stand replacement.

Managing density in new pine stands

Stand characteristics that favour incipient outbreaks of mountain pine beetle are very like those associated with "physiological maturity," which is defined by the point in stand development at which current annual increment declines to below the mean annual increment (Safranyik et al. 1974). Onset of physiological maturity may be delayed by management actions that retain stand vigour, such as density management (Anhold and Long 1996). Density management is a very useful tool for preventive management because it can also be used to direct stand growth to meet specific product, timber supply, or habitat objectives (Farnden 1996).

Figure 5 illustrates how two silvicultural entries to a fully stocked, natural stand of lodgepole pine starting at 5000 trees/ha at breast height age on a site with SI_{50} = 18 m affect stand development. Without treatment ("1" in Fig. 5), the stand would self-thin to about 1500 trees/ha by 80 years of age, just reaching the average diameter where outbreaks typically develop. The stand could then be harvested, yielding 270 m^3/ha with an average piece size of 0.25 m^3. If beetle pressure was low, it could be left to grow with regular monitoring of mountain pine beetle activity. If the same stand is precommercially thinned to 1600 trees/ha ("2" in Fig. 5), it develops to about 1100 treees/ha at age 80 and could be harvested, yielding about 330 m^3/ ha with a larger average piece size, which may be more desirable if sawlogs are the product objective. If it is necessary or desirable to carry this stand to larger piece size or older age to meet some timber supply, habitat, or visual quality objective, a commercial thinning entry at about age 60 is an option. Removing approximately 100 m³ of sawlog material would shift the growth trajectory away from conditions where outbreaks would ordinarily develop ("3" in Fig. 5), and potentially yield about 350 m³/ha with large piece size at 100 years breast height age.

The above example illustrates only three possibilities. When stands are brought under active management, there are many possible pathways for stand development that will lead to acceptable end products with reduced stand and landscape susceptibility to mountain pine beetle.

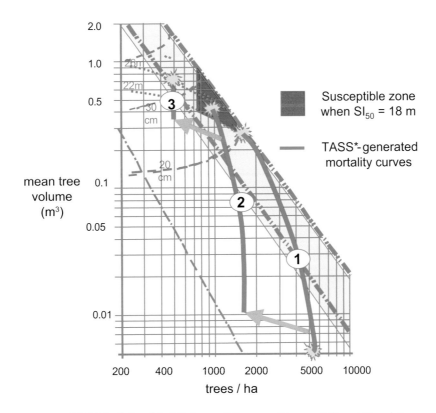

* British Columbia Ministry of Forests - Tree and Stand Simulator

Figure 5. Stand Density Management Diagram for natural-origin lodgepole pine, with TASS-generated mortality curves illustrating how density management can lead to acceptable final products on an 80-year rotation or maintain low susceptibility to mountain pine beetle on an extended rotation (source: Farnden [1996]).

Managing density in existing mature natural stands

Removing susceptible diameter classes from pure pine stands by thinning from above (diameter-limit cutting or "high grading") may reduce susceptibility of mixed or pure stands for a limited time until residual trees grow to susceptible size and another removal is required. However, such a thinning regime generally leaves stands of reduced silvicultural value (Schmidt and Alexander 1985) with uneven stem distributions, and such stands are often vulnerable to wind or snow damage. Consequently, this option may have limited application.

In most of western Canada, it will be difficult to quickly replace all stands of high susceptibility without exceeding other constraints on harvest such as timber supply, visual quality, or habitat. Also, it is often important to hold some mature stands in the harvest queue while older stands or stands at higher risk are recycled. One tactic that has shown considerable promise is thinning some mature stands to a uniform inter-tree spacing at less than 600 trees/ha (also known as "beetle proofing"). The prescription requires thinning from below to enhance individual tree vigour (increasing the trees' ability to produce resins that are the primary defense against attack), and uniform spacing to create stand microclimate conditions (higher temperatures, light intensity, and within-stand winds) that hinder beetle dispersal, attack behaviour and survival (Bartos and Amman 1989; Amman and Logan 1998). To optimize these effects, stands must be opened to at least a 4-m inter-tree spacing (to increase wind penetration, light and temperature), with the largest, healthiest trees retained (for vigour and windfirmness). Damage to leave trees must be minimized to avoid stress. It is important to remember that increasing inter-tree spacing (not thinning to a target density or basal area) achieves the microclimate objectives. This prescription, which takes mature stands down to between 400 and 625 trees/ha, usually removes enough volume of sufficient piece size to ensure a commercially viable operation[2] in timberlands, and leaves stands with higher value for wildlife habitat, recreation and water management.

The Canadian Forest Service has been studying this "beetle proofing" prescription for more than a decade. Whitehead et al. (2004) reported preliminary results of two studies of interest. In the first, three levels of treatment (not treated, spaced to 4 m and spaced to 5 m) were applied in uniform 90- to 110-year-old lodgepole stands at each of three sites in the East Kootenays between 1992 and 1993. Microclimate was monitored in each treatment unit, and trees within each unit were monitored to document tree vigour. Results over the first decade indicated the prescription achieved the desired tree vigour (Fig. 6) and microclimate effects (Fig. 7).

---

[2] Anon. 1999. Case study in adaptive management: Beetle proofing lodgepole pine in southeastern British Columbia. BC Ministry of Forests Extension Note EN-039.

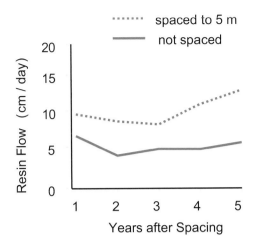

Figure 6. Comparison of resin production in response to wounding in spaced and unspaced stands from the East Kootenay Trial (mean of 10 trees/treatment on each of three sites). Source: L. Safranyik, D. Linton and A. Carroll, Canadian Forest Service, Victoria, unpublished data.

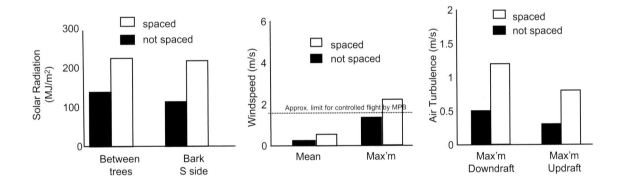

Figure 7. Comparison of three important within-stand microclimate parameters in spaced and unspaced stands from the East Kootenay Trial (5-year average on three sites for days in July and August when air temperature exceeds 18° C). Source: R.A. Benton and B.N. Brown, Canadian Forest Service, Victoria, British Columbia, unpublished data. (MPB = mountain pine beetle.)

The second study was conducted in 2003, when conditions favouring an increase in mountain pine beetle populations had persisted for at least 3 years (Whitehead and Russo 2005). It compared levels of beetle activity since treatment in five existing study areas where side-by-side demonstrations of beetle-proofed and untreated stands had been established between 1991 and 1994. Proportion and number of trees successfully attacked since treatment, and ratio of green attack to red attack over the last year, were both lower in beetle-proofed stands in every case. However, the magnitude of that difference reflected site-specific factors.

At three sites where aggressive direct control of incipient infestations in surrounding areas had kept rising beetle populations relatively low, untreated stands all developed incipient infestations that required direct control; beetle-proofed stands did not. At a fourth site, there was less mature pine in the surrounding area and no direct control program for the preceding two years. There, the proportion and density of trees attacked in the untreated stand was three to four times higher than in the thinned area, but green:red attack ratios were similar (1.8 and 1.4, respectively). In this case, the prescription had called for thinning to 500 trees/ha, rather than spacing to a minimum inter-tree distance and most attacks were found in patches of higher density left to compensate for natural stand openings or removal of damaged trees (i.e., where microclimate was still favourable for host selection and initiation of attack). It is important to remember that beetle proofing depends on final inter-tree spacing to achieve the desired microclimate and that thinning to a target stand density or basal area may not produce the tree distribution required.

The fifth site, located in a large expanse of untreated susceptible pine, was on the edge of a rapidly expanding uncontrolled outbreak and had been subjected to very high beetle pressure for the preceding 2 to 3 years. When the stand was assessed, about 35% of all trees in each unit had been attacked. In the untreated stand, this fraction included nearly three times the total number of attacks in the spaced stand (453/ha vs. 167/ha) and more than 80% of pine over 20 cm in diameter. Although green to red attack ratio was also lower in the spaced stand (1.2 vs. 3.3, respectively), the spaced stand is expected to succumb as the outbreak proceeds. Beetle proofing is intended to prevent transition between endemic and incipient phases of the outbreak cycle, and should not be expected to save stands during an epidemic.

The beetle proofing prescription is a useful tool, suited for limited application in areas where there is a reason to maintain mature forest cover in a specific place (such as maintenance of recreation value, riparian zone integrity, viewscape quality, or timber supply) while the amount and distribution of susceptible stands in the surrounding area are adjusted through stand replacement. Consistent monitoring and aggressive direct control of incipient outbreaks in surrounding areas are an important complement to this prescription.

Summary

The current landscape in western Canada includes an abundance of largely undeveloped older lodgepole pine stands that matured without active silviculture, and this landscape is very susceptible to development of landscape-level outbreaks of mountain pine beetle. Planned stand replacement is required to create a landscape mosaic with less old pine in smaller and more widely separated parcels, where age-class, size and species mixes will not favour development of large-scale outbreaks. Opportunities for reducing future susceptibility of replacement stands include conversion to nonpine species and management of pine on shorter rotations with density management to control stand growth, and attention to stand hygiene. There are also limited opportunities for stand-level management of current mature stands, including pine removal from mixed stands and beetle proofing some mature stands to provide flexibility for integrated management of multiple resource values on a landscape.

References

Amman, G.D. 1972. Mountain pine beetle brood production in relation to thickness of lodgepole pine phloem. Journal of Economic Entomology 65:138-140.

Amman, G.D.; Schmitz, R.F. 1988. Mountain pine beetle-lodgepole pine interactions and strategies for reducing tree losses. Ambio 17:62-68.

Amman, G.D.; Logan, J.A. 1998. Silvicultural control of the mountain pine beetle: prescriptions and the influence of microclimate. American Entomologist 44:166-177.

Amman, G.D.; Anhold, J.A. 1989. Preliminary evaluation of hazard and risk variables for mountain pine beetle infestations in lodgepole pine stands. Pages 22-27 *in* G.D. Amman, comp. Proceedings - Symposium on the management of lodgepole pine to minimize losses to the mountain pine beetle. Kalispell, MT, July 12-14, 1988. USDA Forest Service, General Technical Report INT-262.

Amman, G.D.; McGregor, M.D.; Schmitdtz, R.F.; Oakes, R.D. 1988. Susceptibility of lodgepole pine to infestation by mountain pine beetle following partial cutting of stands. Canadian Journal of Forest Research 18:688-695.

Amman, G.D.; McGregor, M.D.; Cahill, D.B.; Klein, W.H. 1977. Guidelines for reducing losses of lodgepole pine to the mountain pine beetle in unmanaged stands in the Rocky Mountains. USDA Forest Service, General Technical Report INT-36. 19 p.

Amman, G.D.; Safranyik, L. 1985. Insects of lodgepole pine: impacts and control. Pages 107-124 *in* D.M. Baumgartner, R.G. Krebill, J.T. Arnott, and G.F. Weetman, eds. Lodgepole Pine: The Species and its Management, Symposium Proceedings. May 8-10, 1984. Washington State University Cooperative Extension, Spokane, WA.

Anhold J.A.; Long, J.N. 1996. Management of lodgepole pine stand density to reduce susceptibility to mountain pine beetle attack. Western Journal of Applied Forestry 11(2):50-53.

Bartos, D.L.; Amman, G.D. 1989. Microclimate: an alternative to tree vigor as a basis for mountain pine beetle infestations. USDA Forest Service, Intermountain Research Station, Ogden Utah. Research Paper INT-400. 10 p.

Bennett D.D.; McGregor M. D. 1980. A demonstration of basal area cutting to manage mountain pine beetle in second growth ponderosa pine. USDA Forest Service Northern Region, Forest Pest Management Report 88-16. 5 p.

Bollenbacher, B.; Gibson K.E. 1986. Mountain pine beetle: a land manager's perspective. USDA Forest Service. Forest Pest Management Report 81-15. 5 p.

Brown, J.K. 1975. Fire cycles and community dynamics in lodgepole pine forests, Pages 430-456 *in* D. M. Baumgartner, ed. Proceedings Symposium: Management of Lodgepole Pine Ecosystems, Oct. 9-13, 1973. Washington State University Cooperative Extension. Pullman, WA.

Cahill, D.B. 1978. Cutting strategies as control measures of the mountain pine beetle in lodgepole pine in Colorado. Pages 188-191 *in* A.A. Berryman, G.D. Amman and R.W. Stark, eds. Theory and practice of mountain pine beetle management in lodgepole pine forests: Symposium proceedings; April 25-27, 1978; Pullman, WA. University of Idaho, Forest, Wildlife and Range Experiment Station, Moscow, ID.

Carroll, A.L.; Taylor, S.W.; Régnière, J.; Safranyik, L. 2004. Effects of climate change on range expansion by the mountain pine beetle. Pages 21-32 *in* Shore, T.L., J.E. Brooks and J.E. Stone, eds. Challenges and Solutions: Proceedings of the Mountain Pine Beetle Symposium. Kelowna, British Columbia, Canada. October 30-31, 2003. Natural Resources Canada, Canadian Forest Service, Pacific Forestry Centre, Victoria, BC, Information Report BC-X-399. 298 p.

Carter, W. 1978. Potential impacts of mountain pine beetle and their mitigation in lodgepole pine forests. Pages 27-38 *in* A.A. Berryman, G.D. Amman and R.W. Stark, eds. Theory and practice of mountain pine beetle management in lodgepole pine forests: Symposium proceedings, April 25-27, 1978, Pullman, WA. University of Idaho, Forest, Wildlife and Range Experiment Station, Moscow, ID.

Cole, D.M.; McGregor M.D. 1985. Silvicultural practices for lodgepole pine stands in commercial forests. Pages 45-46 *in* M.D. McGregor and D.M. Cole, eds. Integrating management strategies for the mountain pine beetle with multiple-resource management of lodgepole pine forests. USDA Forest Service, General Technical Report INT-174.

Cole, D.M. 1978. Feasibility of silvicultural practices for reducing losses to the mountain pine beetle in lodgepole pine forests. Pages 140-147 *in* A.A. Berryman, G.D. Amman and R.W. Stark, eds. Theory and practice of mountain pine beetle management in lodgepole pine forests: Symposium proceedings, April 25-27, 1978, Pullman, WA. University of Idaho, Forest, Wildlife and Range Experiment Station, Moscow, ID.

Cole, D.M. 1989. Preventive strategies for lodgepole pine/mountain pine beetle problems: opportunities with immature stands. Pages 64-69 *in* G.D. Amman, comp. Proceedings - Symposium on the management of lodgepole pine to minimize losses to the mountain pine beetle. Kalispell, MT, July 12-14, 1988. USDA Forest Service, General Technical Report INT-262.

Cole, W.E.; Amman, G.D. 1980. Mountain pine beetle dynamics in lodgepole pine forests: Part 1. Course of an infestation. USDA Forest Service, General Technical Report INT- 89.

Cole, W.E.; Amman, G.D. 1969. Mountain pine beetle infestations in relation to lodgepole pine diameters. USDA Forest Service, Research Note INT-195. Ogden, UT. 7 p.

Cole, W.E.; Cahill, D.B. 1976. Cutting strategies can reduce probabilities of mountain pine beetle epidemics in lodgepole pine. Journal of Forestry 74:294-297.

Coulson, R.N. 1979. Population dynamics of bark beetles. Annual Review of Entomology 24:217-246.

Coulson, R.N.; Stark, R.W. 1982. Integrated management of bark beetles. Pages 315-349 *in* J.B. Milton and K.B. Sturgeon, eds. Bark beetles in North American conifers. University of Texas Press. Austin, TX.

Eaton, C.B. 1941. Influence of the mountain pine beetle on the composition of mixed pole stands of ponderosa pine and white fir. Journal of Forestry 39:710-713.

Ebata, T. 2004. Current status of mountain pine beetle in British Columbia. Pages 52-56 *in* Shore, T.L., J.E. Brooks and J.E. Stone, eds. Challenges and Solutions: Proceedings of the Mountain Pine Beetle Symposium. Kelowna, British Columbia, Canada. October 30-31, 2003. Natural Resources Canada, Canadian Forest Service, Pacific Forestry Centre, Victoria, BC. Information Report BC-X-399. 298 p.

Fall, A.; Shore, T.L.; Safranyik, L.; Riel, W.G.; Sachs, D. 2004. Integrating landscape-scale mountain pine beetle projection and spatial harvesting models to assess management strategies. Pages 114-132 *in* Shore, T.L., J.E. Brooks and J.E. Stone, eds. Challenges and Solutions: Proceedings of the Mountain Pine Beetle Symposium. Kelowna, British Columbia, Canada. October 30-31, 2003. Natural Resources Canada, Canadian Forest Service, Pacific Forestry Centre, Victoria, BC, Information Report BC-X-399. 298 p.

Farnden, C. 1996. Stand density management diagrams for lodgepole pine, white spruce, and interior Douglas-fir. Natural Resources Canada, Canadian Forest Service, Pacific Forestry Centre, Victoria, BC, Information Report BC-X-360. 37 p.

Gara, R.I.; Littke, W.R. ; Agee, J.K.; Geiszler, D.R.; Stuart, J.D.; Driver, C.H. 1985. Influence of fires, fungi and mountain pine beetles on development of a lodgepole pine forest in South Central Oregon. Pages 153-162 *in* D.M. Baumgartner, R.G. Krebill, J.T. Arnott, and G.F. Weetman, eds. Lodgepole Pine: The Species and its Management, Symposium Proceedings. May 8-10, 1984. Washington State University Cooperative Extension, Spokane, WA.

Geiszler, D.R.; Gara, R.I. 1978. Mountain pine beetle attack dynamics in lodgepole pine. Pages 182-187 *in* A.A. Berryman, G.D. Amman and R.W. Stark, eds. Theory and practice of mountain pine beetle management in lodgepole pine forests: Symposium proceedings; April 25-27, 1978; Pullman, WA. University of Idaho, Forest, Wildlife and Range Experiment Station, Moscow, ID.

Gibson, K.E. 1989. Partial cutting (sanitation thinning) to reduce mountain pine beetle-caused mortality. Pages 45-47 *in* G.D. Amman, comp. Proceedings - Symposium on the management of lodgepole pine to minimize losses to the mountain pine beetle. Kalispell, MT, July 12-14, 1988. USDA Forest Service, General Technical Report INT-262.

Graham, D.A.; Miller, G. 1989. Canada / U.S. mountain pine beetles / lodgepole pine program 1981-1988. Pages 1-3 *in* G.D. Amman, comp. Proceedings - Symposium on the management of lodgepole pine to minimize losses to the mountain pine beetle. Kalispell, MT, July 12-14, 1988. USDA Forest Service, General Technical Report INT-262.

Hopkins, A.D. 1902. Insect enemies of the pine in the Black Hills Forest Reserve. USDA, Division of Entomology Bulletin 32. 24 p.

Hopkins, A.D. 1905. The Black Hills beetle. Washington, D.C. USDA, Bureau of Entomology. Bulletin 56. 24 p.

Hopping G.R.; Beall, G. 1948. The relation of diameter of lodgepole pine to incidence of attack by the bark beetle (*Dendroctonus monticolae* Hopk.). Forestry Chronicle 24:141-145.

Hopping, G.R. 1951. The mountain pine beetle. Forestry Chronicle 27:26-29.

Hopping, G.R.; Mathers, W.G. 1945. Observation on outbreaks and control of the mountain pine beetle in the lodgepole pine stands of western Canada. Forestry Chronicle 21(2):98-108.

Kennedy, R.W. 1985. Lodgepole pine as a commercial resource in Canada. Pages 21-23 *in* D.M. Baumgartner, R.G. Krebill, J.T. Arnott, and G. F. Weetman, eds. Lodgepole Pine, the Species and Its Management. Symposium Proceedings. May 8-10, 1984 Spokane, Washington, USA and May 14-16, 1984 Vancouver, British Columbia, Canada. Washington State University, Pullman, WA.

Koch, P. 1996. Lodgepole pine in North America. Forest Products Society, Madison, Wisconson. Volume 1. pp. 7-28.

Kohler, S. 1981. Montana division of forestry mountain pine beetle program. Pages 9-40 *in* Mountain pine beetle symposium. February 6-7, 1981, Coleman Alberta. Alberta Energy and Natural Resources, Forest Service.

Lotan, J.E.; Brown, J.K.; Neuenschwander, L.K. 1985. Role of fire in lodgepole pine forests. Pages 153-162 *in* D.M. Baumgartner, R.G. Krebill, J.T. Arnott, and G.F. Weetman, eds. Lodgepole Pine: The Species and its Management, Symposium Proceedings. May 8-10, 1984. Washington State University Cooperative Extension, Spokane, WA.

Lotan, J.E.; Critchfield W.B. 1990. Silvics of lodgepole pine (*Pinus contorta*). Pages 302-315 *in* R.M. Burns and B.H. Honkala eds. Silvics of North America Vol. 1. Conifers. USDA, Agriculture Handbook 654.

McGregor, M.D.; Amman, G.D.; Schmitz, R.F.; Oakes, R.D. 1987. Partial cutting lodgepole pine stands to reduce losses to the mountain pine beetle. Canadian Journal of Forest Research 17:1234-1239.

Ono, H. 2004. The mountain pine beetle: scope of the problem and key issues in Alberta. Pages 62-66 *in* Shore, T.L., J.E. Brooks and J.E. Stone, eds. Challenges and Solutions: Proceedings of the Mountain Pine Beetle Symposium. Kelowna, British Columbia, Canada. October 30-31, 2003. Natural Resources Canada, Canadian Forest Service, Pacific Forestry Centre, Victoria, BC. Information Report BC-X-399. 298 p.

Peterman, R.M. 1978. The ecological role of mountain pine beetle in lodgepole pine forests. Pages 16-26 *in* A.A. Berryman, G.D. Amman, and R.W. Stark, eds. Theory and practice of mountain pine beetle management on lodgepole pine forests. Proceedings of the symposium. Washington State University, Pullman, WA.

Powell, J.M. 1961. The mountain pine beetle, *Dendroctonus monticolae* Hopk., in western Canada. Canada Department of Forestry, Entomology and Pathology Branch, Internal Report.

Reid, R.W. 1963. Biology of the mountain pine beetle, *Dendroctonus monticolae* Hopkins, in the East Kootenay region of British Columbia III: Interaction between the beetle and its host, with emphasis on brood mortality and survival. The Canadian Entomologist 95:225-238.

Riel, W.G.; Fall, A.; Shore, T.L.; Safranyik, L. 2004. A spatio-temporal simulation of mountain pine beetle impacts on the landscape. Pages 106-113 *in* Shore, T.L., J.E. Brooks and J.E. Stone, eds. Challenges and Solutions: Proceedings of the Mountain Pine Beetle Symposium. Kelowna, British Columbia, Canada. October 30 –31, 2003. Natural Resources Canada, Canadian Forest Service, Pacific Forestry Centre, Victoria, BC. Information Report BC-X-399. 298 p.

Roe, A.L.; Amman, G.D. 1970. The mountain pine beetle in lodgepole pine forests. USDA Forest Service, Intermountain Forest and Range Experiment Station, Research Paper INT-71. 23 p.

Safranyik, L. 1978. Effects of climate and weather on mountain pine beetle populations. Pages 77-84 *in* A.A. Berryman, G.D. Amman and R.W. Stark, eds. Theory and practice of mountain pine beetle management in lodgepole pine forests: Symposium proceedings, April 25-27, 1978, Pullman, WA. University of Idaho, Forest, Wildlife and Range Experiment Station, Moscow, ID.

Safranyik, L. 2004. Mountain pine beetle epidemiology in lodgepole pine. Pages 33-40 *in* Shore, T.L., J.E. Brooks and J.E. Stone, eds. Challenges and Solutions: Proceedings of the Mountain Pine Beetle Symposium. Kelowna, British Columbia, Canada. October 30 –31, 2003. Natural Resources Canada, Canadian Forest Service, Pacific Forestry Centre, Victoria, BC. Information Report BC-X-399. 298 p.

Safranyik, L.; Shore T.L.; Carroll, A.L.; Linton D.A. 2004. Bark beetle (Coleoptera: Scolytidae) diversity in spaced and unmanaged mature lodgepole pine (Pinaceae) in southeastern British Columbia. Forest Ecology and Management 200:23-38.

Safranyik L.; Shrimpton, D.M.; Whitney H.S. 1974. Management of lodgepole pine to reduce losses from the mountain pine beetle. Canadian Forest Service, Pacific Forest Research Centre, Victoria, BC. Forest Technical Report No. 1.

Safranyik, L.; Shrimpton, D.M.; Whitney, H.S. 1975. An interpretation of the interaction between lodgepole pine, the mountain pine beetle and its associated blue stain fungi in western Canada. Pages 406-428 *in* D.M. Baumgarner, ed. Management of lodgepole pine ecosystems. Symposium Proceedings Oct. 9-13, 1973. Washington State University Cooperative Extension. Pullman, WA.

Schmidt, W.C. 1989. Lodgepole pine: an ecological opportunist. Pages 14-20 *in* G.D. Amman, comp. Proceedings - Symposium on the management of lodgepole pine to minimize losses to the mountain pine beetle. Kalispell, MT, July 12-14, 1988. USDA Forest Service, Intermountain Research Station, Ogden, UT, General Technical Report INT-262.

Schmidt, W.C.; Alexander R.R. 1985. Strategies for managing lodgepole pine. Pages 201-210 *in* D.M. Baumgartner, R.G. Krebill, J.T. Arnott, and G.F. Weetman, eds. Lodgepole Pine: The Species and its Management, Symposium Proceedings, May 8-10, 1984. Washington State University Cooperative Extension, Spokane, WA.

Shepherd, R.F. 1966. Factors influencing the orientation and rates of activity of *Dendroctonus ponderosae* Hopkins (Coleoptera: Scolytidae). The Canadian Entomologist 98:507-518.

Shore T.L.; Safranyik, L. 1992. Susceptibility and risk rating systems for the mountain pine beetle in lodgepole pine stands. Forestry Canada, Pacific Forestry Centre, Victoria, BC. Information Report BC-X-336. 12 p.

Shore, T.; Safranyik, L.; Lemieux, J. 2000. Susceptibility of lodgepole pine stands to the mountain pine beetle: testing of a rating system. Canadian Journal of Forest Research 30:44-49.

Shore, T.L.; Boudewyn, P.A. Gardner, E.R.; Thompson, A.J. 1989. A preliminary evaluation of hazard rating systems for the mountain pine beetle in lodgepole pine stands in British Columbia. Pages 28-33 *in* G.D. Amman, comp. Proceedings - Symposium on the management of lodgepole pine to minimize losses to the mountain pine beetle. Kalispell, MT, July 12-14, 1988. USDA Forest Service, General Technical Report INT-262.

Shore, T.L.; Safranyik, L. 2004. Mountain pine beetle management and decision support. Pages 97-105 *in* Shore, T.L., J.E. Brooks and J.E. Stone, eds. Challenges and Solutions: Proceedings of the Mountain Pine Beetle Symposium. Kelowna, British Columbia, Canada. October 30-31, 2003. Natural Resources Canada, Canadian Forest Service, Pacific Forestry Centre, Victoria, BC, Information Report BC-X-399. 298 p.

Smithers, L. A. 1961. Lodgepole pine in Alberta. Canadian Department of Forestry, Bulletin 127. Ottawa, ON. 153 p.

Stark, R.W. 1978. The mountain pine beetle symposium aspirations. Pages 3-8 *in* A.A. Berryman, G.D. Amman and R.W. Stark, eds. Theory and practice of mountain pine beetle management in lodgepole pine forests: Symposium proceedings, April 25-27, 1978; Pullman, WA. University of Idaho, Forest, Wildlife and Range Experiment Station, Moscow, ID.

Swain, J.J. 1918. Canadian bark beetles II: A preliminary classification with an account of the habits and means of control. Canadian Department of Agriculture, Technical Bulletin No.14. 143 p.

Taylor, S.W.; Carroll, A.L. 2004. Disturbance, forest age, and mountain pine beetle dynamics in British Columbia: a historical perspective. Pages 41-51 *in* T.L. Shore, J.E. Brooks and J.E. Stone, eds. Proceedings of the Mountain Pine Beetle Symposium: Challenges and Solutions. Kelowna, British Columbia, Canada. October 30-31, 2003. Natural Resources Canada, Canadian Forest Service, Pacific Forestry Centre, Victoria, BC, Information Report BC-X-399. 298 p.

Van Hooser, D.D.; Keegan, C.E. III. 1985. Lodgepole pine as a commercial resource in the United States. Pages 15-19 *in* D.M. Baumgartner, R.G. Krebill, J.T. Arnott, and G. F. Weetman, eds. Lodgepole Pine, the Species and Its Management. Symposium Proceedings. Washington State University, Pullman, WA.

Van Sickle, G.A. 1989. Status of mountain pine beetle in western Canada. Pages 6-8 *in* G.D. Amman, comp. Proceedings - Symposium on the management of lodgepole pine to minimize losses to the mountain pine beetle. Kalispell, MT, July 12-14, 1988. USDA Forest Service, Intermountain Forest and Range Experiment Station, Ogden, UT, General Technical Report INT-262.

Wellner, C.A. 1978. Management problems resulting from mountain pine beetles in lodgepole pine forests. Pages 9-15 *in* A.A. Berryman, G.D. Amman and R.W. Stark, eds. Theory and practice of mountain pine beetle management in lodgepole pine forests: Symposium proceedings; April 25-27, 1978; Pullman, WA. University of Idaho, Forest, Wildlife and Range Experiment Station, Moscow, ID.

Whitehead, R.J.; Safranyik, L.; Russo, G.L.; Shore, T.L.; Carroll, A.L. 2004. Silviculture to reduce landscape and stand susceptibility to mountain pine beetle. Pages 233-244 *in* T.L. Shore, J.E. Brooks and J.E. Stone, eds. Proceedings of the Mountain Pine Beetle Symposium: Challenges and Solutions. Kelowna, British Columbia, Canada. Oct. 30 -31, 2003. Natural Resources Canada, Canadian Forest Service, Pacific Forestry Centre, Victoria, BC. Information Report BC-X-399. 298 p.

Whitehead, R.J.; Russo, G.L. 2005. "Beetle-proofed" lodgepole pine stands in interior British Columbia have less damage from mountain pine beetle. Natural Resources Canada, Canadian Forest Service, Pacific Forestry Centre, Victoria, BC. Information Report BC-X-402. 17 p.

Wong, C.; Dorner, B.; Sandmann, H. 2003. Estimating historical variability of natural disturbances in British Columbia. British Columbia Ministry of Forests, Research Branch, Victoria BC. Land Management Handbook No. 53. 45 p.

Chapter 8

Decision Support Systems

Terry L. Shore, Bill G. Riel, Les Safranyik, and Andrew Fall

Natural Resources Canada, Canadian Forest Service, Pacific Forestry Centre,
506 West Burnside Road, Victoria, British Columbia, V8Z 1M5

Abstract

Given the complexity and large number of issues facing forest managers, computerized decision support systems are valuable tools for decision makers. Decision support systems can: provide support for planning, provide rationale for the allocation of scarce resources, allow the exploration of "what if" scenarios, and provide the ability to compare effects of different management strategies. When forest management must consider mountain pine beetle (*Dendroctonus ponderosae* Hopk. [Coleoptera: Scolytidae]), susceptibility and risk rating systems and simulation models are key components of decision support. This chapter reviews mountain pine beetle susceptibility and risk rating systems as well as several different approaches to simulation modelling with a specific focus on products developed and employed as decision support tools in western Canada.

Résumé

Étant donné la complexité et la multitude des problèmes auxquels doivent faire face les gestionnaires des forêts, les systèmes informatisés d'aide à la décision constituent des outils fort précieux pour les décideurs et les décideuses. Ces systèmes peuvent fournir une aide pour effectuer de la planification et une analyse raisonnée de l'allocation de ressources limitées, permettre l'exploration de scénarios de simulation et donner la capacité de comparer les effets des différentes stratégies de gestion. Lorsque la gestion des forêts doit prendre en compte le dendroctone du pin ponderosa (*Dendroctonus ponderosae* Hopk. [Coleoptera: Scolytidae]), les systèmes d'évaluation de la vulnérabilité et des risques d'infestation ainsi que les modèles de simulation deviennent des éléments clés de l'aide à la décision. Dans le présent chapitre, on examine les systèmes d'évaluation de la vulnérabilité et des risques d'infestation de même que différentes approches à la modélisation de simulation, en mettant l'accent sur la gamme de produits développés et utilisés comme outils d'aide à la décision dans l'Ouest canadien.

Introduction

Decision support systems refer to knowledge-based tools, computer-based or otherwise, that provide information to the user to improve the quality and timeliness of decisions. In Figure 1 we show an overview of current decision support systems for the mountain pine beetle. Data requirements include information about the host – forest inventory and geospatial data, and information about the beetle including location and numbers of infested and killed trees. This information can be utilized to develop susceptibility (hazard) and risk rating systems (Fig. 1). Data on climate and management resources, practices and options can be integrated with the beetle and forest inventory information and utilized in various models (Fig. 1). Susceptibility, risk and population dynamics/impact models can be used by managers to set priorities and evaluate management scenarios based on projections of the course of infestations.

The first references to mountain pine beetle (*Dendroctonus ponderosae* Hopk. [Coleoptera: Scolytidae]) in western North America were in 1899 in the United States (Hopkins 1899) and 1912 in Canada (Swaine 1912). Control efforts against the mountain pine beetle were first carried out in Oregon in 1910. From 1910 to the 1970s, most of the focus both in Canada and the USA was on studying the biology of the insect and on direct control activity. Much knowledge was gained on the biology of the beetle and its interaction with its hosts; however, less work was done on packaging this information into tools usable by managers of the forest resource.

Over time this has changed, as systems and models have been developed with the direct goal of supporting management. As computer technology has improved, the ability to encapsulate biological knowledge in tools usable by resource managers has grown in sophistication, leading to the development of decision support systems. Decision support systems typically capture expert knowledge and provide information, risk assessments or projections in a context which facilitates incorporation into the decision making process.

One of the first attempts at producing a management tool for bark beetles in western North America began with the sympatric species western pine beetle, *Dendroctonus brevicomis* Leconte, for which a hazard rating system was developed in the 1930s (Keene 1936). This work related tree characteristics of ponderosa pine to likelihood of western pine beetle attack. Beginning in the 1970s, quantitative work was begun on developing hazard rating systems for the mountain pine beetle. Subsequently, model development began with detailed population dynamics and impact models being produced. Advances in technology have led to spatial modelling tools being incorporated into the mountain pine beetle management environment.

In this chapter we introduce the evolution of mountain pine beetle decision support systems, with emphasis on those used in Canada. These include susceptibility (hazard) and risk rating systems, population dynamics, and impact and management models, both aspatial and spatial, at stand and landscape scales. We include discussion about, and examples of, their use in assisting managers to make informed decisions to minimize the impact of mountain pine beetle on lodgepole pine (*Pinus contorta* Dougl. ex Loud. var. *latifolia* Engelm.) forests.

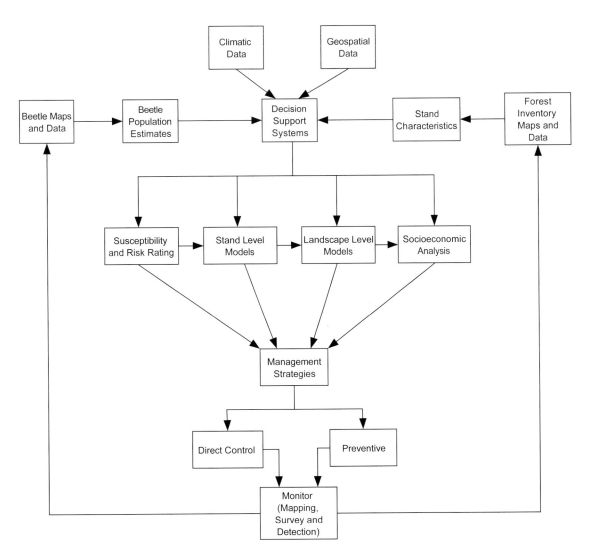

Figure 1. Schematic of decision support systems for the mountain pine beetle.

Susceptibility (Hazard) and Risk Rating Systems

Safranyik et al. (1975) produced a hazard map for mountain pine beetle in British Columbia more than 30 years ago. This map was developed from a model of climatic suitability to the mountain pine beetle based on long-term weather station data. It incorporated a number of climatic variables that were considered important to beetle establishment and survival. A number of hazard or risk rating systems aimed at stand level classification have since been developed for the mountain pine beetle (Amman et al. 1977; Mahoney 1978; Berryman 1978; Schenk et al. 1980; Waring and Pitman 1980; Stuart 1984; Anhold and Jenkins 1987). All of these systems, with the exception of Schenk et al. (1980), were categorical designs where stands would be classified as likely to be attacked or not (Mahoney 1978; Waring and Pitman 1980; Stuart 1984), or assigned to a high, moderate or low (or similar) hazard class (Amman et al. 1977; Berryman 1978; Anhold and Jenkins 1987).

The system of Amman et al. (1977) places the variables of tree diameter, elevation-latitude, and age to rate stands into categories of low, moderate or high hazard. Evaluations of this system generally indicated a low rate of accuracy with a tendency to over-rate stands (Mahoney 1978; Amman 1985; Shore et al. 1989; Bentz et al. 1993). One possible reason for the low accuracy of this system may be the assumption that diameter is related to phloem thickness, the beetle's primary feeding and breeding tissue in the tree. This relationship was not found by other researchers (Katovich and Lavigne 1986; Shrimpton and Thomson 1985).

Mahoney (1978) developed a two-class system based on the variable periodic growth ratio (PGR): the ratio of the most recent 5 years radial growth to the previous 5 years radial growth. Stands having a ratio of 0.9 or less were considered to be in declining vigour and therefore susceptible to attack, and those with a ratio greater than 0.9 were considered resistant to attack. This system was not able to predict losses accurately in subsequent tests (Shrimpton and Thomson 1983; Stuart 1984; Amman 1985; Shore et al. 1989; Bentz et al. 1993). A basic problem with the system is that stands generally decline in growth after about age 30; therefore, a ratio of less than 1.0 would be the norm for stands past this age (Shrimpton and Thomson 1983). Stands less than about 80 years of age, however, are not commonly known to be attacked by mountain pine beetle (Safranyik et al. 1974).

Berryman (1978) developed a theoretical model of stand susceptibility based on phloem thickness and stand resistance. This model had a relatively low rate of success at assigning stands into classes of extreme, high, and low susceptibility in subsequent tests (Amman 1985; Shore et al. 1989; Bentz et al. 1993). A shortcoming in this system may be the variable selected as an index of stand resistance. This variable consisted of the ratio between PGR and stand hazard rating (SHR) (Schenk et al. 1980), described below, and thus inherited the problems described for those indices (Katovich and Lavigne 1986).

The system developed by Waring and Pitman (1980) involves calculating growth efficiency as the ratio of current growth (grams of stemwood produced) to crown leaf surface. These variables are difficult to collect and calculate, and evaluations of this system have produced less than adequate results (Stuart 1984; Amman 1985; Katovich and Lavigne 1986; Shore et al. 1989).

Stuart (1984) developed a discriminant function to describe the probability of a stand falling into a susceptible or non-susceptible class for the mountain pine beetle. This function used the variables of quadratic mean tree diameter and number of rings in the outer one centimetre of radial growth. This relationship can only be considered valid for the small area from which the data was collected.

Anhold and Jenkins (1987) examined the relationship between Stand Density Index (SDI) (Reineke 1933) and beetle-caused tree mortality. They found that SDI was not a good predictor of decreasing or increasing populations; however, ranges of SDI values were found to coincide with low potential for attack, increasing potential for attack, and declining potential for attack. From a theoretical standpoint SDI would not appear to be a useful indicator of stand susceptibility to mountain pine beetle because it is the product of two variables, trees per hectare and quadratic mean diameter. Therefore, a single value of SDI could be determined, for example, by a combination of numerous trees of small diameter or fewer trees of large diameter. It is well known that the beetle shows a preference for larger diameter trees; therefore, it is unlikely that the two stands in this example would have similar susceptibility. It is likely that the findings of Anhold and Jenkins (1987) reflect mainly variations in stand density because only larger diameter trees (>12.7 cm dbh [diameter at breast height]) were included (Safranyik et al. 1974; Amman et al. 1977).

The system designed by Schenk et al. (1980) is the only one that attempted to produce a stand hazard rating (SHR) index that was a continuous variable, and relate it to tree mortality caused by the mountain pine beetle. SHR was calculated using crown competition factor (Krajicek et al. 1961), and the proportion of lodgepole pine basal area in the stand. Tests of this system found that crown competition factor (CCF) and therefore, SHR were inversely related to tree mortality caused by the beetle (McGregor et al. 1981; Shore et al. 1989, Bentz et al. 1993). The problem with the system appeared to be the assumption of a positive relationship between stand density and mountain pine beetle-caused tree mortality (Katovich and Lavigne 1986).

In 1992, Shore and Safranyik published a system incorporating the best features of previous systems. It was considered important to have a continuous variable hazard rating system because a two or three class system is not sensitive enough to provide managers with sufficient information to assign management priorities. Also, it was desirable that the hazard rating index relate to beetle-caused tree mortality. These were features of the Schenk et al. (1980) system. Important variables that are known to affect stand susceptibility are age (Safranyik et al. 1974; Amman et al. 1977; Shrimpton and Thomson 1983), tree diameter (Safranyik et al. 1974; Amman et al. 1977), and climate, which were components of the Amman et al. (1977) system. Some measure of inter-tree competition or stand density was also considered to be important as was attempted in the systems of Berryman (1978), Waring and Pitman (1980), Schenk et al. (1980), and Anhold and Jenkins (1987). In addition, we felt it important from a stand rating perspective to include a measure of the species composition of the stand, as did Schenk et al. (1980).

The Shore and Safranyik (1992) risk rating system incorporated estimators of both stand susceptibility and beetle pressure. The susceptibility rating system provides an index of potential loss of stand basal area in the event of a mountain pine beetle infestation and is, therefore, a long-term rating. The risk rating system provides a short-term index of the likelihood of this event occurring and causing significant losses to the stand.

In British Columbia, Alberta and parts of the western United States, the Shore and Safranyik (1992) system has been incorporated into forest management planning. This system considers stand risk as a function of both stand susceptibility to the mountain pine beetle and beetle population pressure on the stand. The logic behind this is that, from a management perspective, knowledge is required on both the susceptibility of stands and on the size and location of mountain pine beetle populations. A susceptible stand can be at low risk if there is no beetle population present. This general concept of risk as a function of host susceptibility and pest numbers had previously been defined (e.g., Nebeker and Hodges 1985; Paine et al. 1983, 1984). We use the term "susceptibility" synonymously with "hazard" but find it a more self explanatory term to describe the characteristics of a tree, stand or landscape that indicate its level of suitability to the mountain pine beetle. Risk, on the other hand, incorporates a measure of the beetle population into the equation. We define risk as a function of susceptibility and beetle pressure.

In this section we describe the Shore and Safranyik (1992) susceptibility and risk rating system, including a discussion on its use and some modifications. These modifications include the replacement of discrete functions with continuous functions for age, stand density, and beetle pressure, as well as the introduction of an additional susceptibility and risk rating system for the pine component of a stand (pine susceptibility and risk). The rationale for replacing discrete functions with continuous functions for age, stand density, and beetle pressure is to provide more of a gradual transition in susceptibility and risk related to these factors. For example, with the discrete age classes, an 80-year-old stand would be rated considerably less susceptible than an 81-year-old stand with all other factors being equal. With the continuous function for age there will be little difference between the two example stands.

Pine susceptibility and risk are introduced as additional rating systems to address an issue that often causes confusion with the stand susceptibility and risk rating system. In the system, a stand can be rated low and still experience a mountain pine beetle infestation. This is because the stand as a whole is rated; therefore, if only a small part of it is composed of susceptible pine it will be rated low. There will still be a viable stand after the mountain pine beetle. However, this does not address the concern of a forest manager interested in knowing where the susceptible pine is that may contribute to an infestation of mountain pine beetle. By introducing a second system that rates the susceptibility and risk of the pine component of stands, the forest manager can determine where the most susceptible stands are as well as where stands containing susceptible pine are. For further information on the rationale, validation and use of this rating system see Shore and Safranyik (1992) and Shore et al. (2000).

Calculating the stand susceptibility, beetle pressure and stand risk indices

Calculating the stand susceptibility index (SSI)

The susceptibility index for a given stand is based on four variables: relative abundance of susceptible pine basal area in the stand, age of dominant and co-dominant live pine, the density of the stand, and the location (latitude, longitude and elevation) of the stand.

The expression for calculating the stand susceptibility index (SSI) is

$$SSI = P \times A \times D \times L \qquad [1]$$

where

P is the percentage of susceptible pine basal area
A is the age factor
D is the density factor, and
L is the location factor.

Percentage susceptible pine basal area factor (P)

The percentage of susceptible pine basal area (P) is unchanged from the original system and is calculated as:

$$P = \frac{[\text{average basal area/ha of pine} \geq 15 \text{ cm dbh}] \times 100}{[\text{average basal area/ha of all species} \geq 7.5 \text{ cm dbh}]} \qquad [2]$$

where dbh is diameter at breast height.

Age factor (A)

The age factor (A) from the original system was a categorical variable broken into age classes as follows:

Table 1. Determination of the age factor (A) in original Shore and Safranyik (1992) Stand Susceptibility Index.

If the average age of dominant or co-dominant pine is:	Then the age factor (A) is:
less than or equal to 60 years	0.1
61-80 years	0.6
more than 80 years	1.0

The age factor ratings from Table 1 are replaced by a series of equations that result in a continuous function that will prevent jumps in values at the class limits (Table 2).

Table 2. Determination of the age factor (A) using current continuous functions

If the average age of dominant or co-dominant pine is:	Then the age factor (A) is:
40-80 years	$0.1 + 0.1[[\text{age}-40]/10]^{1.585}$
81–120 years	1.0
121-510 years	$1.0 - 0.05[(\text{age}-120)/20]$
Less than 40 or greater than 510	0.1

Density factor (D)

The stand density factor (D) from the original system was a categorical variable broken into several classes as follows:

Table 3. Determination of the density factor (D) in original Shore and Safranyik (1992) Stand Susceptibility Index.

If the density of the stand in stems per ha (all species ≥7.5 cm dbh) is:	Then the density factor (D) is:
less than or equal to 250	0.1
251 - 750	0.5
751 – 1,500	1.0
1,501 – 2,000	0.8
2,001 – 2,500	0.5
more than 2,500	0.1

As with age factor, density factor is now calculated using a series of equations that result in a continuous function that will prevent jumps in values at the class limits (Table 4).

Table 4. Determination of the density factor (D) using current continuous functions

If the density of the stand in stems per ha (sph) (all species ≥7.5 cm dbh) is:	Then the density factor (D) is:
Less than 650	$0.0824 \, [\text{sph}/250]^{2.0}$
650 - 750	$1.0 - 0.7 \, [3-\text{sph}/250]^{0.5}$
751 - 1500	1.0
Greater than 1500	$1.0 / [0.9 + [0.1e^{(0.4796[\text{sph}/250-6])}]]$

Location factor (L)

The location factor (L) remains unchanged from the original system. There is ongoing research that may result in this variable eventually being replaced by a climatic suitability index (Carroll et al. 2004).

There are three possible location factors (1.0, 0.7, and 0.3). The manner in which the location factor varies with latitude, longitude, and elevation is shown in Figure 2 (unlike the figure, the relationship is not limited to British Columbia). To determine the location factor for a particular stand, a parameter (Y) from the following equation is first determined:

$$Y = [24.4 \text{ Longitude}] - [121.9 \text{ Latitude}] - [\text{Elevation (m)}] + [4545.1] \qquad [5]$$

The location factor is then determined from the value of Y using Table 5.

Table 5. Location factor values.

If Y is:	Then the location factor (L) is:
greater than or equal to 0	1.0
between 0 and -500	0.7
less than -500	0.3

Once the variables P, A, D and L are determined for a stand, the Stand Susceptibility Index (SSI) is calculated as the simple product of the four as defined above: SSI = P x A x D x L

Stand susceptibility indices will range from 0 to 100. The highest values indicate the most susceptible stands (Fig. 3).

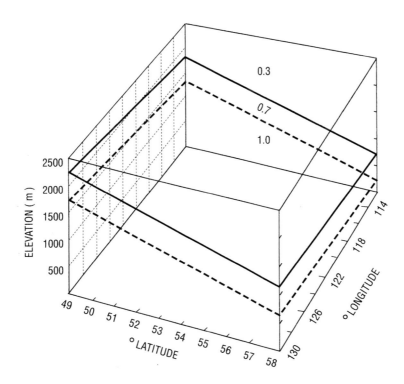

Figure 2. The relationship between latitude, longitude and elevation as related to mountain pine beetle susceptibility in British Columbia (from Shore and Safranyik 1992).

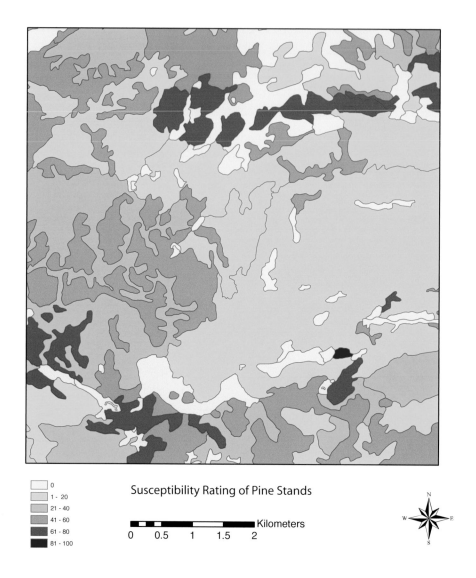

0
1 - 20
21 - 40
41 - 60
61 - 80
81 - 100

Susceptibility Rating of Pine Stands

Kilometers
0   0.5   1   1.5   2

Figure 3. Map showing stand susceptibility index values associated with forest inventory polygons.

Determining the beetle pressure index

Beetle pressure is related to the size and proximity of a mountain pine beetle population that is affecting the stand being rated. To determine the beetle pressure index (B), the size category of the infestation is determined from Table 6. After the size category of the infestation has been determined, the beetle pressure index was previously determined by distance categories in Table 7, but is currently determined using the continuous functions contained in Table 8.

Table 6. Use this table to determine the relative size of a mountain pine beetle infestation within 3 km of the stand being rated.

Number of Infested Trees Outside Stand Within 3 km	Number of Infested Trees Inside the Stand		
	Less than 10	10 to 100	More than 100
Less than 900	Small	Medium	Large
900 to 9,000	Medium	Medium	Large
More than 9,000	Large	Large	Large

Table 7. Categorical table originally used to determine the beetle pressure index (B) from infestation size (determined from Table 6) and the distance from the stand being rated to the nearest edge of the mountain pine beetle infestation.

Relative Infestation Size	Distance to Nearest Beetle Infestation (km)					
	In Stand	0 - 1	1 - 2	2 - 3	3 - 4	4 +
Small	0.6	0.5	0.4	0.3	0.1	0.06
Medium	0.8	0.7	0.6	0.4	0.2	0.08
Large	1.0	0.9	0.7	0.5	0.2	0.10

Table 8. Continuous functions currently used to determine the beetle pressure index (B) from infestation size (determined from Table 6) and the distance from the stand being rated to the nearest edge of the mountain pine beetle infestation.

Relative Infestation Size	Distance (D) to Nearest Beetle Infestation (km)	
	0 – 4.5	4.5 +
Small	0.582 – [0.123 x D]	0.03
Medium	0.803 – [0.163 x D]	0.06
Large	1.003 – [0.209 x D]	0.07

Calculating the stand risk index

The stand risk index (SRI) is calculated as follows:

$$\text{SRI} = 2.74\,[\text{SSI}^{1.77}e^{-.0177\text{SSI}}]\,[\text{B}^{2.78}e^{-2.78\text{B}}] \qquad [6]$$

where: e = the base of natural logarithms = 2.718

B = Beetle pressure index

SSI = Stand Susceptibility index

Alternatively, the stand risk index value can be found in Table 9. If the exact value of the beetle pressure index or stand susceptibility index is not represented in the table, an approximate risk index can be determined using the closest values represented, or it can be interpolated between the two closest values found in the table. The risk index will range between 0 and 100, with the highest values representing stands that would be expected to receive the most damage by the mountain pine beetle in the near future.

Table 9. The mountain pine beetle stand risk index as a function of the stand susceptibility and beetle pressure indices.

Stand Susceptibility (SSI)	Beetle Pressure (B)									
	0.1	0.2	0.3	0.4	0.5	0.6	0.7	0.8	0.9	1
10	<1	<1	2	3	5	6	7	8	8	8
20	<1	3	6	10	14	18	20	22	24	24
30	<1	4	10	17	24	30	35	39	41	41
40	1	6	14	24	34	42	49	54	57	57
50	1	8	18	30	42	52	61	67	70	71
60	2	9	20	34	48	61	70	77	81	83
70	2	10	22	38	53	67	78	85	89	91
80	2	10	24	40	56	71	82	90	95	96
90	2	10	24	41	58	73	85	93	98	99
100	2	11	25	42	59	74	86	94	99	100

Rationale for the stand susceptibility and risk indices

The rationale for selecting the variables, thresholds, weights and models included in the risk rating system are presented here. This section is not a literature review on any of the system components, but a few key references are provided to substantiate the logic and provide a starting point for further reading.

In developing the risk rating system, we chose a heuristic rather than a statistical approach. That is, we selected variables we considered to be key factors and assigned weights to these based on current knowledge, logic, and experience with the beetle.

The following criteria were considered important components of an operational risk rating system:

- it should account for both the beetle pressure and stand susceptibility components of mountain pine beetle damage,

- most of the required data should be obtainable from existing forest inventory data and minimal field work should be required to obtain the remainder,

- a continuous-scale index value should be provided for each stand,

- the risk index should relate directly to basal area and volume killed by mountain pine beetle,

- most of the variables included in the stand susceptibility index should be manipulable by silviculture,

- the beetle pressure component of the risk index should be manipulable by direct control pest management methods.

Susceptibility index

For the stand susceptibility component of our model, we chose four variables as indicators of a stand's susceptibility to mountain pine beetle: relative abundance of larger diameter pine, age of dominant and co-dominant pine, stand density, and location. All four variables may not be key factors for any given stand, but their inclusion in the model provides a responsive system that we believe is generally applicable. The weights for these four variables are simply multiplied together, implying that each variable holds equal weight in its contribution towards stand susceptibility and that the overall effect is multiplicative rather than additive. While this may be arguable in certain situations, overall we considered it to be a reasonable assumption.

Percentage of susceptible pine basal area (P)

Susceptible pine basal area (P) is a complex variable that incorporates the effects of diameter and stand composition on stand susceptibility to mountain pine beetle. Basal area is defined as the cross sectional area of a tree at breast height and is related to volume.

Diameter

The beetles show a visual preference for wider objects (Shepherd 1966). Attack correlates positively with diameter, and trees less than 12.5 cm in diameter are rarely attacked (Hopping and Beall 1943). Trees of larger diameter are attacked to a greater height (Cahill 1960) and more intensely (Cole and Amman 1969) than smaller trees. Mountain pine beetle reproduces and survives better in trees of larger diameter (Cole and Amman 1969), and the beetles produced in these trees are larger and perhaps of better quality (Safranyik and Jahren 1970). Trees of larger diameter generally have thicker phloem, which results in more food for the beetles. They also tend to have thicker bark, which provides better protection from desiccation, cold, and enemies than thin bark provides. Diameter is generally correlated with age and older trees are less resistant to the beetle (Shrimpton 1973). On average, the number of emerging brood beetles only exceeded the number of attacking parent beetles in trees 25 cm dbh and larger (Safranyik et al. 1974). We selected 15 cm as a threshold for the susceptible pine component because trees less than this diameter are not commonly attacked in significant numbers and if they are, they will not support significant brood production.

This threshold may seem low in some regions, but significant mortality can occur in smaller trees during a major epidemic and we felt it was better to be conservative than to underestimate stand susceptibility. The threshold of 7.5 cm for basal area of all species in the stand was selected because this is a common minimum tree diameter for inclusion in forest inventories.

Stand composition

Mountain pine beetle attacks the pine component of mixed lodgepole pine stands as readily as it does pure lodgepole pine stands (Amman and Baker 1972). Nonetheless, it seems logical that the probability of beetles successfully finding and attacking a lodgepole pine tree would diminish as the number of non-host species in a stand increases. Also, the probability of an epidemic arising from an endemic situation in a stand would likely decrease with the number of non-host trees in a stand. Hopping (1961) states that mountain pine beetle outbreaks seldom originate in mixed stands, although we have seen situations where this is the case. The potential for basal area loss to the stand as a whole will be less in a mixed stand than in a pure stand. In other words, even if all the larger diameter pine are killed in a mixed stand, it will still have live basal area in other species or in smaller diameter pine; therefore, risk of loss in the stand is lower than that of a pure stand. Depending on the proportion of the pine killed, a release effect may occur on surviving pine and on the non-host trees which may lessen the impact in mixed stands (Heath and Alfaro 1990). The P variable in the susceptibility index indicates what percentage of a stand's total basal area is susceptible to the beetle or, conversely, whether or not a viable stand would still exist if a mountain pine beetle epidemic resulted in the removal of the large diameter pine.

Age of the dominant and co-dominant pine component of the stand

Age has been shown to be directly related to a tree's ability to resist infection by the fungi carried and introduced into successfully attacked trees by the mountain pine beetle (Shrimpton 1973). These fungi quickly penetrate the conductive tissues thereby killing the tree in a few weeks (Safranyik et al. 1974). Trees 31 to 50 years old were found to be the most resistant to fungal infection; resistance declined progressively in older trees (Shrimpton 1973). Diameter is generally related to age and, as mentioned earlier, beetles prefer larger trees. For stands, the point of physical maturity determined by the intersection of current annual increment and mean annual increment can be considered as an age threshold for attack (Shrimpton and Thomson 1981; 1983). In British Columbia, outbreaks are rarely reported in stands less than 60 years of age (except in cases of severe epidemic). Similarly, beetle-caused mortality is less common between 60 and 80 years of age, but common in stands older than 90 years (Safranyik et al. 1974). We, therefore, assigned values to the pine age component of our susceptibility index such that stands less than 60 years of age have a low age component of susceptibility, stands between 60 and 80 years old have an intermediate age component of susceptibility, and stands over 80 years old have a high age component of susceptibility. Lodgepole pine older than about 150 years, although relatively rare in British Columbia, seem to be less often attacked by the mountain pine beetle. This may reflect the reduced growth rate and relatively thinner phloem associated with these older trees. Our age model reflects this gradual reduction in susceptibility in older stands.

The age model is theoretical and not empirically derived. The equation presented is not meant to imply precision of knowledge of the relationship between age and susceptibility, but to provide smooth interpolation between generally understood relationships as described above.

Stand density

There are a number of ways in which stand density affects the susceptibility of pine stands to the mountain pine beetle. Stand density affects tree diameter: dense stands produce small-diameter trees and low-density stands produce trees of larger diameter. Density also affects tree vigour through the increasingly adverse effects of competition for light and nutrition. Thinned stands have been shown to be more resistant to mountain pine beetle damage (McGregor et al. 1987; Amman et al. 1988a,b) both through improvement in tree vigour (Mitchell et al. 1983) and by altering the microclimate (Amman et al. 1988a; Bartos and Amman 1989). Vigourous trees are more able to resist beetle attacks by producing copious flows of resin to "pitch out" attacking beetles (Reid et al. 1967). Mountain pine beetle is affected adversely by microclimate changes in thinned stands including increased light and temperatures on the bole, and increased wind movement in the stand (Bartos and Amman 1989). An inverse relationship between tree mortality caused by the beetle and stand density, as measured by crown competition factor, has been shown (McGregor et al. 1981; Shore et al. 1989). When low density stands are included, a left-skewed distribution occurs when mortality is plotted against stand density (Anhold and Jenkins 1987), indicating low mortality at low stand densities, rapidly increasing mortality at intermediate stand densities, then tailing off at high stand densities. From thinning studies we know that little mortality from the beetle occurs in stands with fewer than 250 stems per ha (Amman et al. 1988a,b) or in very dense stands of more than 2,500 stems per ha. From a theoretical standpoint, the relationship between beetle-caused tree mortality and stand density has to go through the origin because when there are no trees there can be no mortality. Our observations of basal area mortality suggest that the highest mortality occurs in intermediate stand densities of 750 - 1500 stems per hectare. We considered all of this information in developing our stand density model.

The stand density model is theoretical and not empirically derived. The equation presented is not meant to imply precision of knowledge of the relationship between stand density and susceptibility, but to provide smooth interpolation between generally understood relationships as described above.

Location (elevation, latitude, longitude)

Elevation, latitude and longitude influence stand susceptibility through their effects on mountain pine beetle survival. At higher elevations, or more northerly latitudes, or easterly longitudes, the beetle's development cycle will be extended (Hopkins 1919) and it is more likely to be exposed to cold temperatures during vulnerable stages, which increases mortality (Amman 1973). Also, the extended development cycle exposes the beetle to natural enemies for a longer period of time. Tree mortality from beetles is inversely related to elevation (Amman et al. 1973). The elevation zones between which we have observed differences in beetle survival were adjusted for latitude and longitude using Hopkins' bioclimatic law (Hopkins 1919) to arrive at three location classes (Fig. 2). It is not possible to visually determine the location weighting of a stand from Figure 2 unless the stand is at an extreme point on the graph; therefore, the thresholds between classes were described by a mathematical equation.

Beetle pressure index

We included two variables in our measurement of beetle pressure: beetle population size, and proximity of infested trees to the stand being assessed. There are many other variables that could have been included such as beetle population trend, prevailing wind direction, and the size of the stand that, perhaps, would improve the accuracy and precision of this component of the model. The variables we selected represent a compromise between ease of use and potential accuracy and precision.

Tables 6, 7 and 8 contain several thresholds relating to the size and proximity of infestations surrounding the stand being rated. These attempt to express, in the form of an index, the interaction between number and proximity of infested trees and their relationship to the likelihood of a mountain pine beetle population entering the stand. The likelihood of beetles entering a stand from an infestation 3 km away is obviously greater if that infestation is large rather than just a few trees in size. If, however, just a few trees are infested in the stand, the likelihood of infestation becomes 100 percent. The threshold numbers of trees and distances were based largely on observations made during population and dispersal studies over the past 30 years (e.g., Safranyik 1969; Safranyik et al. 1989).

Risk index

The risk index is an indicator of the short-term risk of loss of stand basal area to the mountain pine beetle. It indicates risk only in the short term because beetle pressure changes annually, and once a stand is being attacked its susceptibility will drop annually as the larger live pine component is reduced.

The risk index is calculated using equation [6], which is based on the susceptibility index and beetle pressure index. This non-linear relationship between these three variables is seen in Figure 4.

Calculating the pine susceptibility and pine risk indices

Pine susceptibility and pine risk rating systems serve a different purpose than stand susceptibility and stand risk rating systems. Pine susceptibility and risk indicate the susceptibility and risk of the pine component of a stand, whereas stand susceptibility and risk rate the stand as a whole. For example, a stand containing a small percentage of mature pine will have low stand susceptibility. In this case, even if mountain pine beetle were to kill all the pine, the stand as a whole would suffer only low levels of mortality. The pine susceptibility would be higher than the stand susceptibility, indicating that there is potential in that stand for mountain pine beetle to become established and cause some level of mortality. This concept will be discussed further in the section, Practical Considerations.

Calculation of the pine susceptibility index (PSI)

Pine susceptibility is defined as the inherent characteristics of the pine component of a stand that affect its likelihood of attack and damage by the mountain pine beetle. It is calculated as follows:

$$PSI = 100.0/(1+EXP(-(P-22.7)/5.3)) \times A \times L \times D \qquad [7]$$

Where:

EXP = base of natural logarithms

P = Percentage of susceptible pine basal area

A = Age factor

L = Location factor

D = Density factor

SSI = Stand susceptibility index

The variables defined above have the following restrictions:

If PSI < SSI then PSI = SSI; if SSI = 0 then PSI = 0

Rationale for the pine susceptibility index

This equation was developed on the premise that the P factor in Shore and Safranyik (1992) reflects the proportion of a stand's total basal area that is composed of susceptible pine. The degree of susceptibility of that pine component is related to the magnitude of this proportion (P) in a non-linear fashion (see Table 10). The following examples illustrate the basis for this relationship. Assume A, L and D = 1 (most susceptible): When P is 100 then all of the pine is deemed susceptible, therefore PSI is also 100. If P is greater than 50 (meaning 50% of the stands basal area is composed of susceptible pine), the susceptibility of the pine component changes very little and remains close to 100%. As the percentage of susceptible pine decreases below 50% however, it is assumed that the mountain pine beetle will have increasing difficulty locating suitable host trees in the stand. This dispersion of host trees in the stand can also disrupt the timing and success of breeding and subsequent dispersal. As a result, the pine component of the stand decreases in susceptibility (PSI) more rapidly as P takes on values lower than 50% (Table 10).

Table 10. The relationship between P (percentage of susceptible pine basal area) and PSI (pine susceptibility index) assuming A, D and L values of 1.

A	D	L	P	SSI	PSI
1	1	1	0	0	0
1	1	1	5	5	5
1	1	1	10	10	10
1	1	1	20	20	37.5
1	1	1	30	30	79.9
1	1	1	40	40	96.3
1	1	1	50	50	99.4
1	1	1	60	60	99.9
1	1	1	70	70	100.0
1	1	1	80	80	100.0
1	1	1	90	90	100.0
1	1	1	100	100	100.0

Pine risk: The short term expectation of pine tree mortality in a stand as a result of a bark beetle infestation.

Calculation of the pine risk index:

$$PRI = 2.74 \, [PSI^{1.77} e^{-.0177PSI}][B^{2.78} e^{-2.78B}] \qquad [8]$$

Where:

PSI = Pine Susceptibility Index (above)

B = Beetle Pressure Index (from Shore and Safranyik 1992)

This equation simply replaces SSI with PSI in the risk equation used for calculating stand risk index.

Practical considerations

Interpretation of susceptibility and risk indices

The stand susceptibility index (SSI) is an indicator of the potential loss in stand basal area or volume that could occur if mountain pine beetle infested a particular stand. This index can be used in preventive management to identify which stands, or groups of stands on a landscape, should receive management priority to reduce potential loss to the beetle (Fig. 3 and see Chapter 7). It could also be considered an index of a stand's capacity to produce beetles in the event it is attacked. In this sense, it could be used to set priorities for direct control treatment during incipient or early epidemic mountain pine beetle infestations.

Susceptibility indices are longer-term than risk indices and need to be periodically updated to reflect changes in stand structure due to growth or depletions. Risk indices incorporate both the susceptibility indices and the beetle pressure indices (Fig. 4).

Stand susceptibility and risk indices indicate the potential for loss to the stand as a whole from the mountain pine beetle. Pine susceptibility and risk indicate the potential for loss to the pine component of a stand. By definition, stands with high stand susceptibility will also have high pine susceptibility. By looking at stands with medium to low stand susceptibility, the pine susceptibility index highlights stands where the mountain pine beetle could build up or spread to other stands. The indices should be used together to provide a more complete picture of potential loss and habitat for the mountain pine beetle on which to base preventive management or direct control decisions.

The range of values for these indices will vary by geographic region so we have not defined ranges of discrete categories such as low, moderate, and high. The highest values may only be in the 40 or 50 range in some areas, whereas in others they may be in the 80 or 90 range. Also, depending on the intended use of the ratings, the sensitivity of the system may be lost by going from a 100-point rating system to a small number of broad categories. Therefore, we have left interpretation to the discretion of the user. Through local knowledge and observation of the relationship between index values and resultant mountain pine beetle-caused tree mortality, logical categories can be derived locally which will relate to operational management decisions.

One important consideration that has become increasingly evident during the current enormous mountain pine beetle epidemic in British Columbia is that the stand susceptibility rating system is not intended for use under such unusual beetle population pressure conditions (Ebata 2004). Susceptibility and risk rating systems are planning tools used to reduce stand and landscape level susceptibility to the beetle during endemic, incipient or early epidemic population conditions or to reduce beetle pressure in expanding population situations. Once a large-scale epidemic is in motion, it is not uncommon for beetles to attack trees as small as 8 to 10 cm, in younger age classes, and in a variety of density classes where hosts become limited in relation to the population of beetles. The mountain pine beetle will not successfully reproduce in most of these stands and the net effect will be that these stands are a "sink" rather than a "source" for beetle populations. Nevertheless, the usefulness of susceptibility and risk indices under these circumstances is diminished.

Validation and interpretation of the stand susceptibility index

The key question, "Does the stand susceptibility index relate to tree mortality caused by the mountain pine beetle?" and the related question, "What does a particular stand susceptibility index value mean?" were addressed by Shore et al. (2000). As stated above, the SSI is a relative value, the range of which could vary widely between forest management units. To a degree, experience with the system and the mountain pine beetle will give a forest manager a sense for which values of SSI may be more cause for concern than others in his or her management unit. Shore et al. (2000) examined 38 stands in which a mountain pine beetle infestation had come and gone and rated the SSI for the stands as they would have been before the beetle infestation. The SSI was then related to the percentage of stand basal area killed. The resultant regression was:

Percent basal area killed = 0.68 x SSI   [9]

This equation reduced the variation in the dependent variable, uncorrected for the mean, by 86% (Steel and Torrie 1980) (Fig. 5).

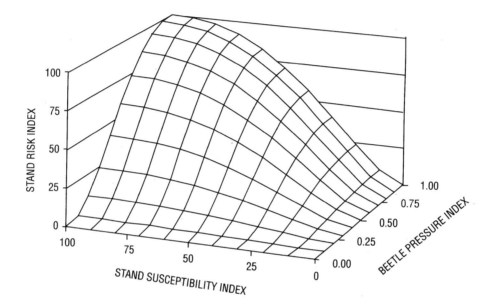

Figure 4. The stand risk index as a function of the stand susceptibility index and the beetle pressure index.

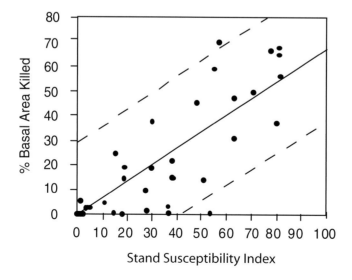

Figure 5. The relationship between the stand susceptibility index and percent basal area killed for 38 stands in the Cariboo region of British Columbia. Solid line represents the regression and broken lines represent the 95% prediction interval.

Putting a 95% prediction interval around this regression, and overlaying an independent data set consisting of data from 41 stands across British Columbia, 40 stands fell within the prediction interval (Fig. 6).

These results indicate that the stand susceptibility index is directly related to the susceptible basal area of the stand and is an index of the maximum mortality (in terms of percentage of stand basal area) a stand would receive in the event of a mountain pine beetle infestation under normal circumstances (see discussion above regarding major epidemic populations). It is useful as a long-term indicator of potential loss in the event of a beetle epidemic.

It is likely that a portion of the variation about the susceptibility versus percent basal area killed regression line is due to variability in mountain pine beetle population levels between stands. Additional variation would likely be attributable to differences in host resistance (Berryman 1978).

The susceptibility versus percent basal area killed model (equation 9) can be used to estimate the potential loss of stand basal area for stands that have been rated with a susceptibility index. A prediction interval can be assigned to the estimate. The 95% prediction interval shown in Figure 5 is rather broad (approximately ± 30 m^2 per ha) for single stand estimates with 95% probability, but this can be reduced considerably if a lower level of confidence is acceptable (e.g., approximately ± 19 m^2 per ha at the 80% probability level). In practice, use of the regression at the individual stand level is limited by its variability. The most likely way this relationship would be used is as an estimator of potential loss of basal area at the landscape level where the average susceptibility of a large number of stands is calculated. A confidence interval would then be constructed about the predicted mean basal area mortality. In such a situation, for a given probability level, the confidence interval around the mean would be considerably less than the prediction level in Figure 5 (Shore et al. 2000).

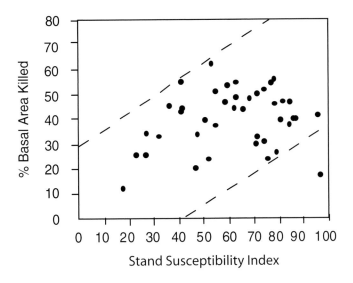

Figure 6. Overlay of data from 41 stands from across British Columbia on the 95% prediction interval shown in Figure 5.

Reduction of stand risk through forest and pest management

By understanding the components of the risk index, a number of forest and pest management activities that will lower the risk of a stand being damaged by the mountain pine beetle will become apparent. These can be grouped into two categories related to the two components of stand risk: reduction of stand susceptibility, and reduction of beetle pressure.

Reduction of stand susceptibility

Of the four variables composing the susceptibility index, the variables of age, density and percentage of the stand's basal area represented by susceptible pine can be altered through silvicultural practices. Through stocking control in young stands, thinning in specific situations, and applying organized clearcuts, age, size, and species mosaics can be created to break up the large, homogeneous, susceptible forest type that has resulted in major mountain pine beetle epidemics (Cole 1978). Reducing the ratio of large diameter pine to other size and species components by thinning "from above" will reduce the susceptibility index of the stand by reducing the relative abundance of susceptible pine, possibly reducing the average age of the pine component of the stand, and lowering stand density. This approach is perhaps best suited to mixed stands where species other than pine could be left that would respond well to removal of the overstory. In pure pine stands removal of larger pine could result in "high-grading", leaving inferior trees to produce a poor stand. The residual, smaller diameter pine may be susceptible to wind and snow breakage. Through stocking control in young stands and partial cutting in older stands, densities can be lowered below 750 stems per ha to reduce stand susceptibility. At these low densities larger and older pine can be left standing and the susceptibility will be relatively low (see Whitehead et al. Chapter 7 for more complete discussion).

Reduction of beetle pressure

Beetle pressure is determined by the size and proximity of the nearest group of trees infested by the mountain pine beetle to the stand being rated. Both the number and proximity of infested trees to a stand can be altered through "direct control" pest management techniques such as fell and burn, treatment with silvicides or insecticides, mechanical debarking and sanitation logging. The effectiveness of these treatments can be improved by the strategic use of semiochemicals such as pheromones (McMullen et al. 1986). See Carroll et al. (Chapter 6) for further discussion of direct control of mountain pine beetle.

Population dynamics, impact and management models

Models simulating mountain pine beetle activity have long been an important component of decision support, and many different types of models have been developed. With improvements in computer technology, more sophisticated modelling approaches have been used, and it is expected that this trend will continue. Following is a brief discussion on some of these approaches and models. This is not intended to be an exhaustive review of mountain pine beetle simulation models, but rather a brief exploration of some of the different modelling approaches that have been employed.

Empirical models based on life tables and life stages have been developed and used (Cole et al. 1985), and are often components of other modelling approaches. More theoretical models have also been developed. Burnell (1977) developed a dispersal-aggregation model based on the following three assumptions:

1. Pioneer beetles attack with random distribution over the available bark surface.
2. Every tree has a threshold of aggregation which is required to trigger aggregation.
3. Any tree which becomes an aggregator (as in assumption 2) will be mass attacked and killed.

Assumption 1 meant that trees would be attacked in proportion to the "barrier" presented to the flying beetles; there would be no active selection on the part of the beetle. However, larger diameter trees would tend to be attacked earlier due to the larger basal area presented. Assumption 2 was not meant to be a measure of the number of insects required to kill a tree, but rather the number and distribution of attacking beetles required to trigger aggregation. Assumption 3 may not be true in some cases, but simplified the model development. This theoretical model was fit to data from four stands that had been attacked by mountain pine beetle and found to provide a reasonable account for tree mortality by diameter class during an outbreak.

Cole and McGregor (1983) used a more empirical approach, and developed a rate of tree loss model that projected tree and volume losses per year and for the duration of an epidemic. At its time of development, this model differed from many other mountain pine beetle models because it did not follow a continuous-infection assumption, something common to models of epidemic processes. In analyzing and verifying this model it became clear that different habitat types displayed different tree mortality patterns during outbreaks. This led to the development of different rate of loss projections for differing habitats. One of the major strengths of this model was the ability to integrate it into existing forest management planning software. This design philosophy is common today (Beukema, et al. 1997; Fall et al. 2004, Riel et al. 2004) and is an important consideration for the development of decision support tools.

Raffa and Berryman (1986) developed a mechanistic model exploring mountain pine beetle population interactions with lodgepole pine stands. This model was based on laboratory and field studies from which equations and model assumptions were developed. This model was not intended to project numerical levels of beetle attack or damage, but rather patterns of population development of both *D. ponderosae* and other primary bark beetle species. It was used to evaluate management practices for controlling mountain pine beetle, and the results suggested that control efforts that directly influence stand vigour were the most effective long term strategies for reducing damage from beetle outbreaks.

Beyond the stand level, landscape scale simulation models have also been developed as decision support tools. Earlier technology did not permit spatially explicit modelling, thus aspatial landscape scale models have been developed. Thomson (1991) published a landscape scale model that explored the general impacts of various management strategies on a mountain pine beetle outbreak. Since then, spatially explicit approaches have become practical. The Westwide Pine Beetle Model (Beukema et al.1997) is one example of such an approach, designed to work within the framework of the Forest Vegetation Simulator (Wykoff et al. 1982) using a contagion paradigm to simulate beetle spread among stands, and to and from the "outside world" (i.e., the area surrounding the target landscape).

In addition, sophisticated mathematical approaches to modelling mountain pine beetle spatial dynamics have been employed. Polymenopoulos and Long (1990) developed a model of population growth with spatial diffusion that allows evaluation of the spatial spread of mountain pine beetle populations and the resulting damage. The variables used in the model are insect density, food availability, and insect diffusivity (spatial spread). For modelling mountain pine beetle dynamics, the density of killed (red-topped) trees was used as an index of population density. The model design is based on spatially discrete areas of mountain pine beetle habitat. Exchange of beetles among stands is assumed to be accomplished through random movement of individuals and an "attractive force" that directs movements toward a favourable environment. Two models were developed: a) a simple diffusion model that describes the number of lodgepole pine that would be killed if mountain pine beetle spread was a passive diffusion process, and b) a diffusion-convection model that describes the density of lodgepole pines that would be killed if mountain pine beetle were attracted to stands with thick phloem trees and if the rate of population increase was a function of the density of living lodgepole pine. The models were used to construct maps of density surfaces for killed lodgepole pine and were compared to a map showing the actual density surface for the same area. The initial results indicated that a 3-year history of mountain pine beetle dynamics (i.e., damage) is adequate for a 1-year projection of the spatial distribution and density of damage.

Powell et al. (1998) developed a spatially dynamic, forest-scale model (referred to as the global model) for mountain pine beetle dispersal and interaction with pine hosts. This is a probabilistic model based on a system of partial differential equations, and represents an attempt to capture the complex host tree-beetle interactions including chemical ecology, attack dynamics, beetle dispersal, resin outflow and resin capacity of individual trees. This model is well suited to broad descriptions of dispersal and attack but it is difficult to make comparisons with field data to assess whether or not the model represents a reasonable description of observed events.

Later, a "local" model, a system of ordinary differential equations, was developed to represent the consequences of the global model at the individual tree level to allow analysis of switching mountain pine beetle attacks from initial foci to nearby hosts (Powell et al. 1998). This theoretical analysis of a two-tree system strongly suggested that stand thinnings are successful mainly because of interference with the mountain pine beetle communication system. Tree vigour was found to play a major role only at very low emergence densities.

Logan et al. (1998) developed a spatially explicit model, based in part on the global model, of forest level interaction between the mountain pine beetle and its host. The model system describes the temporal dynamics of beetle attraction: as a function of the concentration of pheromones, change in the numbers of flying and attacking beetles, host tree resistance, and recovery of trees from attack. This model was used to explore the evolution of the spatial pattern of attacks by simulation. The main results indicated that, at endemic levels, the pattern of successful attacks is determined mainly by the spatial distribution of susceptible hosts. During development of an outbreak, the spatial pattern of successful attacks is driven by the pattern of a self-generated semiochemical landscape. Synchrony of adult emergence was critical for overcoming host resistance and spatial proximity to brood trees was an important factor in subsequent successful attacks.

Powell et al. (2000) combined different mathematical approaches to develop a method for assessing the risk of attack by mountain pine beetle on individual hosts. The dispersal and focusing behaviour of the beetle is achieved by the density-based global model, and local projection of this model predicts the consequences of the density equations at individual trees. Natural division of risk into categories of high, medium and low is accomplished by the so-called bifurcation diagram of the density equations. Preliminary results from this model suggested that host vigour and stand age has much less affect on the risk of mountain pine beetle attack than stand microclimate.

Modelling in western Canada

While models of various scales and approaches have been developed and applied in many locations within the range of mountain pine beetle, we will focus specifically on models developed for (and in current use) in western Canada.

Thomson's (1991) landscape scale model was developed in direct response to a mountain pine beetle outbreak in British Columbia in the 1970s to mid 1980s. This was an aspatial model that operated at a relatively large scale. One advantage of this model was that data requirements were relatively simple and easy to acquire. The model was limited, however, in that the spatial dynamics and interaction between the beetle and management could not be captured. Its main strength was the ability to assess the sensitivity of the mountain pine beetle outbreak to various management strategies.

During the early 1990s, a stand level mountain pine beetle population dynamics model was developed to address questions at a much finer scale than the Thomson model (Safranyik et al. 1999). Even though operating at a much smaller scale, the processes captured in this model later allowed its use as a component in a spatially explicit landscape simulation.

The Safranyik population dynamics model

This population dynamics model (hereafter referred to as the "Safranyik model") is a complex process-based simulation of mountain pine beetle activity on a one hectare stand of pure lodgepole pine. The model simulates the process of host colonization, brood development and survival, predation and parasitism of mountain pine beetle as well as tree mortality (Safranyik et al. 1999). It can be used to explore and compare the effects of various management treatments on both the beetle and host stand.

The Safranyik model is composed of four main sections: two biological sections – the forest stand model and the mountain pine beetle biology model, and two non-biological sections – a management submodel and a section that controls input, output and interactive simulation. The original model was written in FORTRAN to run on a VAX 8650 under VMS. It has since been converted to the Windows platform and possesses a simple to use graphical user interface.

The forest stand submodel is based on variable density yield tables for lodgepole pine developed by Johnstone (1975) and simulates the growth (diameter at breast height, height, natural mortality) and yield of a pure, unmanaged lodgepole pine stand as a function of site quality, initial density, and age. The mountain pine beetle biology and management submodels simulate the processes of host colonization, brood development and survival, tree mortality, and control interventions (direct control, host density manipulation and biological control). The model simulates the course of a beetle infestation in a one hectare stand using a daily time step.

Although the number of adult beetles dispersing out of the area is calculated for each beetle generation, the fate of these beetles is not considered in the model. Stand parameters, temperature regime, host resistance, the initial size of the beetle population, and control interventions by type, magnitude, and duration, can all be specified at the beginning of each run.

The development of this model involved two approaches: 1) empirical models from published sources, and 2) conceptual models. The empirical models were based on regressions such as surface area equations or growth and yield functions, or they consisted of tabular data from which intermediate values were interpolated, such as the data for brood development as a function of temperature. The general structures of conceptual models and their parameters were based on published sources whenever data were available. The functions relating egg and larval survival to attack density were derived in this manner. Where data were not available, the parameters were derived from the known or assumed limits of the dependent variable and its rate of change with respect to the explanatory variable. In situations where only general information was available, the structure and parameters of submodels were developed on hypothetical grounds. For example, to examine the effects of bait on attack density and tree mortality, it was assumed that the inter-bait distance commonly used in operational programs was the practical limit for attraction or repellency, and that relative bait effects increase exponentially with bait density.

Model outputs are in the form of tables showing changes through time in a number of stand and insect variables, which can be plotted against each other, or as functions of time. A large number of variables are included in the simulation; only a subset of these variables, of interest mainly to forest managers and students of insect population dynamics, are output. Figure 7 shows a simplified flow chart, which demonstrates program flow.

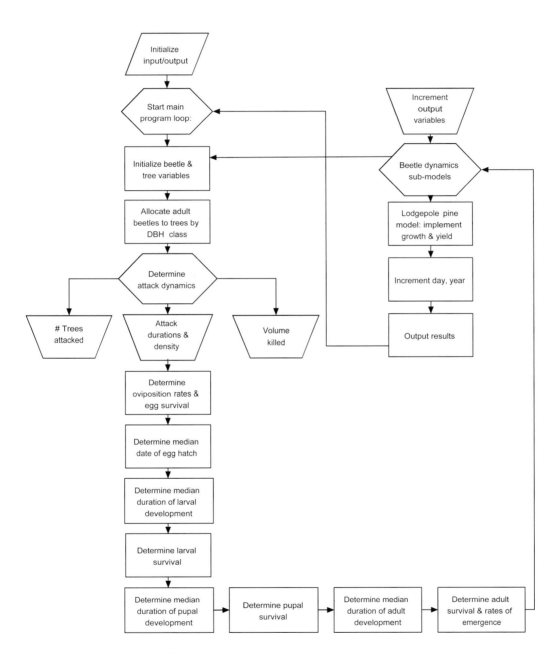

Figure 7. Safranyik model flow diagram (Safranyik et al. 1999).

Stand level simulation: MPBSIM

The Safranyik model represents a sophisticated approach to modelling mountain pine beetle activity and for exploring effects of management intervention at the scale at which it operates. However, the scale of the simulation restricts its utility as a tool for forest managers who must deal with larger stands and stands of mixed tree species. For these reasons, a new simulation called MPBSIM has been developed (Riel et al. 2004). MPBSIM is a stochastic, process based simulation of mountain pine beetle activity at the stand level. Host stands can be mixed species and can range in size from 1 ha to 50 ha. MPBSIM is a much coarser simulation than the Safranyik model; it simulates host selection, brood development and survival and beetle emergence and dispersal out of the stand on a yearly time step. Tree mortality is tracked on a year-by-year basis by different diameter at breast height (dbh) classes.

Similar to the Safranyik model, MPBSIM is composed of four main components: a mountain pine beetle population dynamics sub model, a stand sub model, a beetle management sub model and a graphical user interface for collecting inputs and displaying projected outputs.

MPBSIM input requirements include stand parameters and beetle information. Specifically, the following inputs are necessary for running the simulation:

- Stand size (in hectares);
- Stand age (in years);
- Stand site index (for lodgepole pine, expressed in metres at 50 years breast height age);
- Percent pine;
- Stand density (stems per hectare); and
- Number of attacking beetles (or number of currently attacked trees).

Even though the stand inputs are coarse stand parameters, MPBSIM requires diameter class structure and can use real or simulated tree lists. In the absence of such information, the stand sub model will generate a diameter class structure for the host pine based on the broader stand parameters.

The outputs generated by MPBSIM include:

- Projected duration of outbreak (in years);
- The number of trees killed each year;
- The volume of trees killed each year by diameter class;
- The number of beetles emerging each year; and
- The number of beetles dispersing out of the stand each year.

A highly simplified flow diagram depicting overall program flow in MPBSIM is shown in Figure 8.

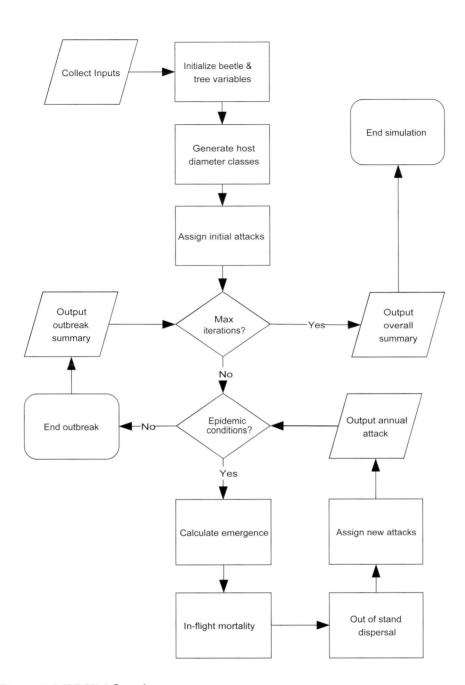

Figure 8. MPBSIM flow diagram.

Landscape level simulation: SELES-MPB

To effectively simulate a mountain pine beetle epidemic, a landscape scale simulation is important. A spatially explicit simulation allows a better platform for evaluating mountain pine beetle impacts and comparing various management strategies because it places the stands in a real world context with geospatial and beetle information. For these reasons, a spatially explicit landscape scale model has been developed using the Spatially Explicit Landscape Event Simulator (SELES) as a development platform (Fall and Fall 2001). SELES is not a model, but a raster-based platform in which to build and execute spatially explicit landscape models (Fall and Fall 2001). Every SELES model consists of three components:

1. Raster layers. These are the landscapes on which the simulation is executed. Layers can be base maps, forest inventory, road networks, etc.

2. Global variables. Global variables describe the state of the system.

3. Landscape events. Landscape events are the dynamic models that operate on (sometimes modifying) the landscape (raster layers). Landscape events can communicate indirectly through modifying the landscape.

The spatio-temporal model of mountain pine beetle spread and impact that was developed consists of several landscape events, including a spatially explicit mountain pine beetle spread model, a spatial timber harvesting model, a spatial mountain pine beetle management model, and an aspatial mountain pine beetle impact simulation. This model is referred to as SELES-MPB.

Model scaling and integration

To provide a satisfactorily detailed projection of mountain pine beetle impacts and to evaluate management effectiveness, it is preferable to generate stand level details of mountain pine beetle impacts even in a landscape model. For this reason, MPBSIM has been linked with the SELES landscape model as a landscape event. Because the purpose of SELES-MPB is to simulate beetle impacts and management strategies on real landscapes with unique climate and topography, it is important that MPBSIM projects beetle development and survival consistent with those conditions. To do this, MPBSIM is calibrated for the specific landscape using the Safranyik model.

The Safranyik model is capable of utilizing recorded daily temperatures for projecting mountain pine beetle development and survival as influenced by climate. To calibrate MPBSIM, temperature data from several weather stations located within the landscape are collected and adapted as inputs to the Safranyik model. A number of simulations are performed in a variety of stand conditions using these temperature data, and the resulting development and survival rates are used to calibrate MPBSIM.

Once MPBSIM has been calibrated to the local landscape climate, it can be incorporated into the landscape model using a loose coupling methodology (Chang 2001). This is accomplished by collecting a complete range of inventory data for the landscape in question and pre-running MPBSIM for as many conditions as possible at a large number of different initial beetle attack levels. This can amount to well over one million different combinations. A variety of values and indicators are output and collated in a large table which includes stand information (number of stems per hectare, stand age, percent pine, site index) and beetle activity information (number of attacking beetles, number of dispersing beetles, number of beetles emerging next year, trees killed and tree volume killed). This table reflects MPBSIM's projection of mountain pine beetle activity for any condition that exists on the landscape. (Fig. 9).

The MPBSIM generated table is integrated into SELES-MPB as a landscape event, along with the spatial harvesting model and management model (Fig. 10). These landscape events do not directly communicate with each other, but can impact each other by making changes on the landscape (spatial landscape layers).

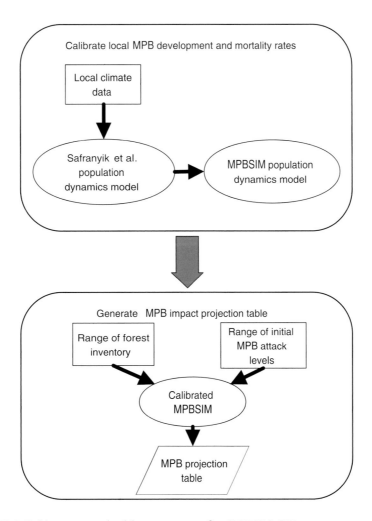

Figure 9. MPBSIM Calibration and table generation for SELES-MPB.

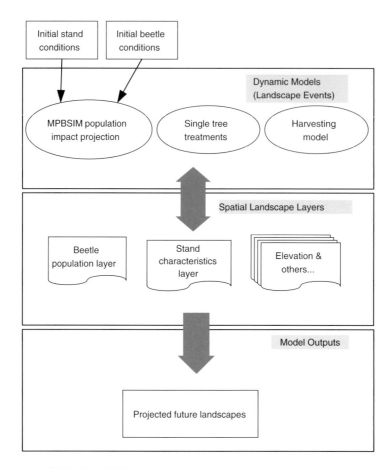

Figure 10. Overview of SELES-MPB.

Model applications

The modelling approach described above has been successfully applied in several districts within the provinces of British Columbia and Alberta (including the Kamloops, Lakes and Morice timber supply areas and the Foothills model forest), exploring the effectiveness of mountain pine beetle management, the impacts of mountain pine beetle on timber supply and other concerns (Fall et al. 2004). In each landscape the questions may be quite different, thus requiring different simulation scenarios, but in every case a "base" scenario is generated and used to compare against other scenarios.

Base scenarios are designed to address primary questions regarding the expected impact of beetle management. These can differ by study area, based on information obtained in workshops held with operational and management personnel. Some common features include application of current forest management policy, operational constraints (e.g., in one forest district, the amount of pine that could be harvested was constrained by a need to address concurrent outbreaks of balsam fir bark beetle [*Dryocoetes confusus* Swaine] and spruce bark beetle [*Dendroctonus rufipennis* Kirby]). Other differences encountered in different landscape simulations include the level of fine-scale treatments applied, harvest levels, differing forest cover constraints, etc. To put the effect of beetle management on the mountain pine beetle in a broad context, base scenarios are compared against a variety of scenarios, including those where no harvesting takes place, where beetle management is abandoned, and where forest policy constraints are disabled.

Outputs are typically tables, graphs and maps that can show a number of indicators including the following:

• Effectiveness of current management,

• Effects of altering harvest level,

• The likely trajectory of the mountain pine beetle across the landscape.

Conclusions

Decision support systems are valuable tools that make the accumulated knowledge of experts available to forest managers to assist them in making good decisions. The essential ingredients to mountain pine beetle decision support systems are reliable data on the forest resource and the location and size of the mountain pine beetle (Fig. 1). These data can be used to develop and assign hazard and risk rating values to stands in the management areas, which enables the manager to begin to set priorities for stand or beetle treatments. As a component of a decision support system, risk rating has a role in both long and short term planning and management.

Data on the forest resource and the beetle are also used as inputs to models, as well as other inputs such as geospatial, climate and management information. Within the context of decision support, modelling mountain pine beetle activity at different scales is important for different management questions. Many different approaches can and have been employed to build valuable decision support tools. Integrating models of different scales allows for a more detailed simulation of finer scale impacts and permits evaluation of management at appropriate levels of detail. For example, SELES-MPB has been used to address many questions surrounding mountain pine beetle activity and its management at relevant scales. Examples of questions addressed include:

• Where should different beetle management strategies be applied?

• What is the effect of an epidemic on the future timber supply?

• Would improved detection help the beetle management effort?

• What are the other resource implications of this epidemic and subsequent harvesting?

• Do any of the policy rules cause difficulties for beetle management?

Through the use of decision support systems we are able to better assign current priorities as well as forecast possible futures under different management scenarios. These models can only improve in the future as new knowledge and technologies become available to us.

References

Amman, G.D. 1973. Population changes of the mountain pine beetle in relation to elevation. Environmental Entomology 2:541-546.

Amman, G.D.; Baker, B.H. 1972. Mountain pine beetle influence on lodgepole pine stand structure. Journal of Forestry 70:204-209.

Amman, G.D.; Baker, B.H.; Stipe, L.E. 1973. Lodgepole pine losses to the mountain pine beetle related to elevation. USDA Forest Service, Intermountain Forest and Range Experiment Station, Research Note INT-171. 8 p.

Amman, G.D.; McGregor, M.D.; Cahill, D.B.; Klein, W.H. 1977. Guidelines for reducing losses of lodgepole pine to the mountain pine beetle in unmanaged stands in the Rocky Mountains. USDA Forest Service, Intermountain Forest and Range Experiment Station, General Technical Report INT-36, 19 p.

Amman, G.D. 1985. A test of lodgepole pine hazard rating methods for mountain pine beetle infestations in southeastern Idaho. Pages 186-200 *in* Safranyik, L., ed. Proceedings of an IUFRO Conference: The Role of the Host in the Population Dynamics of Forest Insects. Sept. 4-7, 1983, Banff, AB. Agriculture Canada, Ministry of State for Forestry, Pacific Forestry Centre, Victoria.

Amman, G.D.; Lessard, G.D.; Rasmussen, L.A.; O'Neil, C.G. 1988a. Lodgepole pine vigour, regeneration, and infestation by mountain pine beetle following partial cutting on the Shoshone National Forest, Wyoming. USDA Forest Service, Intermountain Research Station, Research Paper INT-396, 8 p.

Amman, G.D.; McGregor, M.D.; Schmitz, R.F.; Oakes, R.D. 1988b. Susceptibility of lodgepole pine to infestation by mountain pine beetles following partial cutting of stands. Canadian Journal of Forest Research 18:688-695.

Anhold, J.A.; Jenkins, M.J. 1987. Potential mountain pine beetle (Coleoptera: Scolytidae) attack of lodgepole pine as described by stand index. Environmental Entomology 16:738-742.

Bartos, D.L.; Amman, G.D. 1989. Microclimate: an alternative to tree vigour as a basis for mountain pine beetle infestations. USDA Forest Service, Intermountain Research Station, Research Paper INT-400, 10 p.

Bentz, B.J.; Amman, G.D.; Logan, J.A. 1993. A critical assessment of risk classification systems for the mountain pine beetle. Forest Ecology and Management 61:349-366.

Berryman, A.A. 1978. A synoptic model of the lodgepole pine/mountain pine beetle interaction and its potential application in forest management. Pages 98-103 *in* Berryman, A.A.; Amman, G.D.; Stark, R.W.; Kibbee, D.L., eds. Proceedings: Theory and practice of mountain pine beetle management in lodgepole pine forests. April 25-27, 1978, Pullman, WA. University of Idaho, Moscow, ID.

Beukema, S.J.; Greenough, J.A.; Robinson, D.C.E.; Kurz, W.E.; Smith, E.L.; Eav, B.B. 1997. The westwide pine beetle model: A spatially-explicit contagion model. Pages 126-130 *in* Teck, R.; Moeur, M.; Adams, J., eds. Proceedings: Forest Vegetation Simulator Conference. February 3-7, 1997, Fort Collins, CO. USDA Forest Service, Intermountain Research Station, Ogden, VT. General Technical Report INT-GIR-373. 222 p.

Burnell, D.G. 1977. A dispersal-aggregation model for mountain pine beetle in lodgepole pine stands. Researches on Population Ecology 19:99-106.

Cahill, D.B. 1960. The relationship of diameter to height of attack in lodgepole pine infested by mountain pine beetle. USDA Forest Service, Intermountain Forest and Range Experiment Station, Research Note 78, 4 p.

Carroll, A.C.; Taylor, S.W.; Régnière, J.; Safranyik, L. 2004. Effects of climate change on range expansion by the mountain pine beetle in British Columbia. Pages 223-232 *in* Shore, T.L.; Brooks, J.E.; Stone, J.E., eds. Proceedings of the mountain pine beetle symposium: Challenges and Solutions, October 30-31, 2003, Kelowna, British Columbia, Canada. Natural Resources Canada, Canadian Forest Service, Pacific Forestry Centre, Information Report BC-X-399. 298 p.

Chang, K. 2001. Introduction to Geographic Information Systems. McGraw-Hill. Boston. 348 p.

Cole, D.M. 1978. Feasibility of silvicultural practices for reducing losses to the mountain pine beetle in lodgepole pine forests. Pages 140-147 *in* Berryman, A.A.; Amman, G.D.; Stark, R.W.; Kibbee, D.L., eds. Proceedings: Theory and practice of mountain pine beetle management in lodgepole pine forests. April 25-27, 1978, Pullman, WA. University of Idaho, Moscow, ID.

Cole, W.E.; Amman, G.D. 1969. Mountain pine beetle infestations in relation to lodgepole pine diameters. USDA Forest Service, Intermountain Forest and Range Experiment Station, Research Note INT-95, 7 p.

Cole, W.E.; Amman, G.D.; Chester, E.J. 1985. Mountain pine beetle dynamics in lodgepole pine forests part III: sampling and modelling of mountain pine beetle populations. USDA Forest Service, Intermountain Research Station General Technical Report INT-188, 46 p.

Cole, W.E.; McGregor, M.D. 1983. Estimating the rate and amount of tree loss from mountain pine beetle infestations. USDA Forest Service, Intermountain Forest and Range Experiment Station, General Technical Report INT-318, 22 p.

Ebata, T. 2004. Current status of the mountain pine beetle in British Columbia. 2004. Pages 52-56 *in* Shore, T.L.; Brooks, J.E.; Stone, J.E., eds. Proceedings of the mountain pine beetle symposium: challenges and solutions, October 30-31, 2003, Kelowna, British Columbia, Canada. Natural Resources Canada, Canadian Forest Service, Pacific Forestry Centre, Information Report BC-X-399. 298 p.

Fall, A.; Fall, J. 2001. A domain-specific language for models of landscape dynamics. Ecological Modelling 141(1-3):1-18.

Fall, A.; Shore, T.L.; Safranyik, L.; Riel, W.G; Sachs, D. 2004. Integrating landscape scale mountain pine beetle projection and spatial harvesting models to assess management strategies. Pages 114-132 *in* Shore, T.L.; Brooks, J.E.; Stone, J.E., eds. Proceedings of the mountain pine beetle symposium: challenges and solutions, October 30-31, 2003, Kelowna, British Columbia, Canada. Natural Resources Canada, Canadian Forest Service, Pacific Forestry Centre, Information Report BC-X-399. 298 p.

Heath, R.; Alfaro, R.I. 1990. Growth response in a Douglas-fir/lodgepole pine stand after thinning of lodgepole pine by the mountain pine beetle: A case study. Journal of the Entomological Society of British Columbia 87:16-21.

Hopkins, A.D. 1899. Preliminary report on the insect enemies of forests in the northwest. USDA, Division of Entomology Bulletin, No. 21. 27 pp.

Hopkins, A.D. 1919. The bioclimatic law as applied to entomological research and farm practise. Scientific Monthly 8:496-513.

Hopping, G.R. 1961. Damage agents. Pages 77-99 *in* Smithers, L.A., ed. Lodgepole pine in Alberta. Canada Department of Forestry, Bulletin 127. 153 p.

Hopping, G.R.; Beall, G. 1948. The relation of diameter of lodgepole pine to incidence of attack by the bark beetle *Dendroctonus monticolae* Hopkins. Forestry Chronicle 24:141-145.

Johnstone, W. D. 1975. Variable stand density yields of natural lodgepole pine stands in Alberta. Pages 186-207 *in* Proceedings, Symposium on Management of Lodgepole Pine Ecosystems, October 9-11, 1973. Washington State University, Pullman, WA.

Katovich, S.A.; Lavigne, R.J. 1986. The applicability of available hazard rating systems for mountain pine beetle in lodgepole pine stands of southern Wyoming. Canadian Journal of Forest Research 16:222-225.

Keene, F.P. 1936. Relative susceptibility of ponderosa pines to bark beetle attacks. Journal of Forestry 34(16):919-927.

Krajicek, J.E.; Brinkman, K.A.; Gingrich, S.F. 1961. Crown competition – a measure of density. Forest Science 7:35-42.

Logan, J.A.; White, P.; Bentz, B.J.; Powell, J.A. 1998. Model analysis of spatial patterns in mountain pine beetle outbreaks. Theoretical Population Biology 53:236-255.

Mahoney, R.L. 1978. Lodgepole pine/mountain pine beetle risk classification methods and their application. Pages 106-113 *in* Berryman, A.A.; Amman, G.D.; Stark, R.W.; Kibbee, D.L., eds. Proceedings: Theory and practice of mountain pine beetle management in lodgepole pine forests. April 25-27, 1978, Pullman, WA. University of Idaho, Moscow, ID.

McGregor, M.D.; Amman, G.D.; Cole, W.E. 1981. Hazard-rating lodgepole pine for susceptibility to mountain pine beetle infestation. Pages 99-104 *in* Hedden, R.L.; Barras, S.J.; Coster. J.E., eds. Hazard Rating Systems in Forest Insect Pest Management: Symposium Proceedings. USDA Forest Service, General Technical Report WO-27.

McGregor, M.D.; Amman, G.D.; Schmitz, R.F.; Oakes, R.D. 1987. Partial cutting lodgepole pine stands to reduce losses to the mountain pine beetle. Canadian Journal of Forest Research 17:1234-1239.

McMullen, L.H.; Safranyik, L.; Linton, D.A. 1986. Suppression of mountain pine beetle infestations in lodgepole pine forests. Agriculture Canada, Ministry of State for Forestry, Pacific Forestry Centre, Information Report BC-X-276. 20 p.

Mitchell, R.G.; Waring, R.H.; Pitman, G.B. 1983. Thinning lodgepole pine increases tree vigour and resistance to mountain pine beetle. Forest Science 29:204-211.

Nebeker, T.E.; Hodges, J.D. 1983. Influence of forestry practices on host susceptibility to bark beetles. Zeitschrift-fur-Angewandte-Entomologie 96:194-208.

Paine, T.D.; Stephen, F.M.; Mason, G.N. 1985. A risk model integrating stand hazard and southern pine beetle population level. Pages 201-212 *in* Safranyik, L., ed. Proceedings of the IUFRO Conference: The role of the host in the population dynamics of forest insects. Banff, Alta. 4-7 Sept. 1983. Agriculture Canada, Ministry of State for Forestry, Pacific Forestry Centre, Victoria, BC., Canada.

Paine, T.D.; Stephen, F.M.; Taha, H.A. 1984. Conceptual model of infestation probability based on bark beetle abundance and host tree susceptibility. Environmental Entomology 13:619-624.

Polymenopolous, A. D.; Long, G. 1990. Estimation and evaluation methods for population growth models with spatial diffusion: dynamics of mountain pine beetle. Ecological Modelling 51:97-121.

Powell, J.; Tams, J.; Bentz, B.; Logan, J. 1998. Theoretical analysis of "switching" in a localized model for mountain pine beetle mass attack. Journal of Theoretical Biology 194:49-63.

Powell, J.; Kennedy, B.; White, P.; Bentz, B.; Logan, J.; and Roberts, D. 2000. Mathematical elements of attack risk analysis for mountain pine beetles. Journal of Theoretical Biology 204:601-620.

Raffa, K.F.; Berryman, A.A. 1986. A mechanistic computer model of mountain pine beetle populations interacting with lodgepole pine stands and its implication for forest managers. Forest Science 32(3):789-805.

Reid, R.W.; Whitney, H.S.; Watson, J.A. 1967. Reaction of lodgepole pine to attack by *Dendroctonus ponderosae* Hopkins and blue stain fungi. Canadian Journal of Botany 45:1115-26.

Reineke, L.H. 1933. Perfecting a stand-density index for even-aged forest. Journal of Agriculture Research 46:627-638.

Riel W.G.; Fall, A.; Safranyik, L.; Shore, T.L. 2004. A Spatio-temporal simulation of mountain pine beetle impacts. Pages 106-113 *in* Shore, T.L.; Brooks, J.E.; Stone, J.E., eds. Proceedings of the mountain pine beetle symposium: challenges and solutions, October 30-31, 2003, Kelowna, British Columbia, Canada. Natural Resources Canada, Canadian Forest Service, Pacific Forestry Centre, Information Report BC-X-399. 298 p.

Safranyik, L. 1969. Development of a technique for sampling mountain pine beetle populations in lodgepole pine. Ph.D. Thesis, University of British Columbia, Vancouver, BC. 195 p.

Safranyik, L.; Jahren, R. 1970. Host characteristics, brood density and size of mountain pine beetles emerging from lodgepole pine. Department of Fisheries and Forestry Canada, Bimontly Research Notes 26:(4)35-36.

Safranyik, L.; Shrimpton, D.M.; Whitney, H.S. 1974. Management of lodgepole pine to reduce losses from the mountain pine beetle. Environment Canada, Canadian Forest Service, Pacific Forestry Research Centre, Forestry Technical Report 1, 24 p.

Safranyik, L.; Shrimpton, D.M.; Whitney, H.S. 1975. An interpretation of the interaction between lodgepole pine, the mountain pine beetle and its associated blue stain fungi in western Canada. Pages 406-428 *in* Baumgartner, D.M., ed. Management of lodgepole pine ecosystems symposium proceedings. Washington State University Cooperative Extension Service, WA.

Safranyik, L.; Silversides, R.; McMullen, L.H.; Linton, D.A. 1989. An empirical approach to modelling the local dispersal of the mountain pine beetle (*Dendroctonus ponderosae* Hopk.)(Col., Scolytidae) in relation to sources of attraction, wind direction and speed. Journal of Applied Entomology 108:498-511.

Safranyik, L.; Barclay, H.; Thomson, A.J.; Riel, W.G. 1999. A population dynamics model for the mountain pine beetle, *Dendroctonus ponderosae* Hopk. (Coleoptera: Scolytidae). Canadian Forest Service, Pacific Forestry Centre, Information Report BC-X-386. 35 p.

Schenk, J.L.; Mahoney, R.L.; Moore, J.A.; Adams, D.L. 1980. A model for hazard rating lodgepole pine stands for mortality by mountain pine beetle. Forest Ecology and Management 3:57-66.

Shepherd, R.F. 1966. Factors influencing the orientation and rates of activity of *Dendroctonus ponderosae* Hopkins (Coleoptera: Scolytidae). Canadian Entomologist 98:507-518.

Shore, T.L.; Boudewyn, P.A.; Gardner, E.R.; Thomson, A.J. 1989. A preliminary evaluation of hazard rating systems for the mountain pine beetle in lodgepole pine in British Columbia. Pages 28-33 *in* Amman, G.D., ed. Proceedings of a symposium on the management of lodgepole pine to minimize losses to the mountain pine beetle. July 12-14, 1988 Kalispell, MT., USDA Forest Service, Intermountain Research Station, General Technical Report INT-262.

Shore, T.L.; Safranyik, L. 1992. Susceptibility and risk-rating systems for the mountain pine beetle in lodgepole pine stands. Forestry Canada, Pacific and Yukon Region, Information Report BC-X-336, 12 p.

Shore, T.L.; Safranyik, L.; Lemieux, J.P. 2000. Susceptibility of lodgepole pine to the mountain pine beetle: testing of a rating system. Canadian Journal of Forest Research 30:44-49.

Shrimpton, D.M. 1973. Age- and size-related response of lodgepole pine to inoculation with *Europhium clavigerum*. Canadian Journal of Botany 51:1155-1160.

Shrimpton, D.M.; Thomson, A.J. 1981. Use of physiological maturity to identify hazard of lodgepole pine stands from mountain pine beetle. Pages 149-153 *in* Hedden, R.L.; Barras, S.J.; Coster, J.E., technical coordinators. July 31-August 1, 1980, Athens, GA. Hazard rating systems in forest insect pest management: symposium proceedings. USDA Forest Service, General Technical Report WO-27, 169 p.

Shrimpton, D.M.; Thomson, A.J. 1983. Growth characteristics of lodgepole pine associated with the start of mountain pine beetle outbreaks. Canadian Journal of Forest Research 13:137-144.

Shrimpton, D.M.; Thomson, A.J. 1985. Relationship between phloem thickness and lodgepole pine growth characteristics. Canadian Journal of Forest Research 15:1004-1008.

Steel, R.G.D.; Torrie, J.H. 1980. Principles and procedures of statistics: A biometrical approach. Second edition. McGraw-Hill Book Company, New York, NY.

Stuart, J.D. 1984. Hazard rating of lodgepole pine stands to mountain pine beetle outbreaks in southcentral Oregon. Canadian Journal of Forest Research 14:666-671.

Swaine, J.M. 1912. Notes on some forest insects of 1912. 43rd Annual Report of the Entomological Society of Ontario. pp. 87-91.

Thomson, A.J. 1991. Simulation of mountain pine beetle (*Dendroctonus ponderosae* Hopkins) spread and control in British Columbia. Canadian Forest Service, Pacific Forestry Centre, Information Report BC-X-329. 18 p.

Unger, L. 1993. Mountain pine beetle. Forest pest leaflet No. 76. Forestry Canada, Pacific Forestry Centre. 7 p.

Waring, R.H.; Pitman, G.B. 1980. A simple model of host resistance to bark beetles. Forest Research Laboratory Research Note 65, Oregon State University, School of Forestry, OR.

Wykoff, W.R.; Crookson, N.L.; Stage, A.R. 1982. User's guide to the stand prognosis model. USDA Forest Service, General Technical Report INT-133, 112 p.

Part 3

Socioeconomic Impacts

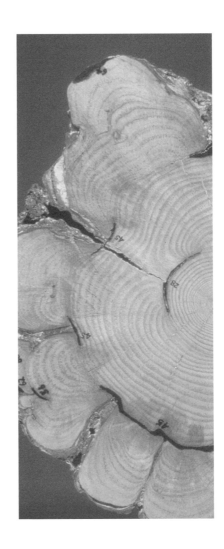

Chapter 9

Characteristics and Utilization of Post-Mountain Pine Beetle Wood in Solid Wood Products

Tony Byrne[1], Cameron Stonestreet[2], and Brian Peter[2]

[1] Forintek Canada Corporation, 2665 East Mall, Vancouver, British Columbia V6T 1W5

[2] Natural Resources Canada, Canadian Forest Service, Pacific Forestry Centre, 506 West Burnside Road, Victoria, British Columbia V8Z 1M5

Abstract

British Columbia is in the midst of the largest outbreak of the mountain pine beetle (*Dendroctonus ponderosae* Hopk. [Coleoptera: Scolytidae]) ever recorded in western Canada. Mature lodgepole pine (*Pinus contorta* Dougl. ex Loud. var. *latifolia*) trees form the bulk of the trees under attack. The mountain pine beetle carries several specific blue stain fungi that decrease wood moisture content and weaken tree defense mechanisms, eventually leading to tree death. Blue stain develops quickly in the sapwood of dying trees. It appears in products made from stained logs, affecting what products can be made and profitably sold. Infested trees also dry and develop splits and checks as the drying stresses are relieved. The physical condition of the wood affects how it can be processed.

This chapter discusses current knowledge of the properties of post-mountain pine beetle wood, its use and marketing. It draws upon information from the literature and current research in Canada that pertains to properties of blue stained and dead wood. Implications for use of post-mountain pine beetle wood for various products are discussed, significant data gaps are identified, and recommendations are made for research to bridge these gaps.

Résumé

La plus importante infestation de dendroctones du pin ponderosa (*Dendroctonus ponderosae* Hopk. [Coleoptera: Scolytidae]) jamais observée dans l'Ouest canadien sévit actuellement en Colombie-Britannique. Les arbres attaqués sont principalement les pins tordus latifoliés (*Pinus contorta* Dougl. ex Loud. var. *latifolia*) mûrs. Le dendroctone du pin ponderosa transporte plusieurs champignons particuliers, agents du bleuissement, qui réduisent le degré d'humidité du bois et affaiblissent les mécanismes de défense des arbres, entraînant finalement leur mort. Le bleuissement apparaît rapidement dans l'aubier des arbres mourants. Il se retrouve dans les produits fabriqués avec du bois bleui, affectant de ce fait le choix des produits à fabriquer pouvant être vendus avec profit. De plus, les arbres attaqués s'assèchent, et des fentes ainsi que des gerces apparaissent dans le bois à la suite du séchage. L'état physique du bois a une incidence sur sa transformation.

Le présent chapitre expose les connaissances actuelles sur les propriétés, l'utilisation et la mise en marché du bois tué par le dendroctone du pin ponderosa. Il s'inspire des informations disponibles dans la littérature spécialisée et les travaux de recherche en cours au Canada sur les propriétés du bois bleui et mort. On y examine des suggestions concernant l'utilisation du bois provenant d'arbres tués par le dendroctone du pin ponderosa pour fabriquer divers produits, on y signale des lacunes importantes en matière de données et on y formule des recommandations en ce qui a trait aux recherches requises pour combler ces lacunes.

Introduction

In western Canada, the main host of mountain pine beetle (*Dendroctonus ponderosae* Hopk. [Coleoptera: Scolytidae]) is lodgepole pine (*Pinus contorta* Dougl. ex Loud. var. *latifolia* Engelm.). Periodic mountain pine beetle outbreaks normally cause catastrophic levels of mortality. Mature lodgepole pine forms the bulk of this mortality. For example, in the central interior of British Columbia in 2003, the beetle attacked an estimated 173.5 million cubic metres of mature lodgepole pine, a 60% increase over the 2002 estimate. The beetle also threatens much of the province's remaining one billion cubic metres of mature pine (Council of Forest Industries 2003). Dealing with the large volume of killed trees has disrupted orderly harvesting plans in British Columbia's central forest regions. Increased annual allowable cuts in infested areas for the medium term will eventually be followed by a sharp decrease in harvest volumes. This fluctuation presents significant economic challenges for regional forest dependent communities.

The mountain pine beetle carries specific blue stain fungi, such as *Ophiostoma clavigerum* and *O. montium*, and possibly also *O. minus* and *O. ips* (Kim et al. 2003; Lee et al. 2003). These fungi weaken tree defense mechanisms, interrupt water translocation and lower wood moisture content. Effects of the fungi, along with damage to inner bark and phloem caused by the beetle, eventually lead to tree death (Unger 1993). Sawmills in mountain pine beetle-infested regions will increasingly be processing beetle-killed lodgepole pine timber. Salvaged timber will be affected by blue stain; this will limit the kind of products that can be made from the wood and profitably sold. Because infested trees also develop splits and checks as drying stresses are relieved, the physical condition of the wood is altered. This, in turn, has implications for how it is processed. In this paper, we review current knowledge about post-mountain pine beetle wood properties for use in solid wood products.

Shelf-life of standing dead lodgepole pine

Because trees deteriorate continuously after death, both recovery volumes and values decrease with the amount of time that dead trees are left standing (Lowery 1982; Sinclair et al. 1977). Moisture, oxygen, and temperature are factors that determine rate and extent of physical and biological deterioration of wood (Giles 1985). Secondary beetles, woodborers, and decay fungi often also develop within the stem. Logs from the dead trees become less suitable for economical manufacture into products, depending on the type of product. How quickly lodgepole pine trees in beetle-affected regions of British Columbia deteriorate is unknown and is likely site specific – associated with microclimate and soil-moisture content. A climate-based index for determining overall decay hazard in wood that is not in contact with the ground (Scheffer 1971) may be a useful predictor of the rate at which decay sets in the part of the stem that is away from the ground. This index is based on mean monthly temperature and precipitation. The Scheffer Index has been calculated for only a few communities within the beetle-affected area (Setliff 1986), but shows large variation across the range of the beetle in the province's interior.

Water or snow storage can be used to control log deterioration over time; however, R & S Rogers (2001) suggests that the economics of storing large volumes of wood in water are not compelling, and that beetle-killed trees can economically be stored only as standing dead. Lumber-recovery studies in the literature demonstrate varying shelf-life results. Significant economic losses have been shown after as little as 1 to 3 years (Fahey et al. 1986). At the other extreme, lumber production using standing dead grey attack lodgepole pine trees before the bark has sloughed off has been shown to be profitable (Dobie and Wright 1978). Current volume and grade recovery information needs to be developed for post-mountain pine beetle lodgepole pine to predict what would occur in modern spruce–pine–fir lumber (SPF) sawmills.

Harvesting and lumber processing

A secondary effect of blue stain fungi on mountain pine beetle-killed wood is excessive dryness; this poses technical challenges to wood use. Reid (1961) reported that the range in moisture content in the outer sapwood of non-infested live lodgepole pine is normally about 85% to 165% of oven-dry weight, with a steep moisture gradient from the outer sapwood to about 30% in the heartwood. In trees that have been infested by mountain pine beetle for one year, sapwood moisture content can be as low as 16%. Seasoning checks develop as the standing dead trees dry below the fibre saturation point (~ 30% moisture content), and grey stage trees usually end up with one or more major checks running from bark to pith (Fahey et al. 1986). The orientation of checks in lodgepole pine logs can be relatively straight or can spiral to varying degrees.

The forest products industry has traditionally been reluctant to handle dry, grey stage logs. Work (1978) gives the following types of losses associated with handling dead trees such as lodgepole pine:

1) Fibre loss and reduced volume of product outturn;

2) Quality loss from blue stain and decay; and

3) Product loss from physical characteristics such as splits and checking.

The biggest value losses in dead logs are associated with handling. Dry, brittle trees are more susceptible to breakage – 11% in four-year-dead trees versus 0% in live trees (Work 1978). The processes of falling, skidding, loading, hauling, decking and feeding mills involve handling the wood with large machinery. Each of these phases is associated with handling losses, ultimately resulting in shorter lumber lengths of lower quality. Additional expenditure on smooth roads and yards has been recommended to reduce breakage during transport (Mancini 1978). Secondary problems with handling dead wood include safety concerns and harvesting costs (Mancini 1978; Kohrt 1978). Toppled trees cause delays in skidding and lower chipping productivity with portable chippers.

Dry logs delivered to the sawmill also present difficulties in the processing stage. Debarkers tend to become less efficient when handling dry logs because the dry fibre is easily damaged. These machines are adjusted to minimize fibre damage as well as remove as much bark as possible – a balance that is especially critical with dry logs (Mancini 1978). Frequent switching between live logs and dead ones is likely to be problematic. Sheets of bark peeling off dead logs can jam debarking equipment (Sinclair and Ifju 1977). Modification of debarkers is required, and log ponds or spray washing of logs have been recommended (Mancini 1978), but because of environmental reasons pertaining to run-off water, modern sawmills are reluctant to follow these suggestions.

Dry wood requires more energy to saw. Saws and chipper and planer blades blunt faster, in part because of dirt and stones lodged in wood checks. Checks and splits in logs open up and reduce board width and length. When checked lumber breaks during processing, pieces can jam sawmill and planer machinery, leading to downtime and reduced productivity. Log scanners and sawing-optimization systems currently in use do not take checking into account; logs are normally processed through sawmills without regard to checks. Mancini (1978) reports more than triple the normal green percentage of economy studs and lower mill productivity (by nearly half, in pure deadwood). The end result is a lower lumber-recovery factor, with smaller board widths and shorter lengths than would be obtained if checks were not present. Spiral checking is a major factor contributing to reduced recovery (Nielson and Wright 1984). Current sawmill-optimization technology may be adaptable to maximize recovery from beetle-killed logs; however, recent data on lumber and grade recovery from post-beetle logs are not available.

As beetle-killed lumber is leaving the sawmill it may need additional sorting based on moisture content prior to kiln drying. Lumber from dead trees results in a disproportionate amount of product re-inspections when received by customers (Wallace 1978). For exporters, re-inspections in the marketplace are expensive, and often result in settlements at lower value than the originally agreed-upon selling price.

A summary of problems cited in a survey on problems associated with processing beetle-killed pine is given in Table 1.

Table 1. Problems cited in processing beetle-killed pine at British Columbia Interior sawmill operations

Problem area	Description
Log handling	• Higher log breakage in yard, log infeed decks • Barkers remove excess wood and cause breakers
Cutting tools	• The dry wood dulls cutting tools more quickly than green wood • When set up to cut frozen wood in winter, dry wood causes saws to heat up and lose stability
Pulp chips	• Dry wood results in more chip fines • Chip volumes increase significantly when processing a high proportion of infected pine
Lumber recovery	• Spiral checking is a major factor contributing to reduced recovery
Grade yields	• A higher % of low grade dimension lumber is produced, and lower % of #2 and better.
Markets	• Blue stain and worm holes not accepted in export markets
Drying	• Uneven final moisture content distribution due to mix of green and partly dry stock; some lumber overdried, some may still be green
Planing	• More breakage and jam-ups at planer; overdried wood reduces planer productivity • Increased trim loss at planer
Small-log salvage	• Higher than normal proportion of small logs results in lower lumber-recovery factor, lower mill productivity and higher unit costs

Source: Neilson and Wright (1984).

Appearance grade and value-added wood products

Within days of successful attack by mountain pine beetle, pigment usually begins to develop in the fungi. This produces the blue colour of blue stained wood (Safranyik et al. 1974). By the time identification of attack can be detected from crown characteristics, more than 50% of the cubic volume or nearly 100% of the sapwood is stained (Harvey 1979). Blue stain is the most visible characteristic of beetle-damaged wood.

After large bark beetle outbreaks in the United States, attempts have been made to market blue stained wood products as an appearance grade or "character grade" product. Blue stained mountain pine beetle pine was reportedly sold in Colorado for exterior siding and fencing, interior paneling, furniture and other products under names such as "Primitive Pine" and "Blue Mountain Pine" (Howe 1978). Currently, no products appear to be marketed under such names, indicating lack of long-term market success. At about the same time, beetle-killed southern yellow pine was promoted, but attempts appear to have been unsuccessful (Levi 1978). The current outbreak in British Columbia has also spawned similar marketing attempts such as "Denim Pine" and "Blue Pine" products. However, markets for blue stained appearance products seem to be limited niche markets with little chance of moving large volumes of wood.

Research on consumer reaction to blue stained wood in appearance-grade products is sparse. Fell (2002) conducted a consumer-preference test of various wood species for appearance-grade end uses and included blue stained lodgepole pine. Heavily blue stained lodgepole pine wood was highly noticeable by survey respondents and largely disliked for all appearance end-uses. Consumers overwhelmingly chose other non-stained wood of any species over heavily blue stained pine. This explicitly demonstrates consumers' willingness to discriminate between wood products on the basis of the blue stain. A small proportion of participants found blue stained wood "interesting" – perhaps indicative of a niche market. Nonetheless, a small amount of lightly blue stained wood could possibly be included in some appearance grades, as respondents noticed lightly blue stained wood less than natural lodgepole pine colour variation between heartwood and sapwood.

Grading rules for appearance products also restrict blue stained products from higher grades. For example, in "B and better – 1 and 2 Clear" select white pine boards, blue stain is limited to "light in an occasional piece over not more than 10% of the face" (National Lumber Grades Authority 2003). Japanese lumber purchasers limit the amount of blue stain in their structural products. They often negotiate a special "J-grade", primarily of the highest-grade timber. This grade is usually very restrictive towards blue stain content and is therefore both an appearance and structural grade.

Although most of the rationale for not choosing blue stained wood is likely aesthetic, some motivations are based on incorrect perceptions. For instance, the Japanese Forestry and Forest Product Research Institute indicates that Japanese customers question the soundness of the wood because they associate blue stain with the first stages of decay. Although this may be the case with other fungal staining, it is not the case with mountain pine beetle blue stain. Further, the Japanese translation of "mountain pine beetle" is similar to that of the Japanese sawyer beetle (*Monochamus alternatus*). This is regrettable given that the *Monochamus* genus is the primary vector for the pinewood nematodes that have caused major losses in pine timber in Japan and China (Dwinell 1997; USDA 2002). Although these perceptions are inaccurate, they create major barriers to entry in markets outside North America.

Clearly, the marketing and sale of a large quantity of blue stained wood for appearance-grade value-added products will require major promotion. As in the past, many consumers may confuse blue stain with mould, thereby reducing demand for the product. Regardless of whether the end use of blue stained wood is structural or visual, appearance problems associated either with misconceptions or with aesthetic displeasure will reduce demand.

Strength of structural products

Most SPF lumber is sold for structural use. Blue stain is not regarded as a defect in most structural softwood lumber-grading rules. For structural lumber, firm blue stained wood is permitted in all grades; only in the "Select Structural" grade is amount of stained sapwood limited. Although the forest products industry assumes that firm blue stained wood is as sound as non-stained wood, until recently, there were no test data available to demonstrate this for Canadian woods.

The effects of blue stain fungi on wood strength are highly dependent on wood and fungus types. Certain blue stain fungi of tropical and hardwood species cause decay that degrades wood strength (e.g., *Botrydiplodia theobromae,* Encinas and Daniel 1995; *Ceratocystis fagacearum,* Sachs et al. 1970; Scheffer 1973). According to the literature, the effect of blue stain fungi on temperate pine species is unclear. However, reduced impact bending strength, a measure of a wood's toughness, has been reported (Wilcox 1978). Some work has found no discernable strength reduction without severe staining; other work found a 30% loss in impact bending strength (Scheffer and Lindgren 1940: Findlay and Pettifor 1937; Chapman and Scheffer 1940). A study on southern pine beetle-killed timber indicated a reduction of 30% to 40% in toughness, of 11% in stiffness or modulus of elasticity, and of 19% in breaking strength or modulus of rupture (McLain and Ifju 1982). None of this work tested lodgepole pine infected by fungi specifically associated with mountain pine beetle. However, Forintek Canada (Forintek 2003; Byrne 2003) recently completed a project on the properties of mountain pine beetle-killed lodgepole pine. Lum (2003) compared mechanical properties of lodgepole pine sapwood containing beetle-transmitted blue stain with those of non-stained sapwood harvested from the same region. No significant difference in density between the two types of wood was found. When standard test methods were used, blue stained and non-stained woods were found to have comparable clear wood-bending strength (modulus of rupture) and stiffness. A 5% lower mean toughness was found in stained specimens, but this was only marginally significant. The small difference in toughness associated with blue stained mountain pine beetle wood clear specimens would likely be masked in full-size pieces of lumber by the differences in mechanical properties of the heartwood and sapwood, and strength-reducing growth characteristics such as large knots. It is important to note that the 5% loss in toughness is much lower than levels reported in the scientific literature for other blue stain fungus–wood species combinations.

Member parts of engineered wood products are glued or mechanically fastened together, and some are highly stressed in tension, so blue stain wood tension-loading capabilities are important. Lum (2003) performed a metal-plate-connected "tension splice" test to examine the holding ability of fasteners on blue stained wood compared to unstained wood. The tension splice is a critical joint found in virtually all metal-plate-connected wood trusses. The truss grip capacity of stained wood was 6% higher and statistically significant; the mean slip at ultimate load was 4% higher, but not significant. When based on the load at a connector plate slip of 0.016 inches (0.4 mm) relative to the wood member, the blue stained sample also had a 6% higher capacity than the non-stained sample. Although the improvement rates found are unlikely to be economically exploitable by industry, they do show blue stain does not weaken the wood.

The overall conclusion is that beetle-transmitted blue stain does affect mechanical properties of lumber. However, these tests were done on material that was probably cut from recently dead trees (green or red stage attack). As the trees proceed towards grey stage attack, and if dead trees are left standing, it is possible that incipient decay will set in and affect strength properties.

Dimensional stability of wood in service

McFarling and Byrne (2003) studied the dimensional stability of blue stained mountain pine beetle wood and observed, initially, that it tended to have different checking patterns than non-stained sapwood. Pieces of blue stained and unstained 2- x 4-in. lodgepole pine lumber were repeatedly subjected to wetting–drying cycles. Amount of bow, crook, cupping, twist, and checking was measured after each cycle. Blue stained wood exhibited both more dimensional stability and greater permeability. In blue stained wood, stresses appeared to be relieved by many micro checks rather than fewer large checks. Field tests of preservative-treated decking were installed to observe wood dimensional stability over extended wet and dry cycles in outdoor exposure. After one year there was little difference between the checking of stained and unstained wood, and no discernible movement was detected due to secure fastening of deck boards.

Gluing and finishing of wood in value-added uses

Lodgepole pine is a wood species well suited to value-added uses requiring gluing and finishing, such as structural glue-laminated beams and furniture. Increased permeability associated with blue stain indicates possible irregular absorption or over-absorption of finishes and glues (Levi 1981). To determine possible effects of higher permeability, Williams and Mucha (2003) examined finishing characteristics of edge-glued panels with alternating stained and non-stained laminates. Finishes were chosen to either enhance the character of the wood or to diminish the contrast between stained and non-stained portions of wood. The increased permeability of blue stained wood did not affect the evenness or adherence of any of the finishes tested. However, finishes containing blue, red, and charcoal tints in the stain, toner, or glaze coatings tended to better mask blue stain. Edge-laminated panels were used to test the strength and durability of glue lines when structural (phenol resorcinol formaldehyde) or non-structural (polyvinyl acetate) adhesives were used. Presence of blue stained lodgepole pine at glue joints made no difference to shear strength and durability of joints with either adhesive. All joints exceeded American Society for Testing and Materials standard test requirements. Clearly, presence of blue stain in lodgepole pine need not hinder furniture production provided a natural finish to highlight blue stain contrast, or a dark finish to mask it, is acceptable to the consumer.

Kiln drying of lumber

Drying of beetle-killed wood provides special challenges for the lumber industry. This is because beetle-killed lodgepole pine typically has a moisture content, on average, of 20% to 30% of oven-dry weight one year after attack – well below normal levels for live-cut lodgepole pine timber (Reid 1961; Tegethoff et al. 1977; Lieu et al. 1979; Lowery and Hearst 1978). Koch (1996) summed up the problem when he wrote, "Dead beetle killed lodgepole pine ... if mixed with green timber and dried on a standard kiln schedule will be degraded from overdrying". Kiln-drying schedules for beetle-killed lodgepole developed by Nielson and MacKay (1986) show the longer drying times required compared to a standard schedule developed by MacKay and Oliveira for live-cut wood (1989).

Apart from difficulties resulting from differing moisture contents in healthy and beetle-killed lodgepole pine, a number of issues must be resolved before kiln-drying properties of mountain pine beetle lodgepole pine can be understood. The higher permeability and microchecking of beetle-killed lodgepole pine (McFarling and Byrne 2003) may affect kiln-drying characteristics. For very dry wood, customized optimum schedules that ensure the lumber achieves the minimum 56° C for 0.5-hour core-wood heating necessary for heat-treatment phytosanitary certification may need to be developed. Resolving these issues should maximize the value of kiln-dried, beetle-killed timber while saving energy costs.

Veneer and plywood manufacture

Various researchers have looked at processing beetle-, fire- and storm-damaged wood for veneer and plywood (Nielson 1985; Nielson and Wright 1984; Giles 1985; Reiter 1986; Walser 1985; Unligil and Shields 1979; Peralta et al. 1993; Snellgrove and Ernst 1983; Walters and Weldon 1982; Woodson 1985). The veneer studies suggest that the most serious problems experienced while processing beetle-killed timber are reduced veneer yield and reduction in full-sheet recovery. Walters and Weldon (1982) found beetle-killed southern pine trees at 90 to 180 days after kill produced 9% less veneer volume, fewer full sheets and a higher percentage of random-width veneer. Snellgrove and Ernst (1983) found a 30% reduction in volume recovery and a higher percentage of random-width veneer in lodgepole pine that had been dead for 3 years prior to harvesting. The increase in random width veneer volumes can be expected to negatively affect mill operating margins. Statistics reported in the trade publication *Random Lengths* indicated a price spread of approximately $60 per m^3 between full sheets and random-width veneer in 2001. A study of beetle-killed spruce carried out at a Prince George, British Columbia plywood plant found that the greatest loss of value came from dry wood and checking (Reiter 1986). Most of the blue stain was lost in roundup. Losses due to more spinouts during peeling of low-moisture content logs were also anticipated.

Wang and Dai (2004) examined veneer-peeling issues for beetle-killed lodgepole pine with the objective to maximize veneer value. Because of increased permeability and dryness, post-beetle salvage logs can be thawed more easily in winter and dried faster than normal logs. These characteristics present an opportunity to reduce costs by using different log conditioning, veneer peeling, and drying parameters. Laboratory tests, pilot plant, and mill trials were conducted to quantify the impact of using post-mountain pine beetle logs for veneer manufacture, and to determine optimum manufacturing strategies for conditioning, peeling, and drying. Wang and Dai (2004) found that:

1) Proper log conditioning is key to improving veneer recovery from beetle-killed logs;

2) Lathe settings have a pronounced effect on veneer quality and veneer recovery; and

3) Compared to the control green veneer, green veneer from mountain pine beetle wood has lower moisture content and smaller moisture content variation.

In general, veneer from mountain pine beetle-killed wood can be clipped more narrowly than normal, with an equivalent of 1% increase in recovery because of smaller width shrinkage, and it can be sorted more accurately, requiring only two green sorts: heart and light sap. Beetle-wood veneer can be dried faster, with a 35% reduction in drying time for the light sap veneer. Despite a 1% increase in recovery from veneer clipping and a 27% increase in productivity from veneer drying, the recovery of mountain pine beetle logs was overall about 8% lower than that of control logs. This lower value represents the higher percentage of narrower random sheets, waste from peeling, and increased manual handling and composing. It was noticed that the blue colour of beetle-wood veneer interfered with camera vision grading systems. Since mountain pine beetle-killed wood is drastically different from other speces in terms of moisture content and subsequent processing characteristics, it is recommended that this wood be sorted in the log yard and handled differently than normal green wood.

Composite wood-based panelboard production

Current trends and related literature provide insights into the feasibility of converting beetle-killed wood into composite wood panel products such as medium density fibreboard (MDF) and oriented strandboard (OSB) but more research is needed. Lodgepole pine has long been identified as having all the desirable characteristics for composite wood product production (Maloney 1981). Additionally, British Columbia and Alberta producers already make use of lodgepole pine residues from lumber production for MDF, and producers in the southern USA make use of other pine species for OSB production. In terms of MDF and OSB capacity, there is reason to believe beetle-killed lodgepole could be used if some adjustments are made in the manufacturing process. The question is whether the blue stained mountain pine beetle lodgepole pine is of appropriate quality to produce these products economically.

If the fibre is suitable, potential exists to make use of some of the beetle-affected volumes – probably less so with MDF than with OSB. There are two MDF mills in western

Canada, with a total capacity of about 260 MSF 3/4". Potential levels of volume utilization are difficult to determine, as MDF mills rely on residues. Existing plants rely on local residues because they are expensive to transport. Although moisture loss is a detriment to strandboard, it could be a boon to fibreboard products: as dead timber dries it becomes lighter, thus reducing transportation costs, and requires less drying time, thus saving production costs. Koch (1996) notes that, although lodgepole pine is not a primary source for fibreboard (i.e., MDF), it is a suitable fibre source. He goes on to write, "one plant in Whitecourt, Alberta uses significant quantities of lodgepole pine," and that after a beetle outbreak in the late 1980s to 1990s, "plants (MDF) in eastern Oregon used high percentages of lodgepole pine salvaged from extensive bark beetle-killed stands."

As discussed above, a small amount of lodgepole pine finds its way into OSB, but the preferred wood species for OSB in Canada is aspen, which is cheap and widely available. Preliminary work at Forintek indicates that the quality of OSB panels derived from 100% mountain pine beetle-killed wood, whether standing dead for 2 or for 20 years, would not be acceptable in the marketplace due to greatly reduced water-resistance properties and dimensional stability. These panels, made using the current aspen panel manufacturing conditions, were not able to meet the Canadian Standards Association (CSA) panelboard standard for OSB thickness swell after a 24-hour water soak, nor meet the standard for modulus of rupture retention after the accelerated-aging test. Only when adhesive loading was increased dramatically did OSB panels made of 100% mountain pine beetle wood meet CSA standards; however, such high adhesive loading is uneconomical.

This experience contrasts with older literature on panel production that needs to be reinterpreted in light of modern product standards, product application requirements, manufacturing economics and industry practices. Thirty years ago, Maloney et al. (1976) conducted a study on making composite panel products from standing dead white pine and dead lodgepole pine in the USA. They concluded that the dead material of both white pine and lodgepole pine could be used effectively in making particleboard, MDF and flakeboard (a precursor to OSB). Their experimental data have great reference value. For example, they showed that lodgepole pine composite panels have relatively poor linear expansion, exceeding commercial standards, except in flakeboard. This would, therefore, raise serious concerns today in the manufacture of particleboard or high-density fibreboard for flooring – applications that are important for these two products now, but were not 30 years ago. In the flakeboard experiments with dead lodgepole pine, high thickness swell and water absorption was observed. This is similar to recent findings at Forintek, and warrants concern in the context of modern product requirements: although boards made by Maloney et al. met the standards of the time (circa 1976), they would not meet the more demanding market standards today.

Koch (1996), in summarizing other authors studying beetle-killed lodgepole, found that "quite acceptable structural flakeboard could be made from the species, whether trees were live or dead at time of harvest" (Koch 1996; Heebink 1974; Ramaker and Lehmann 1976; Price and Lehmann 1978). In his study of comparative economics of manufacturing composition boards from dead timber, Maloney (1981) concluded that equipment modifications for composite-board plants using the dead tree resource would not be major when compared to plants operating conventionally. Furnish preparation using cutting knives would probably be subjected to more wear and maintenance when cutting the dead trees into furnish. Extra screening capacity would also be necessary as more fines are generated, resulting in lower rates of timber-volume utilization. This is due to deterioration of the wood and, in the case of OSB, moisture loss. To be an acceptable product, OSB requires quality strands and the smallest amount of fines. Fines consume excess amounts of resin binder and contribute little to mechanical properties. This is significant, as logs dried to an average 50% moisture content produced nearly double the fines relative to green logs (Knudson and Chen 2001). Beetle-killed lodgepole pines can be at 20% moisture content 1 year after attack (Reid 1961). In addition to these findings, the Forintek preliminary study showed that at least 30% more adhesive would be needed to produce commercially acceptable OSB panel products from dead lodgepole pine. It is estimated that even a 10% increase in resin used to manufacture OSB from mountain pine beetle-killed pine would be uneconomical, increasing costs by approximately $1.7 million per plant per year.

Overall, using beetle-killed lodgepole pine poses potential problems for panel production. Panel products made from beetle-killed lodgepole will contain blue stain and, with lower timber recovery and utilization rates, will result in relatively higher production costs. There is also uncertainty around the potential of creating additional markets for new panel production from British Columbia.

Questions remain that need to be resolved in order to understand the role panel products can play, such as: Does increased permeability of blue stained lodgepole pine (McFarling and Byrne 2003) provide an opportunity for a more breathable sheathing for moisture control in buildings? Does blue stain inhibit properties of adhesives and strength of panel products? How long is beetle-killed timber suitable for making various panel products?

Preservative treatment

Some of the literature indicates that blue stained wood may be less resistant to decay fungi than non-stained wood (Findlay 1939; Scheffer 1940). This is largely due to increased permeability that allows for greater water penetration. Increased permeability of other (non-mountain pine beetle) blue stained wood has been demonstrated (Scheffer 1969) and therefore might be anticipated in products made from beetle-affected wood. Preservative-treated wood products are thus an obvious candidate end use for post-beetle wood; some studies on this have been documented in the literature.

Dead lodgepole pine has been recognized as suitable for preservative-treated products such as fence posts and utility poles (Lowery and Hast 1979). Tegethoff et al. (1977) suggest that decayed parts of dead pines could be trimmed prior to making poles, but recommend that beetle-killed trees suitable for poles should be harvested soon after death to avoid incipient decay. Lowery and Hast (1979) found that pressure treatment of posts and poles from dead lodgepole pine resulted in retentions exceeding minimum specification requirements. McFarling and Byrne (2003) quantified uptake of liquid during soaking or pressure treatment of both blue stained (from mountain pine beetle-killed trees) and non-stained lodgepole pine lumber. Increased permeability of blue stained sapwood was confirmed by data showing enhanced chromated copper arsenate uptake and penetration. These authors suggest that the mechanism for increased permeability is probably the opening up of ray parenchyma cells by blue stain fungi, and the microchecking that could be observed on some lumber samples. One implication of stained sapwood treating more readily than non-stained wood is that stained wood might be over-treated when processed in mixed batches with non-stained wood. CSA standards require treatment of both heartwood and sapwood; consequently, improved sapwood permeability may be of limited advantage to producers, or may even result in higher costs due to excess uptake.

Solid wood products that use preservatives include decking and treated framing lumber (Vlosky and Gaston 2004). Manufacturers in the southern USA treat some framing lumber (which may include imports from Canada) with disodium octaborate; a blue dye is added to the otherwise clear treatment solution to enable the treated wood to be differentiated from non-treated wood. This blue dye would mask blue stain in lumber harvested from infested stands, while the borate would impart durability. Wood for exterior decking is treated with copper-containing preservatives. The green colour of the treated wood also masks the blue stain, creating durable products that may reduce marketing problems associated with blue stain.

Log-home manufacturing

Standing dead lodgepole pine trees are dry, seasoned, plentiful and relatively cheap; as such, they can make ideal material from which to manufacture log homes (Peckinpaugh 1978, Hamilton 2001). Making log homes with dead trees has been done for many decades in the northern USA. Most logs are shaped with a planer, turned on a lathe, or sawn on two sides. Log homes are built at the buyer's site or are pre-built at a construction plant. Poor-quality logs are not used for log homes: a basic level of quality is required. Peckinpaugh (1978) provides the following quality parameters for log-home logs: they should be free from rot, have no spiral checks, have no check larger than 0.635 cm, be at least 17.78 cm in diameter, be at least 4.88 m long, be straight, have no crook, have minimal sweep, and taper less than 7.62 cm in 12.2 m. Douglas-fir is the species most frequently used by British Columbia log-home manufacturers, although cedar, spruce and pine are also used to a significant degree (Thony 2004; Wilson et al. 2001). Beetle-killed trees that meet house-log specifications have been used in the log-home manufacturing sector (Stirling 2002; Thony 2004). However, the log-home industry consumes only a small proportion of the province's total harvest which makes it unlikely to absorb much of the current outbreak volume.

Fuel pellet, wood energy and firewood production

Burning wood for energy has been proposed as a possible use for some volumes of beetle-killed lodgepole pine. Although domestic stoves, furnaces and fireplaces could make use of some logs, the volume will be small. More compelling options involve industrial production of fuel pellets, electricity and heat. Large, commercial-scale wood-pelletization plants already in operation in the beetle-infestation area consume large volumes of residual fibre from other processing facilities. For example, one plant produces 200,000 tonnes of pellets per year, making use of approximately 1.22 times that volume in wood residual feedstock (Community Futures Development Association 2005; BC Hydro 2004; Damen and Faaij 2003). As well, there are multiple co-generation plants and at least one plant producing direct electricity in British Columbia. Stennes et al. (2004) estimate these plants produce 600 to 650 MW per year of provincial woody biomass power capacity, using more than 3 million bone-dry tonnes of wood residues. Although these projects are certainly successful examples, there are a number of issues to be considered before using beetle-killed pine for energy purposes.

Potential for bioenergy from beetle wood in the form of pellets or energy depends heavily on costs for production, not technical feasibility. Most literature points to feedstock costs as a critical factor in economic feasibility of biomass-energy production. In British Columbia, current bioenergy depends on residual wood fibre delivered at little or no cost to production facilities. However, if direct salvaged beetle-killed lodgepole pine were used to procure wood fibre, costs of energy and pellets production could potentially double or triple. Also, given the extensive nature of the beetle-infestation area, costs associated with trying to harvest and transport wood fibre to new centralized bioenergy facilities could be daunting. Related costs include fixed-capital costs for bioenergy facilities, which tend to be exceptionally high in co-generation and electricity plants. Generally, bioenergy facilities need a low-cost feedstock, such as wood residuals, to be feasible and also often need a long-term fibre supply to pay off facility capital costs.

With regard to wood-fibre supply, both direct energy conversion and pelletization face a similar problem: potential long-term fibre-supply shortage. Current estimates show that in 15 years, British Columbia may drop almost 12 million m^3 in annual allowable cut from current beetle-induced uplift cut volumes (Pedersen 2004). Volumes of unused residual wood from pre-uplift levels remain available (B.C. Hydro 2004; Stennes et al. 2004); additional capacity at existing pelletization plants (Community Futures Development Association 2005), coupled with current proposed projects, will likely use these volumes. This is significant, as annual allowable cut reductions in 15 years will ultimately translate into a reduction of residual volumes below pre-increase levels. The result, assuming constant current costs, is that any new bioenergy projects for beetle-killed wood would likely need to pay off their fixed capital costs before the reduction.

Although there are cost and supply concerns, there are also benefits specific to bio-energy products. Fuel pellets offer several benefits over wood chips and other forms of combustible wood material; they are a stable product and have significant advantages in terms of transportation, storage and handling. Processing also reduces phytosanitary concerns associated with the output of "green" wood products. As transport costs of biofuels do not depend on type of product but primarily upon product bulk and moisture content, lower transportation and storage costs are achieved through compacting wood fibre (Suurs 2002). As well, as energy from wood ultimately replaces other energy sources and produces fewer carbon emissions, Canada's Kyoto Protocol commitments could provide a source of carbon credit benefits. Wood-energy options may even be feasible without construction of additional facilities as, with limited modifications, 10% biomass can be co-fired in existing coal plants (Stennes et al. 2004).

Examples of economically feasible wood-energy use exist in British Columbia, but more work needs to be done before additional capacity is installed. Costs associated with accessing the beetle-killed fibre supply, and issues regarding long-term annual allowable cut levels of the supply complicate options. Although carbon credits and lower transportation storage costs may mitigate overall product costs, it is not evident these would be sufficient to make new production facilities economically feasible. As such, use of additional wood fibre residuals may be limited to existing facilities for the time being. On the whole, questions concerning salvage and transportation costs, carbon credit benefits, feasibility of co-firing and the shelf life of beetle-killed wood and biofuel need to be resolved.

Summary and research needs

Challenges associated with manufacturing solid wood products from beetle-affected timber stands exist through all phases of production including harvesting, transportation, log storage, processing, and end-product marketing. However, as timber stands left in the wake of the current mountain pine beetle outbreak represent a significant economic resource, economic uses of this resource need to be carefully considered. A key issue is the amount of time, or shelf life, that is associated with capturing economic values, and how this may vary between locations. Upon reviewing the literature, it is clear that much of the available information is based on research conducted 20 or more years ago. There is need to update the research base to reflect current processing techniques, equipment technology and markets, and to explore research questions that remain unanswered.

With respect to research, high-priority needs include:

- Assessment of the deterioration of post-mountain pine beetle stands as a source of solid wood products, and how this varies across site and stand types;

- Measurement of the impacts of processing grey stage logs on value and volume recovery;

- Examination of mechanical properties of grey attacked wood over time as it goes into mill production;

- Determination of drying properties of blue stained wood versus non-stained wood;

- Examination of post-mountain pine beetle veneer on panel lay-up and hot pressing, product grade, panel stiffness and bonding strength; and

- Measurement of chemical characteristics of post-mountain pine beetle wood and impacts on bondability and wettability in panelboards.

References

B.C. Hydro. 2004. Potential in B.C. website: http://www.bchydro.com/environment/greenpower/greenpower1735.html (Accessed Jan 31, 2005.)

Byrne, A. 2003. Characterising the properties of wood containing beetle-transmitted bluestain: Background, Material Collection, and Summary of Findings. Report to Forestry Innovation Investment Program. Forintek Canada Corp., Western Division, Vancouver, BC.

Byrne, A.; Woo, K.; Uzunovic, A.; Watson, P. 2005. An annotated bibliography on the effect of blue stain on wood utilization with emphasis on mountain pine beetle vectored bluestain. Natural Resources Canada, Canadian Forest Service, Pacific Forestry Centre, Victoria, BC. Mountain Pine Beetle Initiative working paper 2005-4. 58 p.

Community Futures Development Association of British Columbia. 2005. Capitalizing on international opportunities. *In* Branching Out: A newsletter of the Softwood Industry Community Economic Adjustment Initiative. Western Economic Diversification Canada, Vancouver, BC. No. 5 (January).

Chapman, A.D; Scheffer, T.C. 1940. Effect of blue stain on specific gravity and strength of southern pine. Journal of Agricultural Research 61(2):125–133.

Council of Forest Industries (COFI) of BC, Mountain pine beetle task force. 2003. Mountain pine bark beetle update for release Dec. 15, 2003: British Columbia's mountain pine beetle epidemic 60% larger this year. http://www.mountainpinebeetle.com/article_2003_dec15.html (Accessed June 20, 2005.)

Damen, K.; Faaij, A. 2003. A life cycle inventory of existing biomass import chains for "green" electricity. Essent Energie, Universtiteit Utrecht, Copernicus Institute, Department of Science, Technology and Society, Utrecht, The Netherlands. 68 p.

Dobie, J.; Wright, D.M. 1978. Lumber values from beetle-killed lodgepole pine. Forest Products Journal 28(6):44–47.

Dwinell, L.D. 1997. The pinewood nematode: regulation and mitigation. Annual Review of Phytopathology 35:153–66.

Encinas, O.; Daniel, G. 1995. Wood cell wall biodegradation by the blue stain fungus *Botryodiplodia theobromae* Pat. Material und Organismen 29:255–272.

Fahey, T.D.; Snellgrove, T.A.; Plank, M.E. 1986. Changes in product recovery between live and dead lodgepole pine: a compendium. USDA Forest Service, Pacific Northwest Research Station, Portland, OR. Research Paper PNW-353. 25 p.

Fell, D. 2002. Consumer visual evaluation of Canadian woods. Forintek Canada, Vancouver, BC. Report to Natural Resources Canada, Canadian Forest Service, Pacific forestry Centre, Victoria, BC. 110 p.

Findlay, W.P.K. 1939. Effect of sap-stain on the properties of timber. II. Effect of sap-stain on the decay resistance of pine sapwood. Forestry 13:59–67.

Findlay, W.P.K.; Pettifor, C.B. 1937. Effect of sap-stain on the properties of timber. I Effect of sap-stain on the strength of Scots pine sapwood. Forestry 11:40–52.

Forintek Canada Corp. 2003. Properties of lumber with beetle-transmitted blue stain. Forintek Canada Corp., Western Division. Wood Protection Bulletin. Vancouver BC. 4 p. [Also available in Japanese.]

Giles, D. 1986. Harvesting and processing of beetle-killed timber. Pages 15–17 *in* R.W. Nielson, ed. Harvesting and processing beetle-killed timber: Proceedings of a seminar sponsored by Forintek Canada and COFI, Northern Interior Lumber Section, May 10, 1985, Prince George, BC. Forintek Canada Corp., Western Division, Vancouver, BC. Special Publication No. SP-26.

Hamilton, G. 2001. Log home builders turn pestilence into profit. Business section, Vancouver Sun, April 10, 2001. Business section final edition, Page D1/front.

Harvey, R. D., Jr. 1979. Rate of increase of blue stained volume in mountain pine beetle killed lodgepole pine in northeastern Oregon, USA. Canadian Journal of Forest Research 9(3):323–326.

Heebink, G. 1974. Particleboard from lodgepole pine forest residue. USDA Forest Service, Forest Products Laboratory, Madison, WI. Research Paper FPI-221. 14 p.

Howe, J.P. 1978. Uses of dead timber in specialty products. Pages 61–66 *in* The dead softwood lumber resource: proceedings of symposium held May 22–24, 1978, Spokane, WA. USA. Washington State University, Pullman, WA.

Kim, J.J.; Kim, S.H.; Lee, S.; Breuil, C. 2003. Distinguishing *ophiostoma* ips and *O. montium* two bark beetle-associated fungi. FEMS Microbiology Letters 222:187–192.

Knudson, R.M.; Chen, L. 2001. Effect of aspen log moisture content on stranding, strand quality and properties of OSB. Forintek Canada Corp., Western Division, Vancouver, BC. Contract No. 2001–2322.

Koch, P. 1996. Lodgepole pine in North America. 3 Vols. Forest Products Society, Madison, WI.

Kohrt, R. 1978. Harvesting and delivery to plant. Pages 187–192 *in* The dead softwood lumber resource: proceedings of symposium held May 22–24, 1978, Spokane, WA. Washington State University, Pullman, WA.

Lee, S.; Kim, J.J.; Fung, S.; Breuil, C. 2003. A PCR RFLP marker distinguishing *Ophiostoma clavigerum* from morphologically similar *leptographium* species associated with bark beetles. Canadian Journal of Botany 81:1104–1112.

Levi, M. 1978. Blue-flecked paneling: a new market for southern pine beetle-killed trees. South Lumberman 237(2994):70–71.

Levi, M. P. 1981. Southern pine beetle handbook: A guide for using beetle-killed southern pine based on tree appearance. USDA, Washington, DC. Agriculture Handbook 572. 19 p.

Lieu, P.; Kelsey, R.; Shfizadeh, F. 1979. Some chemical characteristics of green and dead lodgepole pine and western white pine. USDA Forest Service, Intermountain Forest and Range Experiment Station, Ogden, UT. Research Note INT-256. 8 p.

Lowery, D.P. 1982. Dead softwood timber resource and its utilization in the west. USDA Forest Service, Intermountain Forest and Range Experiment Station, Ogden, UT. General Technical Report INT-125. 18 p.

Lowery, D.P.; Hast, J.R. 1979. Preservation of dead lodgepole pine posts and poles. USDA Forest Service, Intermountain Forest and Range Experiment Station, Ogden, UT. Research Paper INT-241. 12 p.

Lowery, D.P.; Hearst, A. 1978. Moisture content of lumber produced from dead western white pine and lodgepole pine trees. USDA Forest Service, Intermountain Forest and Range Experiment Station, Ogden, UT. Research Paper INT-212. 11 p.

Lum, C. 2003. Characterising the mechanical properties of wood containing beetle-transmitted bluestain. Report to Forest Innovation Investment. Forintek Canada, Western Division, Vancouver, BC. [W-1984]. 17 p.

Mackay, J.F.G.; Oliveira, L.C. 1989. Kiln operator's handbook for western Canada. Forintek Canada Corp., Vancouver, BC. SP-31. 53 p.

Maloney, T.M. 1981. Comparative economics of manufacturing composition boards from dead timber. Forest Products Journal 31(5):28–36.

Maloney, T.M; Talbott, J.W.; Stickler, M.D.; Lentz, M.D.; Martin, T. 1977. Composition board from standing dead white pine and dead lodgepole pine. Pages 27–104 *in* T.M. Maloney, ed. Proceedings of the 10th Washington State University symposium on particleboard, 1976 March, Pullman, WA.

Mancini, A.J. 1978. Manufacturing and marketing older dead lodgepole pine. Pages 193–196 *in* The dead softwood lumber resource: proceedings of symposium held May 22–24, 1978, Spokane, WA. Washington State University, Pullman, WA.

McFarling, S.; Byrne, A. 2003. Characterizing the dimensional stability, checking, and permeability of wood containing beetle-transmitted bluestain. Report to Forest Innovation Investment. Forintek Canada Corp., Western Division, Vancouver, BC. W-1985. 13 p.

McLain, T.E.; Ifju, G. 1982. Strength properties of bluestained wood from beetle-killed southern pine timber. Pages 55–67 *in* D.E. Lyon and W.L. Galligan, eds. How the environment affects lumber design – assessments and recommendations: proceedings of a workshop held May 28–30, 1980, Madison, WI. Forest Products Laboratory, Madison, WI.

National Lumber Grades Authority. 2003. Standard Grading Rules for Canadian Lumber. New Westminster, BC. 274 p.

Nielson, R.W. 1985. Beetle-killed pine processing problems and opportunities: A British Columbia perspective. Pages 6–9 *in* R.W. Nielson, ed. Harvesting and processing of beetle-killed timber: proceedings of a seminar sponsored by Forintek Canada Corp. and COFI, Northern Interior Lumber Sector, May 10, 1985, Prince George, BC. Forintek Canada, Western Division, Vancouver, BC. Special Publication 26.

Nielson, R.W.; Mackay, J.F.G. 1986. Sorting of dry and green lodgepole pine before kiln drying. Pages 31–34 *in* R.W. Nielson, ed. Harvesting and processing of beetle-killed timber: proceedings of a seminar sponsored by Forintek Canada and COFI, Northern Interior Lumber Sector, May 10, 1985, Prince George, BC. Forintek Canada, Western Division, Vancouver, BC. Special Publication 26.

Nielson, R.W.; Wright, D.M. 1984. Utilization of beetle-killed lodgepole pine. Forintek Canada, Western Division, Vancouver, BC. Report.

Peckinpaugh, S. 1978. The log home market for dead timber. Pages 67–70 *in* The dead softwood lumber resource: proceedings of symposium held May 22–24, 1978, Spokane, WA. Washington State University, Pullman, WA.

Pedersen L. 2004. How serious is the mountain pine beetle problem? From a timber supply perspective. Pages 10–18 *in* Shore, T.L., J.E. Brooks and J.E. Stone, editors. Proceedings of the mountain pine beetle symposium: challenges and solutions, October 30–31, 2003, Kelowna, BC. Natural Resources Canada, Canadian Forest Service, Pacific Forestry Centre, Victoria, BC. BC-X-399. 298 p.

Peralta, P.N.; Syme, J.H.; McAlister, R.H. 1993. Water storage and plywood processing of hurricane-downed southern pine timber. Forest Products Journal 43(4):53–58.

Price, E.W.; Lehmann, W. 1978. Flaking alternatives. Pages 47–68 *in* Structural flakeboard from forest residues: proceedings of a symposium, June 6–8, 1978, Kansas City, MO. USDA Forest Service, Washington, D.C. General Technical Report WO-5.

Random Lengths Publications. 2001. The weekly report on American forest products markets. Volume 57:1–26.

Ramaker, T.; Lehmann, W. 1976. High-performance structural flakeboards from Douglas-fir and lodgepole pine forest residues. USDA Forest Service, Forest Products Laboratory, Madison, WI. Research Paper FPL 286. 21 p.

Reid, R.W. 1961. Moisture changes in lodgepole pine before and after attack by the mountain pine beetle. Forestry Chronicle 37(4):368–375.

Reiter, R. 1986. Processing beetle-killed timber into veneer and plywood. Pages 18–19 *in* R.W. Nielson, ed. Harvesting and Processing Beetle-Killed Timber. Proceedings of a seminar sponsored by Forintek Corp. and COFI, Northern Interior Lumber sector, 1985, in Prince George, BC, Canada, Vancouver, BC. Forintek Canada Corp., Special Publication No. SP-26.

R. & S. Rogers Consulting Inc. 2001. West central British Columbia mountain pine beetle strategic business recommendations report for British Columbia Ministry of Forests, Resource Tenures and Engineering Branch, Victoria, BC. 69 p.

Sachs, I.B.; Nair, M.G.; Kunz, J.E. 1970. Penetration and degradation of cell walls in oaks infected with *Ceratocystis fagacearum*. Phytopathology 60(9):1399–1404.

Safranyik, L.; Shrimpton, D.M.; Whitney, H.S. 1974. Management of lodgepole pine to reduce losses from the mountain pine beetle. Canadian Forest Service, Pacific Forestry Research Centre, Victoria, BC. Forestry Technical Report No. 1. 24 p.

Scheffer, T.C.; Lindgreen, R.M. 1940. Stains of sapwood and sapwood products and their control. USDA, Washington, DC. Technical Bulletin No. 714. 124 p.

Scheffer, T.C. 1969. Protecting stored logs and pulpwood in North America. Material und Organismen 4(3):167–199.

Scheffer, T.C. 1971. A climate index for estimating potential for decay in wood structures above ground. Forest Products Journal 21(5):25–31.

Scheffer, T.C. 1973. Microbiological degradation and its causal organisms. Pages 31-106 *in* D.D. Nicholas, ed. Wood deterioration and its prevention by preservative treatment, (vol. 1), New York, Syracuse University Press.

Setliff, E.C. 1986. Wood decay hazard in Canada based on Scheffer's climate index formula. Forestry Chronicle 62(5):456–459.

Sinclair, S.A.; Ifju, G. 1977. Processing beetle-killed southern pine – an opinion survey in Virginia. Southern Lumberman 235(2916):11–14.

Sinclair, S. A.; Ifju, G.; Heikkenen, H.J. 1977. Bug boards: lumber yield and grade recovery from timber harvested from southern pine beetle-infested forests. Southern Lumberman 234 (2900):9–11.

Snellgrove, T.A.; Ernst, S. 1983. Veneer recovery from live and dead lodgepole pine. Forest Products Journal 33(6):21–26.

Stennes, B.; McBeath, A.; Wilson, B. 2004. Is bioenergy a realistic option for utilizing timber residue from British Columbia's mountain pine beetle epidemic? Presentation to: IEA Bioenergy Task 38 Workshop, Forest Carbon Accounting, Carbon Offset Trading and Opportunities to enhance bioenergy, Sept. 15, 2004. http://www.joanneum.ac.at/iea-bioenergy-task38/workshops/victoria04/11_wilson.pdf. (Accessed June 27, 2005.)

Stirling, J. 2002. Eagle eye for business [online]. Logging and Sawmilling Journal- July/Aug 2002. http://www.forestnet.com/archives/July_Aug_02/spotlight.htm. (Accessed January 24, 2005.)

Suurs, R. 2002. Long distance bioenergy logistics: an assessment of costs and energy consumption for various biomass energy transport chains. Universtiteit Utrecht, Copernicus Institute, Department of Science, Technology and Society, Utrecht, The Netherlands. Student report I-NWS-2002-01. 65 p.

Tegethoff, A.C.; Hinds, T.E.; Eslyn, W.E. 1977. Beetle-killed lodgepole pines are suitable for powerpoles. Forest Products Journal 27(9):21–23.

Thony, P. 2004. Fiber supply issues of the British Columbia log and timber frame home manufacturing industry. Masters thesis, University of British Columbia, Faculty of Forestry, Vancouver, BC. 91 pp.

Unger, L. 1993. Mountain pine beetle. Canadian Forest Service, Pacific Forestry Centre, Victoria, BC. Forest Pest Leaflet 76. 8 p.

Unligil, H. H.; Shields, J.A. 1979. Lumber and wood composite panel from budworm attacked eastern spruce. Forintek Canada Corp. report. DSS contract no ISS79-00072. Ottawa ON.

United States Department of Agriculture (USDA). 2002. Pinewood nematode. Forest Health Update. State and Private Forestry, Northeastern Area, USDA Forest Service. St. Paul, MN.

Vlosky, R.; Gaston, C. 2004. Potential for increased treated wood products usage in US south residential construction. Forintek Canada Report to Value to Wood. Forintek Canada Corp., Western Division, Vancouver BC. 63 p.

Wallace, D.E. 1978. The challenges of marketing products from dead timber. Pages 95–97 *in* The dead softwood lumber resource: proceedings of symposium held May 22–24, 1978, Spokane, WA. Washington State University, Pullman, WA.

Walser, D. 1985. Processing dead timber into veneer and plywood. Pages 20–26 *in* R.W. Nielson, ed. Harvesting and processing of beetle-killed timber: proceedings of a seminar sponsored by Forintek Canada and COFI, Northern Interior Lumber Sector, May 10, 1985, Prince George, BC. Forintek Canada, Western Division, Vancouver, BC. Special Publication 26.

Walters, E.; Weldon, D. 1982. Veneer recovery from green and beetle-killed timber in east Texas. Texas Forest Service, College Station, TX. Circular 257.

Wang, B.; Dai, C. 2004. Maximizing value recovery from mountain beetle-killed pine for veneer products. Natural Resources Canada, Canadian Forest Service, Pacific Forestry Centre, Victoria, BC. Mountain Pine Beetle Initiative working paper 2005-9. 33 p.

Wilcox, W. 1978. Review of literature on the effects of early stages of decay on wood strength. Wood and Fiber 9(4):252–257.

Williams D.; Mucha, E. 2003. Characterizing the gluing and finishing properties of wood containing beetle-transmitted bluestain. Report to Forest Innovation Investment. Forintek Canada Corp., Western Division, Vancouver, BC. 19 p.

Wilson, B.; Stennes, B.; Wang, S.; Wilson, L. 2001. The structure and economic contribution of secondary manufacturing in British Columbia, 1990-1999. Natural Resources Canada, Canadian Forest Service, Pacific Forestry Centre, Victoria, BC. Information Report BC-X-390. 43 p.

Woodson, G. 1985. Utilization of beetle-killed southern pine. USDA Forest Service, Washington, DC. General Technical Report No. WO-47. 27 p.

Work, L.M. 1978. Dead timber evaluation and purchase: firewood or lumber. Pages 179–185 *in* The dead softwood lumber resource: proceedings of symposium held May 22–24, 1978, Spokane, WA. Washington State University, Pullman, WA.

Chapter 10

Impact of the Mountain Pine Beetle on Pulp and Papermaking

Paul Watson

Pulp and Paper Research Institute of Canada
3800 Westbrook Mall, Vancouver, British Columbia, V6S 2L9

Abstract

The mountain pine beetle (*Dendroctonus ponderosae* Hopk. [Coleoptera: Scolytidae]) epidemic poses significant challenges to the pulp and paper industry. In this report, we summarize the current state of knowledge associated with the categories of attack stage (green, red, grey). Early-attacked lodgepole pine sapwood is blue stained and contains a high level of extractives. Grey stage wood exhibits low moisture content. As potentially the largest recipient of blue stained and dry wood, the pulp and paper industry must develop cost-effective utilization strategies to overcome the detrimental effects of these fibre sources. It is recognized that lodgepole pine (*Pinus contorta* Dougl. ex Loud. var. *latifolia*) killed by blue stain vectored by the mountain pine beetle will provide a significant volume of foreseeable fibre supplies. The long-term effects of dry (grey stage) lodgepole pine are of concern. We have identified the critical knowledge gaps and research needs.

Résumé

L'épidémie de dendroctones du pin ponderosa (*Dendroctonus ponderosae* Hopk. [Coleoptera: Scolytidae]) pose de gros défis à l'industrie des pâtes et papiers. Le présent chapitre donne un aperçu de l'état actuel des connaissances associées aux divers stades d'infestation (vert, rouge et gris). L'aubier des pins tordus latifoliés en début d'attaque est bleui et contient des concentrations élevées de matières extractibles. Le bois au stade gris a une faible teneur en eau. À titre de plus grande acheteuse en puissance de bois bleu et de bois sec, l'industrie des pâtes et papiers doit élaborer des stratégies d'utilisation rentables pour compenser les effets néfastes de ces sources de fibres. Il est établi que les pins tordus latifoliés (*Pinus contorta* Dougl. ex Loud. var. *latifolia*) tués par les champignons agents du bleuissement transportés par le dendroctone du pin ponderosa fourniront un volume important et prévisible de fibres. On s'inquiète des effets à long terme de l'utilisation de pins tordus latifoliés secs (au stade gris) sur l'industrie. Les principales lacunes en matière de connaissances et les besoins les plus pressants en matière de recherche y sont signalés.

Introduction

The mountain pine beetle (*Dendroctonus ponderosae* Hopk. [Coleoptera: Scolytidae]) epidemic poses significant challenges to the pulp and paper industry. Pulps prepared from interior British Columbia spruce, lodgepole pine and subalpine fir (SPF) chips command market premium status due to unparalleled kraft and mechanical pulp strength, and intrinsic brightness of mechanical pulps. Located at the end of the forest products value chain, and as a user of high quality sawmill residual chips prepared from the outside of the tree (composed largely of sapwood), as well as chips prepared from low quality roundwood, the pulp and paper industry will be significantly affected by the influx of low quality logs and blue stained sapwood available as a consequence of the mountain pine beetle epidemic. Lodgepole pines (*Pinus contorta* Dougl. ex Loud. var. *latifolia*) attacked by the mountain pine beetle begin to deteriorate before they are dead through the incursion of blue stain; following tree death and decay fungi incursion, moisture content reduces to below the fibre saturation point. Blue stain creates bleaching challenges for mechanical pulp manufacturers whereas dry wood is an undesirable fibre source for both kraft and mechanical pulp mills.

Pulp producers will likely be the largest recipients of blue stained wood from mountain pine beetle killed trees over the long term. Literature on the effects of mountain pine beetle associated blue stain on pulp quality is limited and the results are inconsistent (Troxell et al. 1980). Moreover, existing studies on the evaluation of mechanical and chemical pulping of blue stained wood suggests a wide variation in pulp quality. A majority of the literature suggests that trees that have been dead for up to two years can be used for kraft pulping without affecting pulp yield or paper properties, but to take full advantage of the blue stained resource, rapid removal and processing of this material is compulsory to minimize any possible low moisture content issues. The impact of mountain pine beetle-killed wood on wood chemistry and morphology as well as the appropriate pulping process for dry blue stained wood chips have yet to be fully determined. Given the somewhat forgiving nature of the complex processing required to manufacture kraft pulp in particular, the industry is also ideally situated to add value to such low quality fibre supply if the wood is well characterized in terms of moisture content, basic density and decay content, and is managed by careful metering and monitoring of the process. However, significant processing and product quality challenges still need to be addressed. Understanding the mechanisms of the problems associated with utilizing beetle-killed blue stained and dry wood will assist in developing cost-effective utilization strategies for the pulp and paper industry.

For the purposes of this discussion, lodgepole pine killed by blue stain vectored by the mountain pine beetle can be broadly categorized as early (green or red attack) and late (grey) stage. This classification is based on sapwood moisture content, the key factor that determines wood chip processability and, ultimately, pulp quality. The onset of wood decay is also considered to have occurred within late-attack stage wood.

The impact of early (green and red) attack wood on pulp and paper

Green and red attack wood can be characterized as consisting of sapwood which has both high extractives and blue stain. Green and red attack sapwood, the source of sawmill residual wood chips, comprise significant levels of blue stain. The fungi cause a blue-grayish discolouration of the sapwood, generally thought not to cause structural damage to the wood. Blue staining fungi spread from the initial site of inoculation through the ray parenchyma. Hyphae then penetrate the tracheids through the pit membranes and travel from fibre to fibre. Any damage to tracheid walls can significantly impact pulp quality. Decay fungi are subsequently introduced which cause indiscriminant breakdown of the woody matrix.

The fungi cause substantial reduction in moisture content and disruption of moisture flow within the stem – a major cause of tree mortality. The standing tree dries further, to below the fibre saturation point, which creates significant technical challenges for wood utilization.

The effect of blue stain on pulp processing and production

It is widely assumed that chips prepared from wood with moisture content above the fibre saturation point, regardless of the presence of blue stain, will maintain an acceptable size classification. Chipping studies completed in our (the Pulp and Paper Research Institute of Canada [Paprican]) laboratory have shown conclusively that blue stained wood gives a higher proportion of pinchips and fines, material unsuitable for the production of pulp. Pinchips can be metered back into the pulp chip stream (Watson and Hatton 1996) but fines are only suitable for burning to produce heat and energy.

British Columbia's interior chip supply consists of complex mixtures of spruce, lodgepole pine and subalpine fir (SPF). SPF chips are stored for up to four weeks prior to pulping, depending upon the season, in order to reduce the extractives content. Chip extractives content affects the time required for seasoning, the outdoor storage of chips that allows for hydrolysis and oxidation of extractives to prevent pitch (wood resin deposits), and paper machine friction problems (Back and Allen 2000). However, chip brightness loss and extractives reduction must both be considered. Mechanical pulp mills require bright wood hence storage is kept as short as possible. Kraft mills also prefer to keep chip storage times short – less than two weeks – particularly in the summer months.

Blue stain fungi present in mountain pine beetle infested lodgepole pine sawmill residual chips introduced to uninfested SPF chips will indiscriminantly inoculate clear chips within the pile.

The impact of blue stain on mechanical pulping and pulps

Because of the presence of lignin, both unbleached and bleached mechanical pulps have a characteristic yellow color (yellowish tint) as represented by a high CIE yellow coordinate (b*) value. When bleached mechanical pulps are used along with bleached chemical pulps in high-grade papers, a blue dye has to be added to offset the yellow color (to lower the

CIE b*) and make the paper whiter. Very limited data on the bleaching of pulps made from blue stained logs/chips are available in the literature. Chemithermomechanical pulp (CTMP), made from chips containing blue stained lodgepole pine was reported to have an overall poorer response to sodium hydrosulphite bleaching, but a better response to alkaline hydrogen peroxide bleaching than the control, unstained CTMP (Lougheed et al. 2003). Unfortunately, in this study the species composition of the blue stained CTMP (96% pine and 4% spruce) was drastically different from that of the control pulp (61% pine, 37% spruce and 2% balsam fir). Therefore, it was not clear whether the different bleachability of the blue stained and the unstained CTMP was due to the effect of blue staining or to the difference in species composition.

Paprican has completed a preliminary series of thermomechanical pulping (TMP) and CTMP trials from blue stained and sound lodgepole pine samples. There was no well-defined relationship between refining energy, fibre properties, strength properties, or most surprisingly, optical properties of the TMP and CTMP pulps. It is evident that more research is required involving a larger number of samples where length of time since beetle infestation and the rate of deterioration after beetle infestation are well documented.

At a given freeness, the blue stained lodgepole pine sample had slightly lower scattering coefficient values than those from the sound sample when the comparison was made on either TMP or CTMP pulping processes (Fig. 1).

Chelated, freshly prepared blue stained TMP had an initial brightness of 54.9% ISO, very close to that of the control, unstained TMP (55.2% ISO). Blue stained lodgepole pine TMP

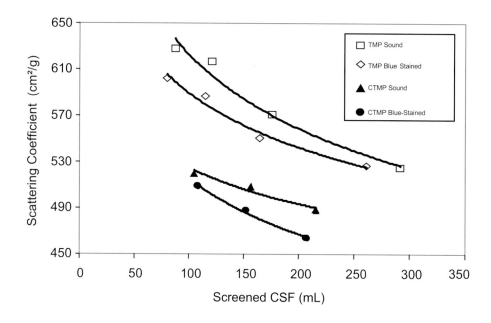

Figure 1. At a given freeness blue stained pine samples had lower scattering coefficient than those from sound pine samples for both TMP and CTMP pulping processes.

responded poorly to sodium hydrosulphite bleaching (a US$7 differential to achieve 60% ISO brightness, Fig. 2), but responded as well as the sound lodgepole pine TMP to alkaline hydrogen peroxide bleaching at high peroxide charges (Fig. 3). The light-stability of the peroxide-bleached, blue stained TMP was identical to that of the peroxide-bleached, sound TMP.

The unbleached, blue stained pine TMP had a lower CIE b* value than the unbleached, unstained pine TMP (Figure 4), indicating that it contained the blue stain. Interestingly, the hydrosulphite-bleached, blue stained pulps also had lower CIE b* values than the unstained pulps bleached to the same brightness level. This suggested that most of the blue stain, if not all, remained with the blue stained pulp after hydrosulphite bleaching.

The poorer bleach response of the blue stained pine TMP means a higher hydrosulphite bleaching cost, but the lower CIE b* of the bleached pulp may provide some downstream savings on blue dyes.

The difference in the CIE b* between the peroxide-bleached, blue stained TMP and the peroxide-bleached, unstained TMP became progressively smaller as the charge of peroxide was increased (Fig. 5). This indicated that more blue stain was dissolved/removed from the blue stained pulp as the charge of alkaline hydrogen peroxide was increased. It is possible that the high concentration of caustic at a high alkaline peroxide charge facilitated the dissolution and removal of acids such as 2, 3-dihydroxybenzoic acids and ceratenolone. These acids, in the form of their ferric chelates, are thought to be responsible for the blue stain (Ayer et al. 1986, 1987).

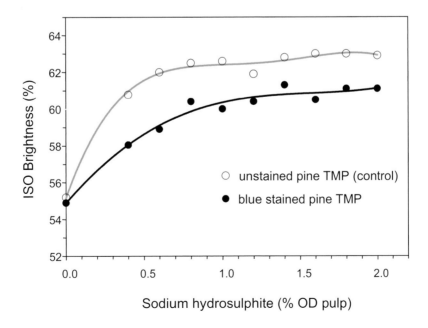

Figure 2. Brightness of the unstained and the blue stained TMP vs. charge of sodium hydrosulphite, $Na_2S_2O_4$.

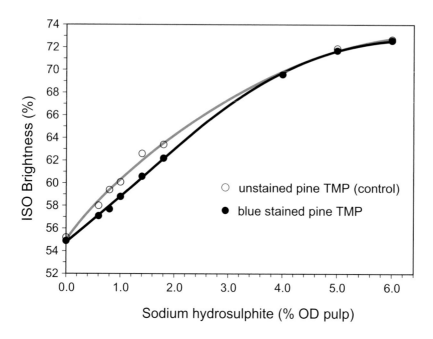

Figure 3. Brightness of the unstained and the blue stained TMP vs. H_2O_2 charge; NaOH charge = H_2O_2 charge.

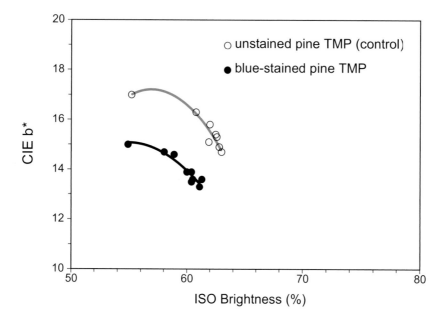

Figure 4. CIE b* vs. ISO brightness of the unstained and the blue stained TMP during sodium hydrosulphite bleaching.

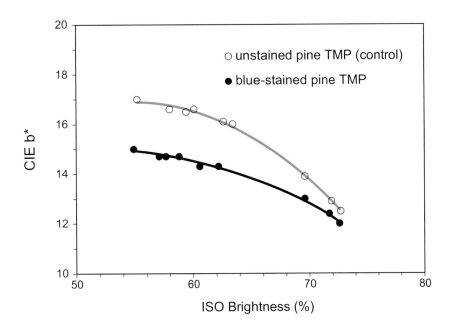

Figure 5. CIE b* vs. ISO brightness of the unstained and the blue stained TMP during alkaline hydrogen peroxide bleaching.

The blue stained pine CTMP had a better response to alkaline hydrogen peroxide bleaching than the unstained pine CTMP, particularly at hydrogen peroxide charges of $\geq$ 4.0% (OD pulp) (Fig. 6). At such charges, the brightness of the bleached, blue stained pulp was ~ 2.0 – 3.0 ISO points higher than that of the bleached, unstained pulp. To achieve the same brightness value, less bleaching chemicals were needed for the blue stained pulp than for the unstained pulp.

The unbleached, blue stained pine CTMP had a lower CIE b* value than the unbleached, unstained CTMP, even though its initial brightness was slightly lower than that of the unstained pulp (Fig. 7). This indicated that the unbleached, blue stained pine CTMP contained the blue stain. A comparison of CIE b* vs. ISO brightness of the peroxide-bleached, unstained and blue stained pulps showed that the difference in the CIE b* between the two pulps became progressly smaller as the charge of peroxide used for the bleaching, and consequently the bleached brightness, was increased. This suggested increased removal of blue stain from the blue stained pulp. No significant difference in peroxide consumptions during bleaching of the two CTMP pulps was found.

Similar to the blue stained TMP, the blue stained CTMP did not respond to sodium hydrosulphite bleaching as well as the unstained pulp, but the hydrosulphite-bleached, blue stained pulp again had a lower CIE b* than the bleached, unstained pulp (Table 1).

Table 1. ISO brightness and CIE b* of the unstained and the blue stained pine CTMP bleached with various amounts of H_2O_2 and NaOH, or with $Na_2S_2O_4$

H_2O_2 / NaOH (% OD pulp)	$Na_2S_2O_4$ (% OD pulp)	Unstained CTMP		Blue stained CTMP	
		Brightness (%ISO)	CIE b*	Brightness (%ISO)	CIE b*
- / -	- / -	54.5[a]	16.2[a]	54.2[a]	15.0[a]
1.0 / 1.0		60.9	15.7	61.6	14.4
1.8 / 1.8		63.9	15.1	65.3	13.6
4.0 / 4.0		68.5	13.1	71.4	11.7
5.0 / 5.0		70.3	12.4	72.3	11.3
6.0 / 6.0		71.4	12.2	74.0	10.9
	1.0	61.8	14.4	61.0	13.0
	2.0	62.5	13.7	60.9	12.5

[a]value for unbleached pulp.

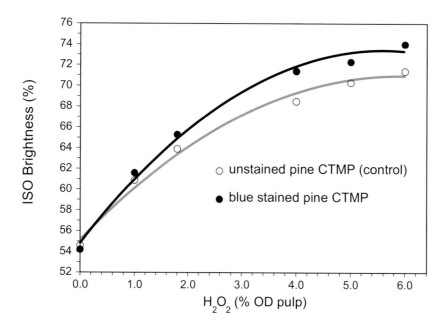

Figure 6. Brightness of the unstained and blue stained CTMP vs. H_2O_2 charge; NaOH charge = H_2O_2 charge.

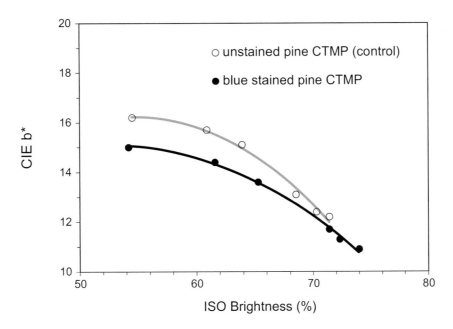

Figure 7. CIE b* vs. ISO brightness of the unstained and the blue stained pine CTMP during alkaline hydrogen peroxide bleaching.

The light-stability of the peroxide-bleached, blue stained pine TMP was identical to that of the peroxide-bleached, unstained pine TMP. Interestingly, the light-stability of the peroxide-bleached, blue stained pine CTMP was slightly higher than that of the unstained pine CTMP bleached to the same initial brightness value.

The impact of blue stain on kraft pulps

It is widely recognized that commercial kraft pulping processes can be forgiving of incoming wood chip quality. However, chip size distribution, incoming wood moisture content, wood density, fibre (tracheid) morphology and wood chemistry all play significant roles in the efficient production of high quality pulps for papermaking. Kraft pulping removes lignin to approximately 2%, creating a brown pulp, prior to entering the beaching plant where residual lignin is removed. Although there are widely conflicting literature reports on the effect of blue stain (Woo et al. 2004), the general operational consensus, confirmed in the Paprican laboratory, is that kraft pulps prepared from blue stained chips which have a starting moisture content above the fibre saturation point, exhibit the same quality as those prepared from fresh lodgepole pine chips and are readily bleached to high final brightness. However, we have observed that currently infested trees had a significantly lower kraft pulp yield, and required more alkali to pulp to a given kappa number than those from late-stage beetle-infested trees. This difference can be attributed to the high extractives level of the chips which contributes to the dry weight (basic density) of the starting chips.

Effect of elevated extractives on pulp and paper processing and production

Although extractives make up only a small percentage of the total chemical composition of wood, they play several significant roles on pulp and paper processing. Extractives can impact the pulping process by causing pulp colour reversion, and give rise to pitch deposits. Economic losses related to pitch problems in kraft mills have been estimated to account for as much as 1% – 2 % of sales (Back and Allen 2000).

The percentage of extractives in sound lodgepole pine varied from 1% – 2% in sapwood and 2% – 4% in the heartwood, corresponding to previous findings (Kim 1988; Shrimpton 1973; Lieu et al. 1979), which indicated that green lodgepole pine contained moderate amounts of extractives, ranging from 1% to 4%. Both Canadian Forests Products Ltd. (Canfor) and Paprican laboratories have determined that the extractives content of lodgepole pine sapwood chips was 1.2% in the grey stage, 7.7% in red attack, 5.4% in green attack, and 3.5% in healthy pine. Thomas (1985) has reported that black liquor tall oil content increased significantly with beetle attack and then decreased with time after attack .

A comprehensive analysis of the individual classes of extractives indicated that the relative proportion of extractives in the infested sapwood had also changed due to the beetle (fungal) infestation (Fig. 8). The results demonstrated a higher proportion of fatty and resin acids, and a lower proportion of sterols, steryl esters and triglycerides compared to sound sapwood. It is fair to conclude that a decrease in these extractives is a result of fungal invasion, such that fungi readily degrade triglycerides, steryl esters and sterols (Shrimpton 1973; Lieu et al. 1979). Wood triglycerides are the most readily degraded extractives component, which results in the liberation and accumulation of fatty acids (Higuchi 1985). Back and Allen (2000) also noted that an increased presence of resin and fatty acids in the sapwood may be due to early death of parenchyma cells.

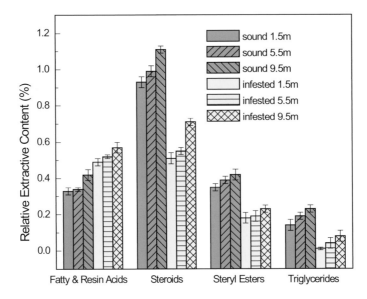

Figure 8. Relative proportion of individual classes of extractives in sound and infested lodgepole pine sapwood at different tree heights. Error bars indicate standard deviation.

During kraft pulping, extractives are either saponified, dissolved into the cooking liquor for subsequent recovery as tall oil, or unsaponified and hence discharged with the waste liquor. Alkali insoluble resin and fatty acids compose most of the unsaponified materials. Of the wood extractives found in pulp mill effluents, resin acids are widely regarded as the most toxic chemicals to aquatic organisms. As early as the 1930s, Ebeling (1931) found that 5mg/L of resin acids in pulp mill effluent killed perch in 40 hours. Leach and Thakore (1973) identified the toxic components of the resin acids in pulp mill effluent from 50% Douglas-fir and 50% western hemlock wood chips. They reported that three resin acid soaps in kraft pulpmill effluent (sodium isopimarate, sodium abietic, and sodium dehydroabietate), compounds also present in effluents from pine-containing pulping processes, caused over 80% of the toxicity to juvenile coho salmon. The toxicity of common resin acids to rainbow trout was 0.5-1.0mg/L during a 96h LC50 test.

As early infested lodgepole pine wood chips have 50%-120% more pitch than healthy pine trees, the discharge of high resin-acid-content effluent could compromise the effectiveness of kraft pulpmill secondary treatment systems. In addition, a problematic secondary treatment system lagoon foam has been reported by many operations. Paprican's preliminary research has confirmed that the foam is largely comprised of steryl esters, fatty alcohol esters, and triglycerides. Gas chromatography/mass spectral analysis suggests that the overall fingerprints are strikingly similar to those obtained from fresh lodgepole pine wood chips, with slight differences in the details likely caused by chemical or biological modification of the extractives. Further investigation is underway to determine if the high concentration of extractives found in the foam sample are, in fact, capable of creating foam.

In mechanical pulp and papermaking operations, extractives are more problematic as they are more readily retained within the pulp. Significant efforts are expended in these operations to ensure that the discharged whitewater is detoxified. Residual resin acids in the pulp can result in pitch accumulation on paper machines which contaminate the paper and can lead to more frequent paper breakage during manufacture.

Of more significant concern are changes to the friction characteristics of the sheet. Friction maintains traction between the paper web and rollers to prevent wandering and misregistration, thus playing a critical role in many web handling, web breaks and winding problems faced by the industry. For example, winding of low friction paper can cause interlayer movement below the paper roll surface, leading to defects such as crepe wrinkles. The coefficient of friction, while dependent on factors such as surface topography and strength, is also significantly influenced by chemistry. Extractives also play a major role. Fatty acids and glycerides on the paper surface generally contribute to a lower coefficient of friction and this effect increases with chain length, whereas the more polar resin acids increase the coefficient of friction. Operations utilizing fresh beetle-killed lodgepole pine have reported significant differences in paper machine runnability performance related to changes in the friction characteristics of their sheets. Research is required to determine the extent of the changes in chemical and morphological composition of these pulps and how they affect paper machine performance.

The impact of grey stage wood on pulp and paper

The substantial reduction in moisture content of the sapwood is believed to be associated with the presence of blue stain in the sapwood (Reid 1961; Nebeker et al. 1993). The moisture content of logs from grey-stage beetle-killed lodgepole pine was frequently below 30% of oven dry weight (fibre saturation point) (Reid 1961; Giles 1986). It has been previously suggested (Nebeker et al. 1993) that the water stress may be due to the blockage of xylem tracheids by toxic fungal metabolites produced by the fungal hyphae, or by aspiration of tracheids when propagating hyphae penetrate cell walls. Either phenomenon may occur after fungal inoculation, but neither has been proven responsible for the loss in moisture content and subsequent tree death (Nebeker et al. 1993).

It has previously been suggested that the decline in density in infested (dead) trees is a function of time since death (Koch 1996). This decrease implies that the chemistry of the infested wood may be altered compared to that of sound wood.

We have confirmed the results of Lieu et al. (1979) who showed a decrease in lignin content in the sapwood following beetle infestation. As blue stain fungi are the primary colonizers in mountain pine beetle killed wood and are known not to degrade lignin, Scott et al. (1996) and Koch (1996) suggested that other decay fungi are likely present and associated with the incipient decay that often is difficult to detect. Therefore, the decrease in lignin content may be attributed to accompanying decay fungi, such as white-rot basidiomycetes which are known to degrade wood lignin.

Earlier studies (McGovern 1951; Lieu et al. 1979) demonstrated that holocellulose (cellulose and hemicellulose) content in sapwood of green lodgepole pine wood had slightly higher carbohydrate content than infested wood. This difference in carbohydrate content suggests that it is due to the removal (consumption) of low molecular, soluble carbohydrates by microorganisms in infested wood. A thorough evaluation of the specific carbohydrates indicated that the infested sapwood had a significant decrease in hemicellulose-derived sugars (Woo et al. 2003). This result is due to the fact that hemicelluose sugars are soluble, and the first material to be consumed by fungi during incipient growth on lignocellulosic material (Higuchi 1985; Zabel and Morrell 1992).

Most decay fungi generally manoeuver through the wood by direct pit penetration, and with the removal of the pit membrane (through enzymatic digestion), the wood becomes more receptive to the movement of fluids. The changes induced by fungal pit degradation results in the infested wood's increased capacity to absorb and desorb liquids more readily than sound wood (Zabel and Morrell 1992) (Fig. 9).

Conclusions by Koch (1996), Flynn (1995), and Rice and D'Onofrio (1996) all support these findings, as they independently indicated that differences in permeability are generally due to differences in aspiration and the total amount of extractives. Resin deposition can vary substantially within the tree, and hydrophobic extractives in wood are known to impede water flow through the cells and to decrease permeability (Flynn 1995; Rice and D'Onofrio 1996; Vologdin et al. 1979).

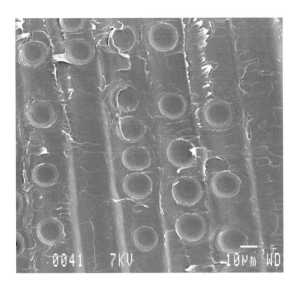
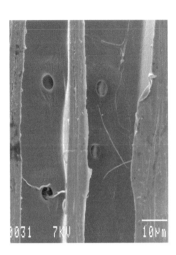

Figure 9. Scanning electron micrograph of aspirated pits in infested lodgepole pine heartwood at mid-bole height (600× magnification) and fungal hyphae in infested lodgepole pine sapwood at mid-bole height (1800× magnification).

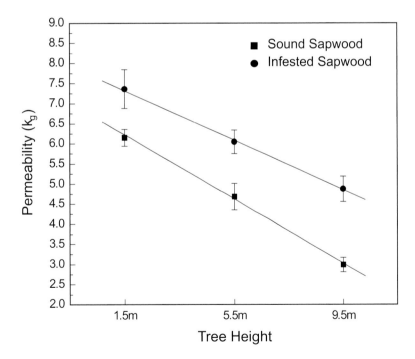

Figure 10. Longitudinal specific permeability of sound and infested lodgepole pine sapwood at different tree heights for a total of 18 samples. Error bars indicate 95% confidence interval.

Kraft pulping

There are limited data available in the literature on kraft pulping of beetle-killed lodgepole pine. Thomas (1985) and McGovern (1951) reported a decrease in pulp yield and pulp quality with time after infestation whereas Lowery et al. (1977) reported no significant differences in pulp properties between sound and dead trees. The presence of sap rot decay in Alaskan white spruce was found to be an important indicator of pulping efficiency and resultant pulp quality. Log deterioration had mixed effects on paper properties, whereas the presence of sap rot increased the kappa number of the pulp and decreased the pulp yield (Scott et al. 1996).

The effects of time since beetle attack on wood characteristics, losses in debarking, and chip quality have been investigated by several researchers (Thomas 1985; Lowery et al. 1977; Dobie et al. 1978). Results obtained at Paprican confirm that the fine and pin chip contents increase with increasing time since beetle attack, whereas wood density decreased with time after attack and are attributed to the variation in wood moisture content; reduced moisture content will increase susceptibility to mechanical damage during the chipping process. The increased pin chip content in a kraft pulping digester will create liquor circulation problems, reduce pulp yield and cause pulping to become non-uniform (Hatton 1975). Paprican has recently completed a preliminary assessment of mountain pine beetle infested trees from the Williams Lake region.

The H-factor (an indicator of kraft cooking rate) vs. kappa number relationship is shown in Figure 11. It is evident that currently attacked, fresher wood chips were more difficult to pulp than the rest of the samples. Consequently, the pulp yields from currently attacked wood chips were significantly lower at a given kappa number than those from the other samples. These chips also consumed more alkali at a given kappa number as shown in Figure 12. The high pulp yield of the 1-year infested sample might be due to inherent yield variability for this species but is most likely due to the lower extractives level in this sample.

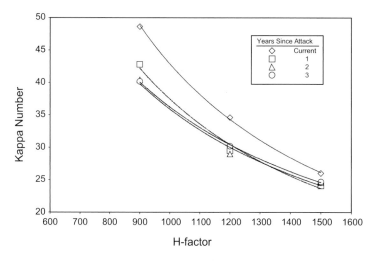

Figure 11. Kappa number/H-factor relationship indicates that currently attacked wood chips were more difficult to pulp to a given kappa number than the rest of the samples.

McGovern (1951) similarly observed that dead wood pulped more quickly. Many studies have indicated that as the wood deteriorates, there will be significant detrimental impact on pulp yield and quality. It is important to note that for laboratory kraft pulping, presteaming after chip impregnation is vastly superior to that of the conventional Kamyr continuous digesters found in the interior of British Columbia. The higher pin chip content and poor impregnation of dry chips leading to chip column hang-ups within the digester and liquor extraction screen plugging can significantly affect production.

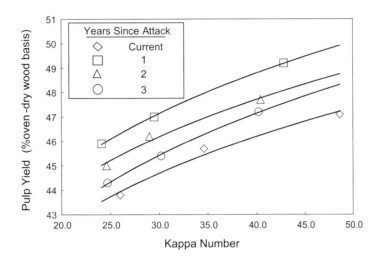

Figure 12. Pulp yield/kappa number relationships show that pulp yield of currently attacked wood was significantly lower at a given kappa number than in any of the other samples.

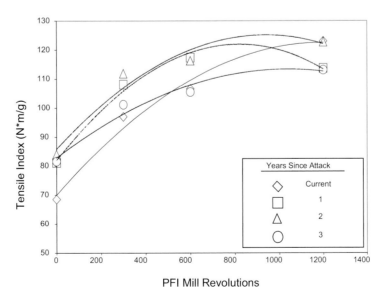

Figure 13. Tensile index/PFI revolutions shows the currently attacked sample had slightly lower tensile strength at lower beating levels than the other samples. However, the difference seems to disappear as the beating level increases.

Thomas (1985) has reported that beetle attack caused no significant differences in the bleachability of kraft pulps. However, he noted that beetle-attacked wood pulp showed poor pressing/drainage characteristics as well.

Figure 13 shows the tensile index as a function of PFI mill beating of unbleached kraft pulp at about 30 kappa number. Although pulp freeness was unaffected (Fig. 14), an unusual response to beating can be seen in the tensile strength properties (Fig. 13). Fully beaten, the current attack pulp produced a superior strength sheet whereas the 1- and 3-year sample exhibited a 10% tensile deficiency, which may, in fact, prove to be the norm for this wood source. The currently attacked sample responded more favourably to refining, creating a better bonded sheet.

Thermomechanical pulping

While several authors (Hattton et al. 1984; Fereshtehkhou et al. 1985; Dines et al. 1984) have investigated the properties of mechanical pulps produced from budworm-killed balsam fir, published literature on mechanical pulping of beetle-killed pine is scarce (Thomas 1985; Troxell et al. 1980). Thomas (1985) reported that there were no clear-cut relationships between strength characteristics and length of time since tree death in chemithermomechanical pulping of lodgepole pine; however, tear index usually decreased with increasing time since attack. Scott et al. (1996) have reported that more decayed Alaskan white spruce required the same or slightly less refining energy to achieve a certain level of freeness. A thermomechanical pulping study of beetle-killed ponderosa pine by Troxell et al. (1980) concluded that dead trees would be suitable for pulp and paper products. Paprican also conducted a preliminary thermomechanical pulping assessment of beetle infested trees from the Williams Lake region.

The data suggest that the 3-year infested sample required slightly less energy to achieve a given freeness than those from the other three samples investigated in this preliminary study. In general, there was no well-defined relationship between the specific refining energy requirement and the length of time since beetle infestation; this confirms our earlier results for refiner mechanical pulps from budworm-killed balsam fir that had been dead for 5 years (Hatton and Johal 1984). In contrast, other investigators have found that 2-year-dead balsam fir required 25% less energy than fresh balsam fir at a given freeness of 80 mL CSF (Canadian Standard Freeness) (Fereshtehkhou et al. 1985). The Paprican study suggested that there was no relationship between chip moisture content and refining energy to a given freeness; one explanation for this could be that pre-steaming equalized the moisture content of the chips before refining. It has been reported by several other researchers that chip moisture content does not have any significant influence on energy consumption and pulp properties, except for shive content of TMP pulps, as long as the moisture content is kept above the fibre saturation point (Eriksen et al. 1981; Hartler 1986).

The tensile index of 3-year infested lodgepole pine samples was generally lower than that from current, 1-year and 2-year samples when the comparison was made at a given freeness (Table 2), a given refining energy, or a given sheet density (Fig. 14), respectively. The tear index at a given freeness from a 3-year lodgepole pine sample was significantly lower than that from current, 1-year and 2-year samples (Table 2).

The lower long-fibre fraction and lower average fibre length values of 3-year lodgepole pine samples are the main contributing factors for the lower tear strength. Surface and cross section images shown in Figure 15 indicate that 3-year sample pulps exhibited more uncollapsed fibres than those from current and 1-year samples, thus being a possible reason

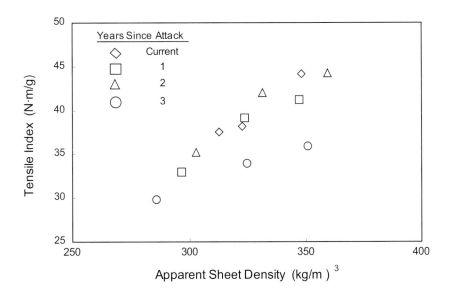

Figure 14. At a given specific refining energy, the tensile index of 3-year samples is significantly lower than those from current, 1-year, and 2-year samples.

Table 2. Properties of themomechanical pulps from beetle-attacked lodgepole pine at a constant freeness of 100 mL CSF.

Years Since Attack	Specific Refining Energy (MJ/kg)	R - 48 Fraction (%)	Fines (P-200) (%)	Length Weighted Fibre Length (mm)	Apparent Sheet Density (kg/m³)	Tensile Index (N·m/g)	Tear Index (mN·m²/ g)	Sheffield Roughness (SU)	Brightness (%)	Scattering Coefficient (cm²/g)	ISO Opacity (%)
Current	11.3	57.8	28.2	1.84	337	43	8.9	239	56	634	96.3
1	11.9	57.6	27.0	1.69	339	41	8.3	239	56	620	96.2
2	11.3	58.8	26.3	1.74	342	43	8.2	244	56	598	96.2
3	11.0	56.2	26.7	1.57	334	35	7.4	226	49	609	98.1

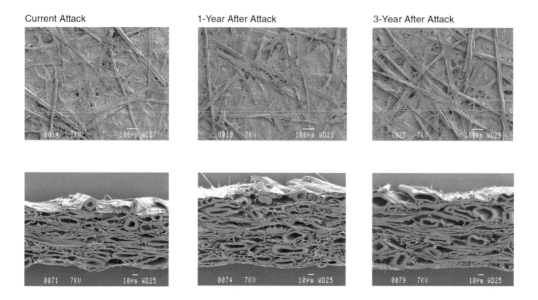

Figure 15: Surface and cross section images of TMP handsheets prepared from current, 1-year and 3-year beetle infested samples.

for strength differences compared to its counterparts. The loss in tensile and tear strengths have been confirmed by other investigators where strength properties from budworm-killed balsam fir were significantly lower for trees that had been dead for two or more years (Dines et al. 1984; Fereshtehkhov et al. 1985). Chemithermomechanical pulps prepared from mountain pine beetle infested lodgepole pine wood samples indicated that tear index decreased with increasing time since infestation (Thomas 1985).

At a given freeness there is no clear-cut relationship between scattering coefficient and length of time since beetle infestation. The brightness of the 3-year sample was seven points lower than that of the current, 1-year, and 2-year samples. Thus, there would be a higher demand of bleaching chemicals for 3-year samples to restore the brightness to about the same level as that of pulps prepared from current, 1-year, and 2-year lodgepole pine samples. Other investigators have reported similar significant brightness losses for budworm-killed balsam fir and beetle infested lodgepole pine (Hatton et al. 1984; Fereshtehkhou et al. 1985; Dines et al. 1984; Thomas 1985).

Summary of information gaps related to pulp and paper utilization of mountain pine beetle infested lodgepole pine

The utilization of wood chips prepared from logs salvaged from insect infested stands is common practice for the pulp and paper industry, and there exist numerous publications on the topic. The potential of the current mountain pine beetle infestation to cause significant detrimental long term processing and product marketing challenges remains. Much of the published research suffers from poor sampling design and selection. Comprehensive literature reviews and detailed consultations with Paprican's affected member company mills, which represent more than 5 million tonnes of SPF wood chip utilization, have highlighted the following technical information gaps:

1. Assessment of the pulping and pulp quality effects of increased lodgepole pine in SPF chip mixtures.
2. Quantification of the effects of blue stain in both kraft and mechanical pulping and pulp bleaching.
3. The development of a wood and fibre quality deterioration (shelf-life) model for infested lodgepole pine by location.
4. Development of portable and on-line rapid assessment devices to quantify blue stain content, moisture content and wood/fibre deterioration in standing trees, decked logs and wood chips.
5. Mechanical pulp pretreatment options for grey stage wood chips (chips below the fibre saturation point).
6. Quantification of kraft cooking of grey stage wood, including an evaluation of pretreatment options for continuous digesters and batch cooking processes.
7. Development of models to quantify blue stain inoculation and extractives losses in wood chip piles by season to maintain fibre quality and reduce pulp processing costs.
8. Quantification of the effect of early attack and grey stage lodgepole pine on tall oil production and quality.
9. Quantification and amelioration of the effect of early attack, high extractives content lodgepole pine on paper machine productivity for mechanical pulp grades.
10. Development of methods to minimize the foam propensity and toxic breakthrough events on secondary lagoons treating lodgepole pine extractives-rich effluents.

References

Ayer, W.A.; Browne, L.M.; Feng, M.C.; Orszanska, H.; Saeedi-Ghomi, H. 1986. The chemistry of the blue stain fungi. Part 1. Some metabolites of *Ceratocystis* species associated with mountain pine beetle infected lodgepole pine. Canadian Journal of Chemistry 64:904-909.

Ayer, W.A.; Attah-Poku, S.K.; Browne, L.M.; Orszanska, H. 1987. The chemistry of the blue stain fungi. Part 3. Some metabolites of *Ceratocystis minor* (Hedgcock) Hunt. Canadian Journal of Chemistry 65:765-769.

Back, E.L.; Allen, L.H. 2000. Pitch control, wood resin and deresination. Tappi Press. Atlanta, GA. Pages 1-83, 186-225, 307-324.

Byrne T.; Woo K.; Uzunovic, A.; Watson, P. 2005. An annotated bibliography of the effect of bluestain on wood utilization with emphasis on mountain pine beetle vectored bluestain. Mountain Pine Beetle Initiative Working Paper 2005-4. Natural Resources Canada, Canadian Forest Service, Pacific Forestry Centre, Victoria, BC.

Dines, R. E.; Tombler, G. 1984. Mechanical and chemimechanical pulping of budworm-killed balsam fir. Preprints of the 70th Annual Meeting, Technical Section, Canadian Paperboard Packaging Association (CPPA), Montreal, QC. B11-B13.

Dobie, J.; Wright, D.M. 1978. Lumber values from beetle-killed lodgepole pine. Forest Products Journal 28(6):44-47.

Ebeling, G. 1931. Results of chemical and bioassay tests on pulp mill effluents. Vom Wasser, 5:192-200.

Eriksen, J.T.; Hauan, S.; Gaure, K.; Mattans, A.L. 1981. Consequences of chip quality for process and pulp quality in TMP production. Proceedings of the International Mechanical Pulping Conference, Session: II, No. 1, Oslo, Norway.

Fereshtehkhou, S.; Neuman, R.D.; Sinclair, S.A. 1985. Thermomechanical pulp properties of spruce budworm-killed balsam fir. Pulp and Paper Canada 86(4):T100-T102.

Flynn, K. 1995. A review of the permeability, fluid flow, and anatomy of spruce (*Picea* spp.). Wood and Fiber Science 27(3):278-284.

Giles, D.R. 1986. Harvesting and processing of beetle killed pine. Harvesting and processing of beetle killed timber seminar proceedings. Prince George, B.C., Forintek Canada Corporation. 26 p.

Hartler, N. 1986. Wood quality requirements in mechanical pulping. Nordic Pulp Paper Research Journal 1(1):4-10.

Hatton, J.V. August 1975. WFPL chip quality analytical procedure: Effect of chipper, wood species and season on production of pin chips and fines. Pulp and Paper Canada 76(8).

Hatton, J.V.; Johal, S.S. 1984. Effects of length of time since tree death on the mechanical pulping of budworm-killed balsam fir. Journal of Pulp and Paper Science 10(6):156-166.

Higuchi, T. 1985. Biosynthesis and biodegradation of wood components. Orlando, Academic Press, Inc. Pages 43-50, 53-58, 441-464, 579-602.

Kim, W. 1988. Chemical characterization of lodgepole pine in North America for use as as industrial raw material. College of Forestry. University of Idaho. Moscow, ID. Pages 1-13, 15-164.

Koch, P. 1996. Lodgepole pine in North America. Madison, Wisconsin, Forest Products Society. Pages 35-45, 213-318, 667-695, 927-940, 1029-1041.

Leach, J.M.; Thakore, A.N. 1973. Identification of the constituents of Kraft pulping effluent that are toxic to juvenile Coho Salmon (*Onorhynchus kisutch*). Journal of the Fisheries Research Board of Canada 30(4):479-484.

Lieu, P.J.; Kelsey, R.; Shafizadeh, F. 1979. Some chemical characteristics of green and dead lodgepole pine and western white pine. Ogden, UT. USDA Forest Service Intermountain Research Station, Research Notes RN 256. 8 p.

Lougheed, M.; Dutton, B.; Huang, Q. 2003. Suitability of blue stained chips for the production of high yield market pulp. Pages 287-292 *in* Proceedings of the International Pulp and Paper Technical Association of Canada. June 2-5, 2003. Montréal, QC.

Lowery, D.P.; Hillstrom, W.A.; Elert, E.E. 1977. Chipping and pulping dead trees of four rocky mountain timber species. USDA Forest Service Research Paper INT-193. Intermountain Forest and Range Experiment Station, Ogden, UT.

McGovern, J.N. 1951. Pulping of lodgepole pine. USDA Forest Service, Madison, Wisconsin. 17 p.

Nebeker, T.E.; Hodges, J.D.; Blanche, C.A. 1993. Host response to bark beetle and pathogen colonization. Pages 157-169 *in* T. D. Schowalter and G. M. Filip, eds. Beetle-pathogen interactions in conifer forests. New York, Harcourt Brace & Company, NY.

Reid, R.W. 1961. Moisture changes in lodgepole pine before and after attack by mountain pine beetle. Forestry Chronicle 37(4):368-375.

Rice, R.W.; D'Onofrio, M. 1996. Longitudinal gas permeability measurements from eastern white pine, red spruce, and balsam fir. Wood and Fiber Science 28(3):301-308.

Scott, G.M; Bormett, D.W.; Sutherland, N.R.; Abubakr, S.; Lowell, E. 1996. Pulpability of beetle-killed spruce. USDA Forest Service Research Paper FPL-RP-557.

Shrimpton, D.M. 1973. Extractives associated with wound response of lodgepole pine attacked by the mountain pine beetle and associated with microorganisms. Canadian Journal of Botany 51:527-533.

Thomas, P.R. 1985. Infestation by pine and spruce bark beetles in British Columbia and its effect on kraft and mechanical pulping. Proceedings, Harvesting and Processing of Beetle-Killed Timber, a seminar sponsored by Forintek Canada Corp., and Council of Forest Industries (COFI) for Northern Interior Lumber Sector. Special Publication No. SP-26.

Troxell, H.E.; Tang, J.L.; Sampson, G.R.; Worth, H.E. 1980. Suitability of Beetle-Killed Pine in Colorado's front range for wood and fibre products. U.S. Forest Service Resource Bulletin, RM-2.

Vologdin, A.I.; A.F. Razumova; Charuk, E.V. 1979. Importance of extractives for permeability of pine and spruce woods. Holztechnology 20(2):67-69.

Watson, P.; Hatton, J. 1996. Increasing the use of supplemental fibre sources in pulping. The Forestry Chronicle 72(5):501.

Woo, K.; Watson, P.; Mansfield, S. 2003. The effects of mountain pine beetle and associated blue staining fungi on wood morphology and chemistry: Implications for wood and fiber quality. Wood and Fiber Science 37(1):112-126.

Zabel, R.A.; Morrell, J.J. 1992. Wood microbiology: Decay and its prevention. New York, Academic Press, Inc. NY. Pages 22-261, 326-339.

Chapter 11

Economics in the Management of Mountain Pine Beetle in Lodgepole Pine in British Columbia: A Synthesis

William L. Wagner, Bill Wilson, Brian Peter, Sen Wang, and Brad Stennes

Natural Resources Canada, Canadian Forest Service, Pacific Forestry Centre, 506 West Burnside Road, Victoria, British Columbia, V8Z 1M5

Abstract

Economic theory has played only a minor role in developing British Columbia's forest strategy for managing the mountain pine beetle (*Dendroctonus ponderosae* Hopk. [Coleoptera: Scolytidae]). Forest economics literature addresses the forest management problem caused by the beetle in lodgepole pine (*Pinus contorta* Dougl. ex Loud. var. *latifolia* Engelm.) from a number of perspectives. The standard methods are concerned with maximizing the value of harvesting a single forest site under the risk of bark beetle. The second viewpoint extends this value-maximizing approach to incorporate multiple uses of, and benefits from, a larger forest system. In this second approach, management policy suggests systems that reduce risk and reduce impact, rather than increase physical product. This chapter discusses literature from these two viewpoints and identifies issues, opportunities and concerns of applying forest economic theory to the mountain pine beetle problem in British Columbia.

Résumé

La théorie économique n'a joué qu'un rôle mineur dans l'élaboration d'une stratégie de lutte contre le dendroctone du pin ponderosa (*Dendroctonus ponderosae* Hopk. [Coleoptera: Scolytidae]) en Colombie-Britannique. La littérature traitant d'économie forestière aborde, de divers points de vue, le problème que pose le dendroctone du pin ponderosa dans la gestion des forêts de pins tordus latifoliés (*Pinus contorta* Dougl. ex Loud. var. *latifolia* Engelm.). Un des points de vue indique que les méthodes classiques visent à maximiser la valeur de la récolte des arbres d'une forêt donnée exposés au risque que représente le dendroctone du pin ponderosa. Un second point de vue élargit cette approche de la maximisation de la valeur de façon à intégrer les multiples utilisations et avantages associés à un système forestier plus vaste. Dans cette seconde approche, la politique d'aménagement propose des méthodes visant à réduire le risque et l'impact que représente le dendroctone du pin ponderosa plutôt qu'à accroître les volumes exploitables. Le présent chapitre porte sur les divers ouvrages qui traitent de ces deux points de vue, et on y précise les questions, les possibilités et les difficultés reliées à l'application de la théorie économique forestière au problème que représente le dendroctone du pin ponderosa en Colombie-Britannique.

Introduction

Forest resources and their associated products are extremely important to British Columbia's economy. Between 1992 to 2001, forest products exports from the province brought in an average of $14.4 billion per year and accounted for 43% of the export base of the province (Baxter and Ramlo, 2002). This large amount of economic activity associated with commercial forest use suggests an economic perspective that may give meaningful insight to understanding most provincial forestry issues including the current epidemic of mountain pine beetle (*Dendroctonus ponderosae* Hopk. [Coleoptera: Scolytidae]).

The relationship between lodgepole pine (*Pinus contorta* Doug. ex Loud. var. *latifolia* Engel.) forests and the mountain pine beetle has been developing in western Canada since the retreat of the ice thousands of years ago (Cwynar and MacDonald 1987). Beetle population outbreaks have been recorded in some parts of British Columbia since 1910, and evidence of mountain pine beetle activity going back hundreds of years is found in strip scars on lodgepole pine trees (Mitchell et al. 1983) and tree-ring analyses (Heath and Alfaro 1990). On the other hand, extensive forest management of lodgepole pine has been ongoing for less than 60 years, hardly time for scientific understanding of the interrelationships in and between complex bio-economic systems.

Lodgepole pine is found in many forest types of interior British Columbia. Mulholland (1937) states:

> At elevations from 3,500 to 5,500 feet increased precipitation produces denser stands, and the larch and fir give place to spruce and alpine fir, forming a type similar to the northern forest. Large areas of this type have been replaced by pure lodgepole pine as a result of fires, and this species is also found in varying proportions among the spruce and alpine fir. The majority of the immature stands throughout the whole Interior are pure lodgepole pine, often in dense thickets; for this reason lodgepole pine will be of importance in future management of Interior forests.

The stands to which Mulholland alluded are almost 70 years older now. Many of them are considered mature; some are being attacked by mountain pine beetle and others are already dead.

Lodgepole pine covers more than 14 million ha and, by volume makes up between 15% and 25% of the province's total standing timber inventory. Lodgepole pine volumes are proportionally higher in interior portions of the province and are critical to the timber supply of the interior British Columbia forest sector (British Columbia Ministry of Forests 1995). Province-wide, the contribution of lodgepole pine stands to the annual harvest has increased from approximately 14 million m^3 in 1980 to over 20 million m^3 in 2001 (Fig. 1). The species is thus very important from an economic point of view.

During the early years of the development of forestry in British Columbia, many stands of lodgepole pine were immature, a result of fires that burned throughout western North America before the turn of the century (Agee, 1993). In the last 75 years, one of the major

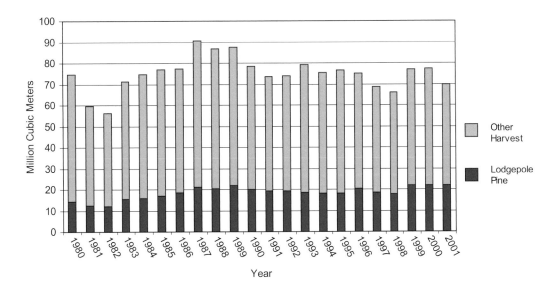

Figure 1. Lodgepole pine component of annual timber harvest in British Columbia (Source: British Columbia Ministry of Forests Annual Reports 1980-2001).

goals of forestry in the province has been to minimize wildfire damage. As a consequence, stand-replacing fires common in the 19th century were for the most part not duplicated in the 20th century. Because the development in the province's interior forests was delayed until after World War II, many juvenile stands of lodgepole pine matured, while older stands became over-mature.

Historically, lodgepole pine has also ranked low as a commercial species. As a result, the species was often by-passed in favour of more economically valuable species during the early stages of provincial forest sector development. Thus, it should not be surprising that a large fraction of the species now exists as mature and over-mature age classes. These older mature trees are most susceptible to beetle attack (Amman 1977; Amman and Safranyik 1985).

For the past 25 years, British Columbia's pine forests have suffered increasing losses in value from a variety of disturbance events. These include wildfires and wind, which are physical in nature, and insects and diseases, which are biological. As forests age, they become increasingly vulnerable to disturbance agents (Christiansen et al. 1987). Disturbance agents, such as wind, insects and fire, often work in combination, but their cumulative effect has been only rarely investigated quantitatively (Bebi et al. 2003; McCullough et al. 1998; Safranyik et al. 2001).

Figure 2 indicates the rate of mountain pine beetle population increase in the west-central interior of British Columbia during recent years. With 4 million ha of red attacked lodgepole pine in 2003[1] (British Columbia Ministry of Forests 2004), the current outbreak is the largest in British Columbia's short history of record keeping. Petersen (2003b) noted that

---

[1] The 2003 estimate is based on red attack resulting from beetle flight in 2002. Thus, the estimate understates the infestation produced by the 2003 beetle flight.

within the 4.2 million ha surveyed in 2003, the intensity level of attack varied. Intensity was rated as 64% light (1% to 10% of trees being dead), 18% moderate (11% to 29% being dead) and 18% severe (over 30% being dead). Work based on global circulation models suggests the cold weather events required to control beetle populations will become less frequent (Carrol et al., 2003).

It appears unlikely that conditions will combine to reduce the expansion of this population to unaffected but susceptible pine forests in the near future. Nonetheless, understanding how beetle biology, lodgepole pine biology and economics interact is important for improving our response to the beetle.

Because many existing lodgepole pine stands are mature, the disturbance threat is ecologically significant. Regardless of whether or not an effective management strategy exists to deal with the mountain pine beetle outbreak, the epidemic will result in considerable socioeconomic impacts, especially in regional communities that depend upon the forest for their livelihood.

Along with the unintended impact of fire exclusion, which resulted in dense forests of older lodgepole pine with heavy fuel conditions, there appears to be a trend of global warming. Average temperatures seem to be above the level of natural variability in the climate system (Crowley, 2000). Carroll et al. (2003) suggest this trend contributes to the current outbreak of mountain pine beetle. If this is the case, then the already catastrophic mountain pine beetle problem in British Columbia has the potential to elevate and spread throughout the boreal forest across western Canada. The potential ecologic and economic crisis resulting from mountain pine beetle outbreak in the boreal forest would increase already major forest health challenges.

While many issues associated with mountain pine beetle deserve attention from economists, the purpose of this chapter is to provide a synthesis of the economic aspects of the issue from a forest management viewpoint. Forest economics is an applied field of economics that deals with economic problems associated with forestland. Nautiyal (1988) divides forest economics into two categories of interest: industry and management, which have both positive and normative aspects. Forest industry economics deals with the study of manufacturing logs from standing forests, their conversion into products, and their trade. Forest management economics deals with economic problems associated with the growing of forests and generating products and services from forestland resources. To the forest economist, humans and many human institutions are equally important to the natural relationships in and between forests.

Mactavish (1965) suggested the application of economic tools such as the minimum-cost-plus-loss criterion to fire control in Canada 40 years ago. The idea would have been appropriate for establishing management levels to form a strategy to protect against large scale increases in beetle populations. Of course, the efficiency of application of this criterion to beetle management would depend upon the generation of quality socioeconomic information. Commenting on a mountain pine beetle epidemic in the province that occurred in the early 1980s, Manning (1982) stated, "…what we do not know about the

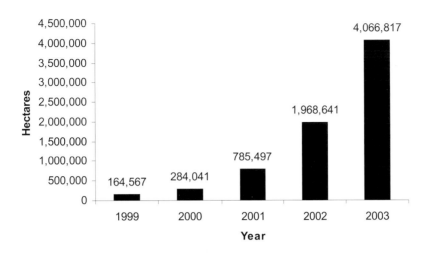

Figure 2. Hectares affected (red attack) by mountain pine beetle in British Columbia (British Columbia Ministry of Forests 2004).

economic impact of the mountain pine beetle far exceeds what we do know, and figures developed from panicky, half-baked analyses have a way of becoming 'gospel'."

This chapter begins with a brief presentation of the biological problem of mountain pine beetle management in lodgepole pine. Next, current knowledge concerning mountain pine beetle in British Columbia is discussed. The promise of recent advances in theory relating to economic decision-making in disturbance management is presented after a brief discussion on economics and sustainable forest management. The chapter concludes with a discussion of the future of research in forest economics and economic decision-making in mountain pine beetle management in British Columbia.

The biological problem and strategies for managing mountain pine beetle

Endemic in stands of lodgepole pine and most pine species throughout western North America, the mountain pine beetle is normally limited to highly stressed trees within the pine forest ecosystem (Koch 1996; Raffa and Berryman 1983). However, when certain circumstances combine, such as large areas of mature pine, unregulated fire suppression, and consecutive warm winters, population outbreaks make the beetle a very destructive biological agent in mature pine forests. Logan and Powell (2001) propose that mountain pine beetle plays a regulatory role in the fire ecology of lodgepole pine. First, dead needles of beetle-killed trees provide a highly combustible source of fine fuels. Later, standing dead trees provide vectors for ground fires to reach the forest canopy that would result in stand replacing crown fires that usually favour lodgepole pine regeneration. Goyer et al. (1998) observed that the ecological roles of mountain pine beetle are to open the canopy, thin dense stands of stressed trees, and initiate decomposition. Thus, mountain pine beetle can be viewed as a natural agent of disturbance in the lodgepole pine life cycle.

Abundance and distribution of mountain pine beetle are largely determined by ecological characteristics of lodgepole pine stands and by changes in these characteristics. Lodgepole pine has considerable ecological amplitude that is reflected in the variety of successional conditions under which it thrives. Pfister and Daubenmire (1975) recognize four successional roles of lodgepole pine: minor seral, dominant seral, climax, and persistent. In turn, mountain pine beetle and fire are primary factors affecting the dynamics and successional status of lodgepole pine (Hagle et al. 2000: Mata et al. 2003). Depending on its successional role and its abundance in a stand, mountain pine beetle's impact on stand structure and composition may be predicted (Amman 1977; Logan and Powell 2001). Unfortunately, the larger the area involved, the lower the predictive value of a stand characteristic. Prediction of lodgepole pine mortality, therefore, appears to be most reliable by individual stand basis (Amman and Anhold 1989).

Increased knowledge of mountain pine beetle ecology has led to two very different tactics for reducing lodgepole pine timber losses: direct control and preventive silviculture. Direct control means killing, attracting or repelling the beetles. The effectiveness of direct control is usually only temporary; it may slow the spread and intensity of mountain pine beetle outbreak in susceptible stands until they can be treated silviculturally or salvage logged. Preventive management attempts to keep populations below injurious levels by limiting food source through forest activities intended to maintain or improve tree resistance. Once the beetle population has developed into a large outbreak, salvage logging of just-infested material will not reduce future timber losses (Safranyik, 1982). As with fighting a fire, beetle management should include reducing the potential food supply for the beetles. To be successful in reducing economic and ecological impacts of mountain pine beetle, strategic management approaches must be conceived. These approaches can be tested and built up from the stand level with non-spatial models, such as the British Columbia Ministry of Forests' Forest Service Simulator (British Columbia Ministry of Forests 2004), and with spatial models, such as SELES (Fall, A.; Shore, T.; Safranyik, L.; Riel, B.; Sachs, D. 2002. Application of the MPB/SELES landscape-scale mountain pine beetle model in the Kamloops Forest District, British Columbia Ministry of Forests, unpublished report.).

The Canadian Forest Service published "Management of lodgepole pine to reduce losses from the mountain pine beetle" for public use and application (Safranyik et al. 1974, 1980). These papers discuss a methodology for conserving forest production and are valuable in the effort to manage mountain pine beetle impact on timber production at the stand level. Complements to this work are examinations of costs and benefits, and addressing the question of complex landscape impacts.

Whitehead et al. (2001) discussed landscape susceptibility and suggested the strategy of "…creating a landscape mosaic where age-class, size, stand density, and species distributions do not favour the development of large scale outbreaks." Such a strategy requires money and time. Mitchell (1994) looked at costs associated with commercial thinning to reduce susceptibility to attack by mountain pine beetle, but did not compare costs with the benefits of holding the stand until regeneration harvest.

Cole and Koch (1995) suggest solutions to management of individual lodgepole pine stands so that probability of reaching planned rotation age remains high, despite serious risk from mountain pine beetle and wildfire. To do this, they looked at product yield per unit area of managed lodgepole pine by site class in Montana. Product yield and other values vary throughout British Columbia, but the technique has merit in determining the benefits of a stand-level protection program.

The Canadian Forest Service also maintains a web site that lists some 110 publications on mountain pine beetle. The references offer insight into the mountain pine beetle biology and problem. While some of the literature on the British Columbia mountain pine beetle situation deals with the impact of the bark beetle on production, little of it deals with prices, injury appraisal or economic approaches to evaluating forest-protection alternatives.

The mountain pine beetle in British Columbia

The British Columbia forest situation provides a unique setting in which forest policies are developed. In the province, about 95% of the forestland base, or a total forest area of about 98.4 million ha, is owned by the provincial government. About 53 million ha are considered commercially productive, although only 25 million ha are classified as commercial forest that is designated as the timber harvesting land base (THLB). Mountain pine beetle is attacking pine in all categories of ownership and forest class in the interior of British Columbia. Any strategy for managing the mountain pine beetle must consider that lodgepole pine is found in parks, reserves and other unmanaged areas as well as on the THLB. In the British Columbia context, institutions such as timber tenures and institutional arrangements related to tenures are as important in a socioeconomic analysis as markets, because public forests are managed for multiple values and cannot be treated as solely commercial enterprises.

Until the 1980s, British Columbia public forest managers used a kind of forester's rotation (the age at which current annual increment is equal to the mean annual increment) to determine allowable annual cut (AAC). Inputs from economic analyses, and those from local people were discouraged or not taken into account. This has changed with the new Timber Supply Review processes, which began in 1992.

Also during the 1980s and 1990s, the British Columbia government made substantial decisions about protected areas and forest practices. These included doubling the area covered by protected areas and establishing land-use planning processes such as the Commission on Resources and Environment (CORE) and Land and Resource Management Planning (LRMP). The province's AAC decision process is driven by land-use and forest practices, not the other way around (Pedersen, 2003). Thus, changing forest practices impact the AAC in the various timber tenures initiated as a response to mountain pine beetle. The long-term timber supply on those tenures also has costs and benefits that can be estimated.

Along with a significant public ownership, another element important to the British Columbia context is that only a small domestic market for forest products exists. The province's forest sector is a major exporter of products, most going to the United States. At present, despite increasing integration of the North American economy, Canada and the USA are embroiled in a trade controversy over the export of Canadian softwood lumber (Hoberg, 2000). The dispute has been almost continuous for the last 25 years, with the most recent trade investigation producing countervailing and anti-dumping duties averaging about 27.2% levied on exports of British Columbia softwood lumber and a suite of forest products to the USA. The resulting constrained access to the American softwood market has severely limited management options available for controlling the mountain pine beetle epidemic in British Columbia.

One result of the continuing softwood lumber controversy is that the British Columbia Ministry of Forests is attempting to create a functional market for timber from the majority of public timber tenures in British Columbia, since April 1, 2004. Although economic ramifications of many changes in forest policy direction are often poorly understood, this does not have to be the case (Haley, 1996). Economic analyses of issues surrounding the beetle epidemic are no exception. Largely because of studies associated with the Forest Practices Code Act, there is emerging understanding of non-market incentives that are embodied in institutions and institutional arrangements in the British Columbia context (Hoberg 2002; Tollerson, 1998) that could be included in economic analyses.

Until the late 1990s, there seems to have been little understanding about how the biology of mountain pine beetle and lodgepole pine relates to forest economics. The British Columbia Ministry of Forests "Socioeconomic Analysis of Mountain Pine Management in British Columbia" web site concludes:

The annual expenditure of $4.5 million from the current control program results in a net benefit of $72 million province-wide in stumpage and lumber value (British Columbia Ministry of Forests, 1998).

The analysis was based on a study conducted for the government by Miller et al. (1993). This report examined mountain pine beetle in the Morice and Merritt timber supply areas, and used a modified susceptibility and risk rating system developed by Shore and Safranyik (1992) to project the expansion of beetle damage with the Ministry's non-spatial timber supply analysis technique, Forest Service Simulator (FSSIM). The Shore–Safranyik (1992) susceptibility rating system was validated in 2000, but the effects of modifications made during analysis are uncertain (Shore et al. 2000).

In an effort to glean socioeconomic impacts of beetle management on communities, Miller et al. (1993) interviewed 30 individuals (9 from the forest industry, 12 from various natural resource government departments), and expanded the study to include the whole province. Again, the Miller report suggested large rewards for a modest control program. Unfortunately, the province's control effort has proven to be not very effective in managing the current outbreak. This outbreak is causing far more forest injury and is far more eruptive than previous attacks. As Manning (1982) pointed out more than 20 years ago, much of the problem is due to a lack of reliable information, which results in unreliable economic analyses.

Administration and management

The British Columbia government recognized an additional need to determine if there was a business case or financial argument to support investment in a management strategy that targets mountain pine beetle. To do that, the government commissioned two studies: one by R. & S. Rodgers (2001), and another by Sterling Wood Group. (Mountain pine beetle epidemic: An estimation of the financial outcomes alternative levels of intervention, British Columbia Ministry of Forests, unpublished report).

The methodology used in the development of the Rodgers' report built on work done through consultations with a cross-section of primary stakeholders. The results of these consultations were presented at three workshops held in the central interior of the province. The objectives of the report revolved around assessing key business issues and their related constraints and identifying viable options for managing the business implications of a worst-case scenario. The report recognized that North American lumber producers currently have excess production capacity and, therefore, recommends that:

> … the British Columbia Ministry of Forests and industry exhaust all efforts to maximize the harvest of green attack timber within the framework of revised cost recognition, tenure and operating area transfers and small business forest enterprise program revenue focused licence opportunities before further AAC uplifts are proposed (R. & S. Rodgers 2001).

The Sterling Wood Group study used inventory and cost estimates supplied by the British Columbia Ministry of Forests or implied by various policy statements, assumptions about rate of spread, and assumptions about volume recovery, to construct a matrix for each policy showing the financial impacts to government. The report deals with uncertainty and sensitivity – two problems seldom discussed in government reports. Sterling Wood Group also recommends a "strong plus" intervention, which would mean harvesting 3 million m^3 per year from recent green attack stands and transferring an additional 3 million m^3 of current production logging into stands infested in previous years. The sensitivity analyses suggest that, in redirecting cut, if the original stumpage is less than double the beetle-wood net stumpage, then the Crown would still benefit by making the transfer. Both these two studies recommend the redirecting of existing cut to deal with the beetle epidemic, with the Sterling recommending further uplifts.

British Columbia's chief forester began to clarify some of the major timber-supply impacts of the current mountain pine beetle outbreak in late 2003 (Pedersen 2003a). Although the chief forester's report presented physical terms rather than economic ones, it is an excellent step in coming to economic terms with the nature of the epidemic associated in 12 management units in the central interior of British Columbia. The report sets the stage and allows costs of an uncontrolled epidemic to now begin to be estimated. The study models the flow of pine under a number of assumptions and uncertainties. It suggests that over 200 million m^3 of beetle-killed pine will not be harvested. Under that scenario, harvest would be increased for 15 years by 6.8 million m^3 per year. Then, after 15 years, the flow of timber will decline by 4.5 million m³ per year for 65 years – a 19% reduction from current levels of harvest. It is interesting to note that short-term harvests are being increased by 6.8 million m³ even though redirection of cut is also occurring.

Because the study looks only at the impact of the bark beetle on timber supply and not at other socioeconomic implications of the outbreak, the simulation is one step in assessing the immensity of the problem. Again, although there may be biological and engineering solutions to the mountain pine beetle issue, more work is required to examine what alternatives may mean in terms of costs and benefits to the human communities impacted, and to the province as a whole.

The British Columbia Ministry of Forests defined its strategies and tactics for managing the mountain pine beetle in the Kamloops Forest Region in a handbook (Kamloops Forest Region, 2003). Although it included little about costs and values associated with mountain pine beetle management, the handbook did illustrate how to develop a mountain pine beetle plan, thereby permitting estimation or determination of costs and benefits of mountain pine beetle management at the landscape level. Thus, there is now a basic foundation for analyzing the economic implications of the mountain pine beetle management in the Kamloops Forest Region.

Sustainable forest management and the ecosystem approach

Globally, the field of forest economics is changing. Shifting from an emphasis on stands, the study of landscapes is now required. The production of trees for fibre is no longer the focus: many non-market forest goods and services are becoming objectives in management and stewardship. The move to sustainable forest management (SFM) or ecosystem management requires inclusion of human institutions that would include local municipal governments, firms and households into forest economic alternatives and recommendations.

A major barrier to information diffusion has been that there exists no specialized discipline of "forest protection economics". To get information on disturbances such as bark beetles, the literature of agriculture, silviculture, entomology, or general forest economics must be reviewed and, even then – especially in the silviculture and entomology literature – economic approaches are often just sidebars to the real purposes of the study. With adoption of ecosystem or sustainable forest management, a new literature, with very different fundamental principles, is developing. Schowalter et al. (1997) discuss integrating ecological roles of insects, pathogens and mycorrhizae into the management of forests; they even cite Mattson and Addy (1975) in challenging the view of mountain pine beetle as pests, suggesting that, in some cases, these organisms actually increase primary productivity through pruning, nutrient cycling and changing species composition. Still, understanding of the interactions between mountain pine beetle–lodgepole pine biology and socioeconomic systems has been slow in developing.

There have been considerable advances in economic analysis of non-priced goods over the past few decades that could clarify an ecosystem approach to the mountain pine beetle issue. Adamowicz et al. (2003) discusses a number of methods for valuing non-timber resources. They define value in terms of the trade-offs people are willing to make and estimate implicit value.

Like Manning, Adamowicz et al. also cite the lack of meaningful data to be applied to analysis, and highlight the problem of only a small pool of qualified workers that work as important factors in the under-incorporation of environmental values into forest decision-making.

There are several ways to analyze the economics of issues that are associated with mountain pine beetle. Although many of the important economic issues associated with mountain pine beetle revolve around the question of value, the problem of approach in identifying what values are to be measured and how also exists. Clearly, at least in the USA, forestry has diverged into two approaches with very different goals. Federal USA forestry is changing to an ecosystem emphasis by identifying and protecting physical, biological and social forest and forest-related values. Although industrial forest owners still focus on increasing forest productivity for wood fibre through application of various cultural tools (Perry 1998), managers and stewards of both jurisdictions remain concerned with long-term sustainability or sustainable forest management (SFM). This trend has become even more pronounced during past two decades (Kant 2003).

Forest managers have traditionally identified the values attached to forests through economic and political systems. Unfortunately, neither forestry nor forest economics has been able to keep up with the paradigm shift to SFM, largely because traditionalists continue to rely heavily on neoclassical economics when examining societal relationships with forests (Kant 2003; Robson et al. 2000). As Kant (2003) notes, "The new forest management paradigm has transformed forest management from timber management to forest ecosystem management, from sustained yield timber management to SFM, and from forest management by exclusion to management by inclusion of user groups."

Forest economics is becoming more a way of thinking about defining issues than it is a set of dogmas that are instantly applicable to policy development. As Davidson (2002) observes, "Policies deserve to be appraised on their merits. Some will invite more public intervention, others, less. Neither market nor government solutions are without flaw – or merit." Much of the economics literature on mountain pine beetle has been developed under the "old" paradigm of forest stands in a neoclassical economic world.

The SFM literature suggests at least three reasons for the economic valuation of natural systems and their services (Pritchard et al, 2000). The first has to do with linking natural systems to human welfare; there is a real and close relationship between natural systems and economic well-being of humans (Costanza et al. 1997). Because this relationship is important, natural system values need to be represented in decision-making processes.

Another reason for valuation is to describe the relative importance of various ecosystem types. Lodgepole pine comprises about 25% of standing inventory in the province and is significant in both its contributions to the economic development and maintenance of the forest sector and to provision environmental services of the natural landscape. If mountain pine beetle management is to have long-term impacts on quantity and quality of forest products harvests, this type of valuation is critical in developing and examining management alternatives.

The final reason, which is also the more traditional approach to valuation, is that economic valuation can justify or critique a particular decision or policy direction. Although this third methodology is less useful in ecosystem or SFM approaches to forestland management, it is a necessary first step in developing forest policy, and is critical in establishing institutional arrangements in forest protection (Kimmins, 2002). As such, this method of valuation can be described and justified in terms of gains and losses from a management strategy, as expressed in financial terms. It can be used to help to determine if protection efforts are adequate to the values at risk or, perhaps, suggest alternative courses to current forest-protection direction.

Traditional forest economics and mountain pine beetle

The literature of forest economics on protection and catastrophic disaster is considerable. Forest economics literature deals with the forest management problem caused by mountain pine beetle in lodgepole pine from a number of perspectives. Standard methods are concerned with maximizing value of harvesting a single forest site under the risk of bark beetle. Another viewpoint extends this value-maximizing approach to incorporate multiple uses of, and benefits from, a larger forest system. In this approach, management policy suggests systems that reduce risk in the form of impact reduction rather than product increase. Thus, management costs can be balanced against the reduction of impact – a least-cost-plus-loss economic approach as discussed earlier, which is usually combined with marginal analysis (Herrick 1981; Mactavish 1965).

Both these lines of analysis have roots in forest-rotation models developed around Faustmann's (1849) optimal rotation formula for a single stand and one criterion. Although Calish et al. (1978) demonstrated that the Faustmann approach could be modified to consider joint values in order to determine economic rotations, there are fundamental weaknesses in this traditional damage appraisal model. First, it does not consider the depressing effect that large amounts of salvage timber from catastrophic events may have on the equilibrium market price of wood products in the marketplace; thus, it fails to estimate benefits to consumers and costs to those holding undamaged timber (Holmes 1991). Secondly, it almost totally neglects non-market ecosystem or sustainable forest management values.

Economic damage that results from catastrophe occurs in two ways: through production losses in timber and through costs associated with increasing risks of carrying an economically mature stand to the forester's rotation. When damages are widespread, they can impact timber prices both with and without salvage efforts. Because most of the forests in the province are publicly owned, welfare effects of price variation due to a widespread catastrophe can be significant

(Holmes, 1991). Government's overwhelming participation in public forest management and protection means its policies influence ecosystems on private lands, as well as timber supply and prices from public lands. Thus, examination of welfare effects of forest-protection policies – even if these policies are to do nothing or are unsuccessful – is also critical.

In economic terms, managing situations like the current mountain pine beetle epidemic in lodgepole pine uses scarce resources. Not only are resources being used by management but the flow of future values associated with timber supply and ecosystem health is changing. The matter of direction in which mountain pine beetle control proceeds is a choice. Rational choice by management suggests some criterion for comparing and evaluating alternatives. For effective and efficient selection among alternatives, size and intensity of the outbreak, subsequent impacts, and cost and effectiveness of control alternatives should be considered together as a system. This type of valuation requires use of a large number of variables, which increases probability of error.

Economic decision-making and integrated pest management

Mountain pine beetle becomes a "pest" when the results of its natural activities begin to counter goals and objectives of owners and managers of the forest ecosystem. The promise of integrated pest management (IPM) as a process that brings together information on the ecology of a pest, the pest's impact on societal values, available management tactics and impacts of management on the pest and related ecosystems has been successfully implemented in agricultural systems (Kogan 1998). IPM attempts to develop criteria from which to derive decisions to manage vegetation such as forests to reduce or maintain pest impacts at acceptable levels. To do this, risk assessment methods are used in IPM, based on principles of insect-population dynamics. Risk assessment involves understanding the causes of the damaging event and formulating a predictive model based on this understanding (Berryman and Stark 1985). Shore and Safranyik (1992) devised and tested (Shore et al. 2000) a susceptibility-and risk-rating system for the mountain pine beetle in lodgepole pine stands in British Columbia. Important from an economic perspective, the Shore-Safranyik risk-rating system also provides a tool to predict landscape-level loss due to mountain pine beetle.

Two economic concepts that are well developed in the economic literature of agriculture entomology could be useful in the lodgepole pine case because they provide information on quantifiable aspects of the pest situation. These ideas are termed economic injury level (EIL), defined as the lowest population density of pests that will cause economic damage, and economic threshold (ET).

Peterson and Higley (2002) define economic damage as the amount of injury that justifies the financial cost of control. Linking pest population to degree of damage explicitly recognizes a relationship between pest biology, host biology and economics. Economic injury level, therefore, is a cost–benefit relationship that suggests a level of injury at which the pest management cost equals the cost from losses in forest yield without pest management. Economic threshold is the density of pests at which control measures should be taken to prevent the pest population from reaching EIL. Nautiyal (1988) suggests that ET is "the point in the development of an outbreak at which control should be initiated." ET is critical to the EIL concept. Mumford and Norton (1984) consider ET an ideal operational decision rule in agriculture. Fox et al. (1997) develop a framework for applying the ET concept to forest pest management. Economic threshold is a very difficult number or range of numbers to derive, and varies under different conditions (Pedigo, 1996); however, given the work of Shore and Safranyik (1992) and Fox et al. (1997), forest economists are close to creating a useful decision-making tool.

Stern (1973) describes how the ET concept was used in California ponderosa pine (*Pinus ponderosa* Laws) and Jeffrey pine (*Pinus jeffreyi* Balf.) in developing crown classification systems for ponderosa pine under threat of attack from the western pine beetle (*Dendroctonus brevicomis* Lec.) in eastern California. If successfully established in a tree, activities of western pine beetle, similar to those of mountain pine beetle, results in tree death. The importance of classifications discussed by Stern was that a light cut of beetle-susceptible trees for the purpose of sanitation and salvage became possible. Stern concludes that these preliminary cuttings were intended to proceed or delay rotation cutting, and that undesirable clearcut units were not necessary.

Berryman and Stark (1985) use the concept of threshold to assess the risk of eruptive lodgepole pine stand destruction by mountain pine beetle. They define outbreak in terms of gradient, cyclical or eruptive. Because mountain pine beetle is an eruptive outbreak, they suggest a model for developing risk assessment that integrates stand, site and insect numbers, and use lodgepole pine as an example. They define threshold in this case as the beetle population density required to invade a stand of given resistance.

Neither IPM nor its important economic ideas of ET and EIL have yet been fully integrated into forest management and protection plans in British Columbia, although a promise of blending fire, insects, disease and other disturbance factors into forest ecosystem management began to crystallize in the 1960s. By the 1980s, the co-development of the ecosystem concept in natural resources management and radical improvements in computational technology suggested that the integration of forest protection into management plans and operations seemed near to realization (Gara et al. 1985).

Unfortunately, largely because of data requirements in determining ET, that promise has not yet been realized in British Columbia nor in most of North America's public forests. Although there may be numerous other reasons for this, in the USA, the new management paradigm – ecosystem management – coupled with lower timber harvests on federal forests, along with growing demand and economic timber values, are all contributing to the delay. Increasing forest product values in the British Columbia situation are further complicated by a high proportion of public forest compared to private forest, and by complex timber-tenure arrangements that appear to retard ability of either public landlord or private licensee to strategically respond to landscape-level disturbances such as mountain pine beetle in lodgepole pine (Ainscough 1976).

Table 1. Variables in the SELES Model (Fall, A.; Shore, T.; Safranyik, L.; Riel, B.; Sachs, D. 2002. Application of the MPB/SELES landscape-scale mountain pine beetle model in the Kamloops Forest District, British Columbia Ministry of Forests, unpublished report.). (MPB = mountain pine beetle).

Landscape structure
1. Biogeoclimatic classification by variant
2. Elevation in metres

Forest state
3. Age in years
4. Inventory type group
5. Height and volume
6. Percent pine
7. Stand density
8. Site index (height in 50 years)
9. Analysis unit (sites with similar stand conditions, management history and site index.)

MPB population
10. MPB population (beetles per cell)
11. Time since attack in years
12. MPB Susceptibility
13. MPB Risk

Harvest availability
14. Potential treatment type
15. Salvageable volume

Timber harvesting landbase
16. Percentage of landbase in each cell

Management zone
17. Visual quality objective
18. Integrated resource management zone
19. Biodiversity options
20. Landscape units
21. Productive forest (each cell is classed as productive operable, productive inoperable or non-productive)

Management parameters
22. Annual allowable cut
23. Beetle management unit strategies
24. Minimum harvest age
25. Management constraints
26. Management preferences

Roads
27. Distance to existing road in metres

Future research: Determining economic thresholds in lodgepole pine

Thompson et al. (1992) demonstrates how computer-based analytical models could be used to investigate economic problems and assist with the design of silviculture programs. Phelps et al. (Phelps, S.E.; Thompson, W.A.; Webb, T.M.; McNamee, P.J.; Tait, D.; Walter, C.J., British Columbia silviculture planning model structure and design. British Columbia Ministry of Forests, unpublished report.) developed a computer simulation model to examine silvicultural investment options for forests at the broad strategic level. The model included a subroutine for studying the economics of bark beetle impacts in terms of prices and delivered wood costs. Brumelle et al. (1991) used the Canadian context to review major issues and analytical techniques in silvicultural investment decision making; they observe, "The socioeconomic system involved in the silvicultural investment problem is even more complex and less understood than the biological system" (Brumelle et al. 1991).

Many discussions and techniques described by Brumelle et al. are important in the application of silviculture to beetle protection in stands. Especially relevant is the chapter on silviculture decision making and discussions about risk and uncertainty, sensitivity, discount rate and decision making in a hierarchy. Discussions and allowances for these parameters are largely absent in the Phelps, S.E.; Thompson N.A.; Webb, T.M.; McNamee, D.J.; Tait, D.; Walters, C.J. 1991. "British Columbia silviculture planning model structure and design." Unpublished report) model, which is basically a bookkeeping device to predict consequences of specified assumptions at the provincial level.

Although not specifically related to barkbeetle dynamics, Stone (1996) completed an economic analysis of commercial thinning of pine for the British Columbia Ministry of Forests. Despite good arguments for commercial thinning at the stand level, the author suggests that at the forest level, commercial thinning will reduce the amount of final harvests allowed in any year. He points out that this economic reversal of going from stand to forest level is an incongruity associated with using total-cut control as a major forest management tool in the province. Stone's landscape assessment did not include mountain pine beetle risk to lodgepole pine as a factor in the assessment.

By building on the work of Berryman and Stark (1985), and Shore and Safranyik (1992), and by incorporating some of the concepts of Brumelle et al. (1991) into the model developed by Fall, A.; Shore, T.; Safranyik, L.; Riel, B.; Sachs, D. (Application of the MPB/SELES landscape-scale mountain pine beetle model in the Kamloops Forest District, British Columbia Ministry of Forests unpublished report.) it would seem that the concepts of economic threshold and economic injury level could become important contributors to economic decision making in lodgepole pine forests. For the economist, the fact that the biological relationship between mountain pine beetle and lodgepole pine can be modelled is good news. The bad news is the large number of variables that have to be addressed. The large number of variables creates daunting levels of complexity and uncertainty.

Bell Randall (2000) outlines successional functions of mountain pine beetle in lodgepole pine stands with and without fire history and creates about eight scenarios. She points out that in stands where lodgepole pine is a minor stand component, mountain pine beetle can have a positive impact by thinning pine out of the stand and driving the system toward climax. Fall, A.; Shore, T.; Safranyik, L.; Riel, B.; and Sachs, D. (Application of the MPB/ SELES landscape-scale mountain pine beetle model in the Kamloops Forest District, British Columbia Ministry of Forests unpublished report) lists 27 variables used in the spatially explicit landscape event simulator model of the mountain pine beetle in the Kamloops Forest District (see Table 1). A set of complex and considerable data are required on the physical side, and still more variables to do with costs and benefits would be required to allow analysis.

In order to use the SELES model, the data should be both adequate and available, but for many areas of the province, this is not the case. In developing strategic business recommendations for the province, Rogers (2001:12) commented:

> …it is absolutely critical to the strategic management of this and other MPB (mountain pine beetle) epidemics to be able to adequately and consistently measure and quantify the level of beetle infestation across the province. While we heard that it is better to over-estimate the scope of the epidemic than to underestimate it, we do <u>not</u> concur with that premise. We believe that if you cannot measure the parameters of the infestation you cannot properly manage it.

The number of variables and data availability or lack of confidence in the data if it exists is a major stumbling block to economic appraisal of the mountain pine beetle issue. On the other hand, strategic models such as that of Phelps, S.E.; Thompson N.A.; Webb, T.M.; McNamee, D.J.; Tait, D.; Walters, C.J., British Columbia silviculture planning model structure and design. British Columbia Ministry of Forests, unpublished report. are available and can be refined with use of models such as the mountain pine beetle SELES approach to begin to assess socioeconomics of the mountain pine beetle epidemics and assess economic implications of adopting some types of strategies and tactics used for managing lodgepole pine and mountain pine beetle.

Conclusions

The relationship between mountain pine beetle, lodgepole pine and wildfire has been developing in western North America for thousands of years. The attempt to exclude fire from British Columbia forests during much of the 20th century has brought about serious economic implications in landscapes that support significant populations of maturing lodgepole pine. This chapter could be seen as a proposal to use economic theory and its related techniques in the landscape management of the mountain pine beetle in the various ecosystems that support stands of lodgepole pine. However, that would be just half a step. Traditionally, the economic aspect of forest decisions focused upon the expected treatment/response relationship in impacted forest stands along with the direct financial costs of the management strategy. This approach often failed to account for uncertainties associated with the selected treatment strategy and usually failed to examine the total economic significance of a selected strategy.

The literature cited in this chapter suggests that there has only been a limited use of economics in mountain pine beetle management in the province. However, using economic theory in conjunction with recent predictive models of beetle behaviour has the potential to guide decision making during the current outbreak and aid with developing a management strategy for lodgepole pine in the future. Cautious interpretation of the strategy in its application to field conditions is also required, as predictive models can be subject to uncertainty from factors that include errors in model input and an incomplete understanding of beetle dynamics and epidemic behaviour. However, even with these uncertainties, models can help understand the complex interactions and outcomes from alternative management scenarios. When coupled with economic analyses, these studies can inform choices and help define strategies that may reduce the impacts of the current epidemic, while considering economic tradeoffs.

Manning (1982), commenting on the mountain pine beetle outbreak of that time, identified five major components of economic impact. These were: 1) impact on allowable cut and value of output, 2) impact on resource flows, 3) impact on product values, 4) changes in protection costs, and 5) changes in forest management costs. If social values were added to the list, Manning's approach would be one useful way to organize an analysis of the socioeconomics of the mountain pine beetle issue in lodgepole pine.

Areas where further research is required include strategies for utilization and market access given the post-beetle timber profile, the social implications of the epidemic to resource-based communities, and the socioeconomic implications of various management strategies. Some of these research topics are currently under the Government of Canada's Mountain Pine Beetle Initiative. Where salvage harvesting is inappropriate like in parks and remote areas, alternative treatments such as the use of fire, or simply leaving the disturbed areas to natural processes, are being explored from both an economic and ecological perspective. Research into longer-term management of affected areas and strategies to minimize risk from future epidemics is also being conducted.

Mountain pine beetle is an important ecological component of lodgepole pine forests, but it also has tremendous economic implications. While silvicultural investments may have the potential to offset some of the timber supply reductions forecast in the aftermath of severe outbreaks, the costs and benefits of such programs are complex and not always apparent at first glance. A careful examination of the economic and social welfare effects of expenditures and investments is needed to guide public managers, particularly where future gains may be subject to increased risk from agents like mountain pine beetle under climatic change.

References

Adamowicz, W.L.; Armstrong, G.W.; Messmer, M.J. 2003. The economics of boreal forest management. Pages 181-211 *in* Burton, P.J. Messier, C., Smith, D. and Adamowicz, W., eds. Towards sustainable management of the boreal forest. NRC Research Press, Ottawa, ON.

Agee, J.K. 1993. Fire ecology of Pacific Northwest forests. Island Press, Washington, DC.

Amman, G.D. 1977. The role of mountain pine beetle in lodgepole pine ecosystems: Impact on succession. Pages 1-19 *in* Mattson, W.J., ed. The Role of Arthropods in Forest Ecosystems. Springer-Verlag, NY.

Amman, G.D.; Anhold, J.A. 1989. Preliminary evaluation of hazard and risk-rating variables for mountain pine beetle infestations in lodgepole pine stands. Pages 3-18 *in* Amman, G.D., ed. Symposium proceedings, The management of lodgepole pine to minimize losses to the mountain pine beetle. USDA Forest Service General Technical Report INT-36.

Amman, G.D.; Safranyik, L. 1985. Insects of lodgepole pine: impacts and control. *In* Baumgartner, D.M., Krebill, R.G., Arnott, .T. and Weetman, G.F., eds. Lodgepole pine: the species and its management: Symposium proceedings, May 8-10, 1984, Spokane, WA and Vancouver, BC. Washington State University, Pullman, WA.

British Columbia Ministry of Forests. 2004. Forest health aerial overview survey. BC Ministry of Forests, Forest Practices Branch, Victoria, BC. http://www.for.gov.bc.ca/hfp/forsite/ overview/overview.htm. (Accessed 26 May 2004.)

Baxter, D.; Ramlo, A. 2002. Resource dependency: the spatial origins of BC's economic base. The Urban Futures Institute, Report 55, Vancouver, BC.

Bebi, P.; Kulakowski, D.; Verlen, T. 2003. Interactions between fire and spruce beetles in a subalpine Rocky Mountain forest landscape. Ecology 84(2):362-371.

Bell Randall, C.B. 2000. Mountain pine beetle in lodgepole pine: Succession functions. *In* Hagle, S.K., Schwandt, J.W. Johnson, T.L. Kegley, S.J. Randall, C.S., Taylor, J.E. Lockman, I.B. Sturdevant, N.J. and Marsden, M.A., eds. Succession functions of forest pathogens and insects. USDA Forest Service, Northern Region, FHP Report No. 00-11.

Berryman, A.A.; Stark, R.W. 1985. Assessing the risk of lodgepole pine stand destruction by pests. Pages 163-169 *in* Baumgartner, D.M., Krebill, R.G., Arnott, T. and Weetman, G.F., eds. Lodgepole pine: the species and its management: Symposium proceedings May 8-10, 1984. Spokane, WA and Vancouver, BC. Washington State University, Pullman, WA.

British Columbia Ministry of Forests, Kamloops Forest Region. 2003. Strategies and tactics for managing the mountain pine beetle. Online: http://www.for.gov.bc.ca/ftp/hfp/external/ !publish/MPB_booklet/. (Accessed November 12, 2003.)

British Columbia Ministry of Forests. 2003a. Timber supply and the mountain pine beetle infestation in British Columbia. http://www.for.gov.bc.ca/hts/. (Accessed October 30, 2003.)

British Columbia Ministry of Forests. 2003b. British Columbia's Forests and their Management. Crown Publications, Victoria, BC.

British Columbia Ministry of Forests. 1998. Socioeconomic analysis of mountain pine management in British Columbia. http://www.for.gov.bc.ca/hfp/pubs/interest/mpbecon/ index.htm. (Accessed October 23, 2003.)

British Columbia Ministry of Forests. 1995. Forest, range and recreation resource analysis. Crown Publications, Victoria, BC.

Brumelle, S.L.; Carley, J.S.; Vertinsky, I.B.; Wehrung, D.A. 1991. Evaluating silvicultural investments: a review in the Canadian context. Forest Products Abstracts 14 (5): 217-270.

Calish, S.; Fight, R.D.; Teeguarden, D.E. 1978. How do nontimber values affect Douglas-fir rotations? Journal of Forestry 76(4):217-221.

Carroll, A.L.; Taylor, S.W.; Régnière, J.; Safranyik, L. 2004. Effects of climate change on range expansion by the mountain pine beetle in British Columbia. Pages 223-232 in Shore, T.L., Brooks, J.E. and Stone, J.E., eds. Proceedings of the mountain pine beetle symposium: Challenges and solutions. Natural Resources Canada, Canadian Forest Service, Pacific Forestry Centre, Victoria, BC. 298 p.

Christiansen, E.; Waring, R.H.; Berryman, A.A. 1987. Resistance of conifers to bark beetle attack: Searching for general relationships Forest Ecology and Management 22:89-106.

Cole, D.M.; Koch, P. 1995. Managing lodgepole pine to yield merchantable thinning products and attain sawtimber rotations. USDA Forest Service, Research Paper, INT-RP-482.

Costanza, R.; d'Arge, R.; de Groot, R.; Farber, S.; Grasso, M.; Hannon, B.; Limburg, K.; Naeem, S.; O'Neill R.V.; Paruelo, J.; Raskin, R.G.; Sutton, P.; vanden Belt, M. 1997. The value of the world's ecosystem services and natural capital. Nature 387:253-260.

Crowley, T.J. 2000. Causes of climate change over the past 1000 years. Science 289:270-277.

Cwynar, L.C.; MacDonald, G.M. 1987. Geographical variation of lodgepole pine in relation to population history. The American Naturalist Vol. 129 (3):463-469.

Davidson, P. 2002. Restating the purpose of the JPKE after 25 years. Journal of Post Keynesian Economics 25 (1):3-7.

Fox, G.; Beke, J.; Hopkin, T.; McKenney, D. 1997. A framework for the use of economic threshold in forest pest management. The Forestry Chronicle 73(3):331-339.

Faustmann, M. 1849. On the determination of the value which forest land and immature stands possess for forestry. Translated by Gane, M. Oxford University, UK. Oxford Institute Paper 42, 1968.

Gara, R.I.; Littke, W.R.; Agee, J.K.; Geiszler, D.R.; Stuart, J.D.; Driver, C.H. 1985. Influence of fires, fungi and mountain pine beetles on development of a lodgepole pine forest in south-central Oregon. Pages 153-162 in Baumgartner, D.M., Krebill, R.G., Arnott, T. and Weetman, G.F., eds. Lodgepole pine: the species and its management: Symposium proceedings May 8-10, 1984, Spokane, WA and Vancouver, BC. Washington State University, Pullman, WA.

Goyer, R.A.; Wagner, M.R.; Schowalter, T.D. 1998. Current and proposed technologies for bark beetle management. Journal of Forestry 96 (12):29-33.

Hagle, S.K.; Schwandt, J.W.; Johnson, T.L.; Kegley, S.J.; Randall, C.S.; Taylor, J.E.; Lockman, I.B.; Sturdevant, N.J.; Marsden, M.A. 2000. Succession functions of forest pathogens and insects. USDA Forest Service, Northern Region, FHP Report No. 00-11.

Haley, D. 1996. Paying the piper: The cost of the British Columbia Forest Practices Code. Forum September/October 3(5):26-28.

Heath, R.; Alfaro, R. 1990. Growth response in a Douglas-fir/lodgepole pine stand after thinning of lodgepole pine by the mountain pine beetle: A case study. Entomological Society of British Columbia Journal 87:16-21.

Herrick, O.W. 1981. Forest pest management economics – application to the gypsy moth. Forest Science 27(1):128-138.

Hoberg, G. 2002. Finding the right balance: Designing policies for sustainable forestry in the new era. Faculty of Forestry Jubilee Lecture Series, September 12, 2002. University of British Columbia, Vancouver, BC.

Hoberg, G. 2000. Canada and North American integration. Canadian Public Policy (26): S35-S50.

Holmes, T.P. 1991. Price and welfare effects of catastrophic forest damage from southern pine beetle epidemics. Forest Science 37(2):500-516.

Kant, S. 2003. The economics of sustainable forest management. Ecoforestry, Spring 2003: 12-16.

Kant, S. 2003a. Extending the boundaries of forest economics. Forest Policy and Economics 5: 39-56.

Kimmins, J.P. 2002. Future shock in forestry. Where have we come from; where are we going; is there a right way to manage forests? Lessons from Thoreau, Leopold, Toffler, Botkin and Nature. Forestry Chronicle 78:263-271.

Koch, P. 1996. Lodgepole pine in North America. Forest Products Society, Madison, WI.

Kogan, M. 1998. Integrated pest management: Historical perspectives and contemporary developments. Annual Review of Entomology 43:243-70.

Logan, J.A.; Powell, J.A. 2001. Ghost forests, global warming and the mountain pine beetle. American Entomologist 47:160-172.

Mactavish, J.S. 1965. Economics and forest fire control. Catalogue No. 47-1114, Queen's Printer, Ottawa, ON.

Manning, G.L. 1982. Impact of the mountain pine beetle on the economy of British Columbia. Pages 22-23 *in* Proceedings of the joint Canada/USA workshop on mountain pine beetle related problems in western North America. Environment Canada, Pacific Forest Research Centre, Victoria, BC. Information Report BC-X-230.

Mata, S.A.; Schmid, J.M.; Olsen, W.K. 2003. Growth of lodgepole pine stands and its relation to mountain pine beetle susceptibility. RMRS-RP-42. USDA Rocky Mountain Research Station, Fort Collins, CO.

Mattson, W.J.; Addy, N.D. 1975. Phytophagous insects as regulators of forest primary production. Science 190:515-522.

McCullough, D.G.; Werner, R.A.; Neumann, D. 1998. Fire and insects in northern and boreal forest ecosystems of North America. Annual Review of Entomology 43:107-127.

Miller, D.R.; Carlson, J.A.; Stemeroff, M. 1993. Socioeconomic analysis of mountain pine beetle management in British Columbia. Phero Tech and Deloitte and Touche Management Consultants, Guelph, ON.

Mitchell, R.G.; Martin, R.E.; Stuart, John. 1983. Catfaces on lodgepole pine – fire scars or strip kills by the mountain pine beetle? Journal of Forestry 81:598-601.

Mitchell, J.L. 1994. Commercial thinning of mature lodgepole pine to reduce susceptibility to mountain pine beetle. FRDA Report 224. Natural Resources Canada, Canadian Forest Service, Pacific Forestry Centre, co-published with the BC Ministry of Forests. Victoria, BC.

Mulholland, F.D. 1937. The forest resources of British Columbia. King's Printer, Victoria, BC.

Mumford, J.D.; Norton, G.A. 1984. Economics of decision making in pest management. Annual Review of Entomology 29:157-174.

Nautiyal, J.C. 1988. Forest economics: principles and applications. Canadian Scholars Press Inc., Toronto.

Pedersen, L. 2003b. Allowable annual cuts in BC – the agony and the ecstasy. Faculty of Forestry Jubilee Lecture Series, March 20, 2003. University of British Columbia, Vancouver, BC.

Pedersen, L. 2003a. How serious is the mountain pine beetle problem? From a timber supply perspective. Pages 10-18 *in* T.L. Shore, J.E. Brooks and J.E. Stone, eds. Proceedings of the mountain pine beetle symposium: Challenges and solutions, October 30-31, 2003. Kelowna, British Columbia, Natural Resources Canada, Canadian Forest Service, Pacific Forestry Centre, Victoria, BC. Information Report BC-X-399 298 p.

Pedigo, L.P. 1996. General models of economic thresholds. Pages 41 -57 *in* Higley, L.G and Pedigo L. P., eds., Economic thresholds for integrated pest management. University of Nebraska Press, Lincoln, NE.

Perry, D.A. 1998. The scientific basis of forestry. Annual Review of Ecological Systems 29:436-466.

Peterson, R.K.D.; Higley, L.G. 2002. Encyclopedia of pest management. D. Pimentel, Ed., Marcel Dekker, Inc. New York, NY.

Pfister, R.D.; Daubenmire, R. 1975. Ecology of lodgepole pine. Pages 27-46 *in* Baumgartner, D.M., ed. Management of lodgepole pine ecosystems, proceedings. Washington State University, Pullman, WA.

Pritchard Jr., L.; Folke, C.; Gunderson, L. 2000. Valuation of ecosystem services in an institutional context. Ecosystems 3:36-40.

R. & S. Rodgers Consulting Inc. 2001. West central B.C. mountain pine beetle strategic business recommendations report. Report to the British Columbia Ministry of Forests. http://www.for.gov.bc.ca/hfp/bark_beetles/finalreport.pdf. (Accessed online November 5, 2003.)

Raffa, K.F.; Berryman, A.A. 1983. The role of host plant resistance in the colonization behavior and ecology of bark beetles. Ecological Monographs 53(1):27-49.

Robson, M.; Hawley, A.; Robinson, D. 2000. Comparing the social values of forest-dependent, provincial and national publics for socially sustainable forest management. Forestry Chronicle 76:615-622.

Safrankyik, L. 1982. Alternative solutions – preventive management and direct control. Pages 29-32 *in* Proceedings of the joint Canada/USA workshop on mountain pine beetle related problems in western North America. BC-X-230. Environment Canada, Pacific Forest Research Centre, Victoria, BC. 87 p.

Safranyik, L.; Shrimpton, D.M.; Whitney, H.S. 1974. Management of lodgepole pine to reduce losses from the mountain pine beetle. Forestry Technical Report 1, Department of the Environment, Pacific Forest Research Centre, Victoria, BC.

Safrankyik, L.; Linton, D.; Shore, T.; Hawkes, B. 2001. The effects of prescribed burning on mountain pine beetle in lodgepole pine. Natural Resources Canada, Canadian Forest Service, Pacific Forestry Centre, Victoria, BC. Information Report BC-X-391.

Schowalter, T.; Hansen, E.; Molina, R.l.; Zhang, Y. 1997 Pages 171-189 *in* Kohm, K.A. and Franklin, J. F., eds., Integrating the ecological roles of phytophagous insects, plant pathogens and mycorrhizae in managed forests. Creating a forestry for the 21st century. Island Press, Covelo, CA.

Shore, T.L.; Safranyik, L. 1992. Susceptibility and risk rating systems for the mountain pine beetle in lodgepole pine stands. Forestry Canada, Pacific Forestry Centre, Victoria, BC. Information Report BC-X-336.

Shore, T.L.; Safranyik, L.; Lemieux. 2000. Susceptibility of lodgepole pine stands to the mountain pine beetle: testing of a rating system. Canadian Journal of Forest Research 30(1):44-49.

Stone, M. 1996. Commercial thinning of lodgepole pine: An economic analysis. Victoria, B.C.: Natural Resources Canada, Canadian Forest Service, Pacific Forestry Centre, Victoria, BC. FRDA Working Paper no. 6-017. 153 pp.

Tollerson, C. 1998. The wealth of forests. University of British Columbia Press, Vancouver, BC.

Thompson, W.A.; Pearse, P.H.; van Kooten, G.C.; Vertinsky, I. 1992. Rehabilitating the backlog of unstocked forest lands in British Columbia: A preliminary simulation analysis of alternative strategies. Pages 99-130 *in* Nemetz, P.N., ed., Emerging issues in forest policy. University of British Columbia Press, Vancouver, BC.

Whitehead, R.; Martin, P.; Powelson, A. 2001. Reducing Stand and Landscape Susceptibility to Mountain Pine Beetle. British Columbia Ministry of Forests, Victoria, BC. 12 p.

Index